The Abingdon Song Book

Edited by
CHARLES C. WASHBURN

ABINGDON-COKESBURY PRESS
NEW YORK ● NASHVILLE

Printed in the United States of America

Contents

Indexes

Preface

UNLESS there be deep purpose in any undertaking, that project will perforce fail of accomplishment. There has been definite purpose behind the assembling of the hymns and songs in THE ABINGDON SONG BOOK from sources both ancient and modern, that it may speak the language of yesterday and of today, seeking to emphasize the continuing Christian thought and aspiration.

The literature of sacred song has, throughout its history, reflected the heart and mind of that group of people which constitutes the Church; and succeeding generations, building on the best thought of the old, have persistently accomplished an evolution in this field which not only expresses the current intentions but prepares the way for future development.

This book seeks, in a limited content, to cover such field with two strong emphases—that of worship in Spirit, and worship in activity, brotherhood, and service.

Much of olden hymnody has been retained, edited with tried carefulness for the thinking of the present day; and contemporary hymns and songs, voicing in noble sentiment the insistent urge of Christian youth, have been carefully selected to perfect a balance.

Special thought has been given to the inclusion of ten Negro Spirituals, which, it is thought, will add to the value of the SONG BOOK as worship material. There has been a tendency to regard these songs as means of entertainment, but they are gradually growing into the worship services of the Church, and this group is designed for such use. They are the arrangement of Mr. John W. Work, of Fisk University, and are not to be reprinted from this volume without permission.

There has been no attempt to suit any "school" of theological thinking, but a vision of the Church in its varied wholeness, in its many and varied phases and personalities, has actuated the compilation. To minister in this manner has been the deepest desire in the assembling of its pages.

If there are phrases in some of the more recent songs that elders question, it is quite as true that the expressions of a former day do not always find ready echo in the heart of Christian youth, whose earnest and devout consecration the Church recognizes with gladness. We are expanding in our Church-wide programs, and the "renewing gospel," to borrow a happy phrase, meets and blesses and glorifies that expansion.

Careful consideration of the "permissions" will indicate to how many friends acknowledgment is due. Such acknowledgment is given with gratitude.

A few outlines, suggesting worship programs on differing themes, are included, but no attempt has been made to furnish the full material for such programs, the purpose being to leave to the initiative and imagination of those seeking assistance and guidance in this field, the completion and adaptation of the subject in hand.

A few changes have been made in the associations of well-known hymns and tunes, changes that may prove not popular with certain groups, but which will be quite welcomed by others.

Minor alterations have been made in some texts, based on changing attitudes and emphases, and endorsed by the editing of other compilers in former days.

THE ABINGDON SONG BOOK is sent forth with fervent prayer that to many it may become the timely interpreter of the gospel message.

CHARLES C. WASHBURN.

100. $\displaystyle\int \frac{dx}{x^2\sqrt{a+bx}} = -\frac{\sqrt{a+bx}}{ax} - \frac{b}{2\,a}\int \frac{dx}{x\sqrt{a+bx}}.$

101. $\displaystyle\int (a+bx)^{\pm\frac{n}{2}}\,dx = \frac{2}{b}\int y^{1\,\pm\,n}\,dy = \frac{2\,(a+bx)^{\frac{2\,\pm\,n}{2}}}{b\,(2\pm n)}.$

102. $\displaystyle\int x\,(a+bx)^{\pm\frac{n}{2}}\,dx = \frac{2}{b^2}\left[\frac{(a+bx)^{\frac{4\,\pm\,n}{2}}}{4\pm n} - \frac{a\,(a+bx)^{\frac{2\,\pm\,n}{2}}}{2\pm n}\right].$

103. $\displaystyle\int \frac{x^m\,dx}{\sqrt{a+bx}} = \frac{2\,x^m\sqrt{a+bx}}{(2\,m+1)\,b} - \frac{2\,ma}{(2\,m+1)\,b}\int \frac{x^{m-1}\,dx}{\sqrt{a+bx}}.$

104. $\displaystyle\int \frac{dx}{x^n\sqrt{a+bx}} = -\frac{\sqrt{a+bx}}{(n-1)ax^{n-1}} - \frac{(2n-3)b}{(2n-2)a}\int \frac{dx}{x^{n-1}\sqrt{a+bx}}$

105. $\displaystyle\int \frac{(a+bx)^{\frac{n}{2}}\,dx}{x} = b\int (a+bx)^{\frac{n-2}{2}}\,dx + a\int \frac{(a+bx)^{\frac{n-2}{2}}}{x}\,dx.$

106. $\displaystyle\int \frac{dx}{x\,(a+bx)^{\frac{m}{2}}} = \frac{1}{a}\int \frac{dx}{x\,(a+bx)^{\frac{m-2}{2}}} - \frac{b}{a}\int \frac{dx}{(a+bx)^{\frac{m}{2}}}.$

107. $\displaystyle\int f(x,\ \sqrt[n]{a+bx})\,dx = \frac{n}{b}\int f\left(\frac{z^n-a}{b},\ z\right)z^{n-1}\,dz,$

    where $z^n = a+bx.$

108. $\displaystyle\int (a+bx)^{\frac{m}{n}}\,dx = \frac{n\,(a+bx)^{\frac{m+n}{n}}}{b\,(m+n)}.$

109. $\displaystyle\int f(x,\ (a+bx)^{\frac{m}{n}},\ (a+bx)^{\frac{p}{q}},\ \cdots)\,dx$

$$= \frac{s}{b}\int f\left(\frac{y^s-a}{b},\ y^{\frac{ms}{n}},\ y^{\frac{ps}{q}},\ \cdots\right)y^{s-1}\,dy,$$

where $y^s = a+bx$, and s is the least common multiple of n, q, etc.

B.—**Expressions Involving Both** $\sqrt{a + bx}$ **and** $\sqrt{a' + b'x}$.

Let $u = a + bx$, $v = a' + b'x$, and $k = ab' - a'b$, then

110. $\displaystyle\int \sqrt{uv}\,dx = \frac{k + 2\,bv}{4\,bb'}\,\sqrt{uv} - \frac{k^2}{8\,bb'}\int \frac{dx}{\sqrt{uv}}.$

111. $\displaystyle\int \frac{\sqrt{v}\,dx}{\sqrt{u}} = \frac{1}{b}\sqrt{uv} - \frac{k}{2\,b}\int \frac{dx}{\sqrt{uv}}.$

112. $\displaystyle\int \frac{x\,dx}{\sqrt{uv}} = \frac{\sqrt{uv}}{bb'} - \frac{ab' + a'b}{2\,bb'}\int \frac{dx}{\sqrt{uv}}.$

113. $\displaystyle\int \frac{dx}{\sqrt{uv}} = \frac{2}{\sqrt{bb'}}\log\left(\sqrt{bb'u} + b\sqrt{v}\right)$

$$= \frac{2}{\sqrt{-bb'}}\tan^{-1}\sqrt{\frac{-b'u}{bv}}, \text{ or } \frac{2}{\sqrt{bb'}}\tanh^{-1}\sqrt{\frac{b'u}{bv}}$$

$$= \frac{1}{\sqrt{-bb'}}\sin^{-1}\frac{2\,bb'x + a'b + ab'}{k}.$$

114. $\displaystyle\int \frac{dx}{v\sqrt{u}} = \frac{1}{\sqrt{kb'}}\log\frac{b'\sqrt{u} - \sqrt{kb'}}{b'\sqrt{u} + \sqrt{kb'}} = \frac{2}{\sqrt{-kb'}}\tan^{-1}\frac{b'\sqrt{u}}{\sqrt{-kb'}}.$

115. $\displaystyle\int \frac{dx}{v\sqrt{uv}} = -\frac{2\sqrt{u}}{k\sqrt{v}}.$

116. $\displaystyle\int v^m\sqrt{u}\,dx = \frac{1}{(2\,m + 3)\,b'}\left(2\,v^{m+1}\sqrt{u} + k\int \frac{v^m\,dx}{\sqrt{u}}\right).$

117. $\displaystyle\int \frac{\sqrt{u}\,dx}{v^m} = -\frac{1}{(2\,m - 3)\,b'}\left(\frac{2\sqrt{u}}{v^{m-1}} + k\int \frac{dx}{v^m\sqrt{u}}\right)$

$$= \frac{1}{(m - 1)\,b'}\left(-\frac{\sqrt{u}}{v^{m-1}} + \tfrac{1}{2}\,b\int \frac{dx}{v^{m-1}\sqrt{u}}\right).$$

118. $\displaystyle\int \frac{v^m\,dx}{\sqrt{u}} = \frac{2}{(2\,m + 1)\,b}\left(v^m\sqrt{u} - mk\int \frac{v^{m-1}\,dx}{\sqrt{u}}\right).$

119. $\int \dfrac{dx}{v^m \sqrt{u}} = -\dfrac{1}{(m-1)k}\left(\dfrac{\sqrt{u}}{v^{m-1}} + \left(m - \tfrac{3}{2}\right)b\int \dfrac{dx}{v^{m-1}\sqrt{u}}\right).$

120. $\int v^m u^{n-\frac{1}{2}}dx = \dfrac{1}{(2m+2n+1)b'}\Big(2\,v^{m+1}u^{n-\frac{1}{2}}$

$$+ (2n-1)k\int v^m u^{n-\frac{3}{2}}dx\Big).$$

121. $\int v^m u^{-(n+\frac{1}{2})}dx = \dfrac{1}{(2n-1)k}\Big(2\,v^{m+1}u^{-(n-\frac{1}{2})}$

$$- (2m-2n+3)b'\int v^m u^{-(n-\frac{1}{2})}dx\Big)$$

$$= \dfrac{2}{(2n-1)b}\Big(-v^m u^{-(n-\frac{1}{2})}$$

$$+ mb'\int v^{m-1}u^{-(n-\frac{1}{2})}dx\Big).$$

122. $\int v^{-m}u^{(n-\frac{1}{2})}dx = \dfrac{-1}{(2m-2n-1)b'}\Big(2\,u^{n-\frac{1}{2}}v^{-(m-1)}$

$$+ (2n-1)k\int u^{n-\frac{3}{2}}v^{-m}dx\Big)$$

$$= \dfrac{1}{(m-1)b'}\Big(-u^{n-\frac{1}{2}}v^{-(m-1)}$$

$$+ \left(n-\tfrac{1}{2}\right)b\int u^{n-\frac{3}{2}}v^{-(m-1)}dx\Big).$$

123. $\int v^{-m}u^{-(n+\frac{1}{2})}dx = \dfrac{1}{(2n-1)k}\Big(2\,v^{-(m-1)}u^{-(n-\frac{1}{2})}$

$$+ (2m+2n-3)b'\int v^{-m}u^{-(n-\frac{1}{2})}dx\Big).$$

C. — Expressions Involving $\sqrt{x^2 \pm a^2}$ and $\sqrt{a^2 - x^2}$.

124. $\displaystyle\int \sqrt{x^2 \pm a^2}\, dx = \tfrac{1}{2}\left[x\sqrt{x^2 \pm a^2} \pm a^2 \log\left(x + \sqrt{x^2 \pm a^2}\right)\right].$*

125. $\displaystyle\int \sqrt{a^2 - x^2}\, dx = \tfrac{1}{2}\left(x\sqrt{a^2 - x^2} + a^2 \sin^{-1}\frac{x}{a}\right).$

126 a. $\displaystyle\int \frac{dx}{\sqrt{x^2 + a^2}} = \log\left(x + \sqrt{x^2 + a^2}\right),$ or $\sinh^{-1}\dfrac{x}{a}.$*

126 b. $\displaystyle\int \frac{dx}{\sqrt{x^2 - a^2}} = \log\left(x + \sqrt{x^2 - a^2}\right),$ or $\cosh^{-1}\dfrac{x}{a}.$*

127. $\displaystyle\int \frac{dx}{\sqrt{a^2 - x^2}} = \sin^{-1}\frac{x}{a},$ or $-\cos^{-1}\dfrac{x}{a}.$

128. $\displaystyle\int \frac{dx}{x\sqrt{x^2 - a^2}} = \frac{1}{a}\cos^{-1}\frac{a}{x}.$

129. $\displaystyle\int \frac{dx}{x\sqrt{a^2 \pm x^2}} = -\frac{1}{a}\log\left(\frac{a + \sqrt{a^2 \pm x^2}}{x}\right).$*

130. $\displaystyle\int \frac{\sqrt{a^2 \pm x^2}}{x}\, dx = \sqrt{a^2 \pm x^2} - a\log\frac{a + \sqrt{a^2 \pm x^2}}{x}.$*

131. $\displaystyle\int \frac{\sqrt{x^2 - a^2}}{x}\, dx = \sqrt{x^2 - a^2} - a\cos^{-1}\frac{a}{x}.$

132. $\displaystyle\int \frac{x\, dx}{\sqrt{a^2 \pm x^2}} = \pm\sqrt{a^2 \pm x^2}.$

133. $\displaystyle\int \frac{x\, dx}{\sqrt{x^2 - a^2}} = \sqrt{x^2 - a^2}.$

---

* $\log\left(\dfrac{x + \sqrt{x^2 + a^2}}{a}\right) = \sinh^{-1}\left(\dfrac{x}{a}\right);$ $\log\left(\dfrac{x + \sqrt{x^2 - a^2}}{a}\right) = \cosh^{-1}\left(\dfrac{x}{a}\right);$

$\log\left(\dfrac{a + \sqrt{a^2 - x^2}}{x}\right) = \operatorname{sech}^{-1}\left(\dfrac{x}{a}\right);$ $\log\left(\dfrac{a + \sqrt{a^2 + x^2}}{x}\right) = \operatorname{csch}^{-1}\left(\dfrac{x}{a}\right);$

$\log z = \sinh^{-1}\left(\dfrac{z^2 - 1}{2z}\right) = \cosh^{-1}\left(\dfrac{z^2 + 1}{2z}\right);$ $\tanh^{-1} z = -i\cdot\tan^{-1}(zi).$

134. $\int x \sqrt{x^2 \pm a^2}\, dx = \tfrac{1}{3} \sqrt{(x^2 \pm a^2)^3}.$

135. $\int x \sqrt{a^2 - x^2}\, dx = -\tfrac{1}{3} \sqrt{(a^2 - x^2)^3}.$

136. $\int \sqrt{(x^2 \pm a^2)^3}\, dx$

$$= \tfrac{1}{4} \left[x \sqrt{(x^2 \pm a^2)^3} \pm \frac{3\, a^2 x}{2} \sqrt{x^2 \pm a^2} + \frac{3\, a^4}{2} \log (x + \sqrt{x^2 \pm a^2}) \right].^{*}$$

137. $\int \sqrt{(a^2 - x^2)^3}\, dx$

$$= \tfrac{1}{4} \left[x \sqrt{(a^2 - x^2)^3} + \frac{3\, a^2 x}{2} \sqrt{a^2 - x^2} + \frac{3\, a^4}{2} \sin^{-1} \frac{x}{a} \right].$$

138. $\int \dfrac{dx}{\sqrt{(x^2 \pm a^2)^3}} = \dfrac{\pm\, x}{a^2 \sqrt{x^2 \pm a^2}}.$

139. $\int \dfrac{dx}{\sqrt{(a^2 - x^2)^3}} = \dfrac{x}{a^2 \sqrt{a^2 - x^2}}.$

140. $\int \dfrac{x\, dx}{\sqrt{(x^2 \pm a^2)^3}} = \dfrac{-1}{\sqrt{x^2 \pm a^2}}.$

141. $\int \dfrac{x\, dx}{\sqrt{(a^2 - x^2)^3}} = \dfrac{1}{\sqrt{a^2 - x^2}}.$

142. $\int x \sqrt{(x^2 \pm a^2)^3}\, dx = \tfrac{1}{5} \sqrt{(x^2 \pm a^2)^5}.$

143. $\int x \sqrt{(a^2 - x^2)^3}\, dx = -\tfrac{1}{5} \sqrt{(a^2 - x^2)^5}.$

144. $\int x^2 \sqrt{x^2 \pm a^2}\, dx$

$$= \frac{x}{4} \sqrt{(x^2 \pm a^2)^3} \mp \frac{a^2}{8} x \sqrt{x^2 \pm a^2} - \frac{a^4}{8} \log (x + \sqrt{x^2 \pm a^2}).^{*}$$

145. $\int x^2 \sqrt{a^2 - x^2}\, dx$

$$= -\frac{x}{4} \sqrt{(a^2 - x^2)^3} + \frac{a^2}{8} \left(x \sqrt{a^2 - x^2} + a^2 \sin^{-1} \frac{x}{a} \right).$$

* See Note on page 20.

146. $\displaystyle\int \frac{\sqrt{a^2 \pm x^2}\, dx}{x^3} = -\frac{\sqrt{a^2 \pm x^2}}{2\, x^2} \pm \frac{1}{2}\int \frac{dx}{x\sqrt{a^2 \pm x^2}}$

147. $\displaystyle\int x^3 \sqrt{a^2 \pm x^2}\, dx = (\pm \tfrac{1}{5} x^2 - \tfrac{2}{15} a^2)\sqrt{(a^2 \pm x^2)^3}.$

148. $\displaystyle\int \frac{dx}{x^3 \sqrt{a^2 \pm x^2}} = -\frac{\sqrt{a^2 \pm x^2}}{2\, a^2 x^2} \mp \frac{1}{2\, a^2}\int \frac{dx}{x\sqrt{a^2 \pm x^2}}$

149. $\displaystyle\int \frac{dx}{x^3 \sqrt{x^2 - a^2}} = \frac{\sqrt{x^2 - a^2}}{2\, a^2 x^2} + \frac{1}{2\, a^3}\cos^{-1}\frac{a}{x}.$

150. $\displaystyle\int \frac{x^2 dx}{\sqrt{x^2 \pm a^2}} = \frac{x}{2}\sqrt{x^2 \pm a^2} \mp \frac{a^2}{2}\log(x + \sqrt{x^2 \pm a^2}).\,{}^{*}$

151. $\displaystyle\int \frac{x^2 dx}{\sqrt{a^2 - x^2}} = -\frac{x}{2}\sqrt{a^2 - x^2} + \frac{a^2}{2}\sin^{-1}\frac{x}{a}.$

152. $\displaystyle\int \frac{dx}{x^2 \sqrt{x^2 \pm a^2}} = \mp \frac{\sqrt{x^2 \pm a^2}}{a^2 x}.$

153. $\displaystyle\int \frac{dx}{x^2 \sqrt{a^2 - x^2}} = -\frac{\sqrt{a^2 - x^2}}{a^2 x}.$

154. $\displaystyle\int \frac{\sqrt{x^2 \pm a^2}\, dx}{x^2} = -\frac{\sqrt{x^2 \pm a^2}}{x} + \log(x + \sqrt{x^2 \pm a^2}).\,{}^{*}$

155. $\displaystyle\int \frac{\sqrt{a^2 - x^2}}{x^2}\, dx = -\frac{\sqrt{a^2 - x^2}}{x} - \sin^{-1}\frac{x}{a}.$

156. $\displaystyle\int \frac{x^2 dx}{\sqrt{(x^2 \pm a^2)^3}} = \frac{-x}{\sqrt{x^2 \pm a^2}} + \log(x + \sqrt{x^2 \pm a^2}).\,{}^{*}$

157. $\displaystyle\int \frac{x^2 dx}{\sqrt{(a^2 - x^2)^3}} = \frac{x}{\sqrt{a^2 - x^2}} - \sin^{-1}\frac{x}{a}.$

* (See Note on page 20.)

158. $\int \dfrac{f(x^2)\,dx}{\sqrt{a + cx^2}} = g \int f\left(\dfrac{au^2}{g^2 - cu^2}\right) \dfrac{du}{(g^2 - cu^2)}$,

where $u = \dfrac{gx}{\sqrt{a + cx^2}}$.

159. $\int \dfrac{xf(x^2)\,dx}{\sqrt{a + cx^2}} = \dfrac{1}{c} \int f\left(\dfrac{u^2 - a}{c}\right) du$, where $u^2 = a + cx^2$.

D. — Expressions Involving $\sqrt{a + bx + cx^2}$.

Let $X = a + bx + cx^2$, $q = 4\,ac - b^2$, and $k = \dfrac{4\,c}{q}$. In order to rationalize the function $f(x, \sqrt{a + bx + cx^2})$ we may put $\sqrt{a + bx + cx^2} = \sqrt{\pm\, c}\,\sqrt{A + Bx \pm x^2}$, according as c is positive or negative, and then substitute for x a new variable z, such that

$z = \sqrt{A + Bx + x^2} \pm x$, if $c > 0$.

$z = \dfrac{\sqrt{A + Bx - x^2} - \sqrt{A}}{x}$, if $c < 0$ and $\dfrac{a}{-c} > 0$.

$z = \sqrt{\dfrac{x - \beta}{a - x}}$, where α and β are the roots of the equation

$A + Bx - x^2 = 0$, if $c < 0$ and $\dfrac{a}{-c} < 0$.

160. $\int \dfrac{dx}{\sqrt{X}} = \dfrac{1}{\sqrt{c}} \log\left(\sqrt{X} + x\sqrt{c} + \dfrac{b}{2\sqrt{c}}\right)$,

or $\dfrac{1}{\sqrt{c}} \sinh^{-1}\left(\dfrac{2\,cx + b}{\sqrt{q}}\right)$.

161. $\int \dfrac{dx}{\sqrt{X}} = \dfrac{-1}{\sqrt{-c}} \sin^{-1}\left(\dfrac{2\,cx + b}{\sqrt{-q}}\right)$.

162. $\displaystyle \int \frac{dx}{X\sqrt{X}} = \frac{2\,(2\,cx + b)}{q\,\sqrt{X}}.$

163. $\displaystyle \int \frac{dx}{X^2\sqrt{X}} = \frac{2\,(2\,cx + b)}{3\,q\,\sqrt{X}}\left(\frac{1}{X} + 2\,k\right).$

164. $\displaystyle \int \frac{dx}{X^n\sqrt{X}} = \frac{2\,(2\,cx + b)\,\sqrt{X}}{(2\,n - 1)\,q\,X^n} + \frac{2\,k\,(n - 1)}{2\,n - 1}\int \frac{dx}{X^{n-1}\sqrt{X}}.$

165. $\displaystyle \int \sqrt{X}\,dx = \frac{(2\,cx + b)\,\sqrt{X}}{4\,c} + \frac{1}{2\,k}\int \frac{dx}{\sqrt{X}}.$

166. $\displaystyle \int X\sqrt{X}\,dx = \frac{(2\,cx + b)\,\sqrt{X}}{8\,c}\left(X + \frac{3}{2\,k}\right) + \frac{3}{8\,k^2}\int \frac{dx}{\sqrt{X}}.$

167. $\displaystyle \int X^2\sqrt{X}\,dx$

$\displaystyle = \frac{(2\,cx + b)\,\sqrt{X}}{12\,c}\left(X^2 + \frac{5\,X}{4\,k} + \frac{15}{8\,k^2}\right) + \frac{5}{16\,k^3}\int \frac{dx}{\sqrt{X}}.$

168. $\displaystyle \int X^n\sqrt{X}\,dx = \frac{(2\,cx + b)\,X^n\sqrt{X}}{4\,(n + 1)\,c} + \frac{2\,n + 1}{2\,(n + 1)\,k}\int \frac{X^n\,dx}{\sqrt{X}}.$

169. $\displaystyle \int \frac{x\,dx}{\sqrt{X}} = \frac{\sqrt{X}}{c} - \frac{b}{2\,c}\int \frac{dx}{\sqrt{X}}.$

170. $\displaystyle \int \frac{x\,dx}{X\sqrt{X}} = -\frac{2\,(bx + 2\,a)}{q\,\sqrt{X}}.$

171. $\displaystyle \int \frac{x\,dx}{X^n\sqrt{X}} = -\frac{\sqrt{X}}{(2\,n - 1)\,c\,X^n} - \frac{b}{2\,c}\int \frac{dx}{X^n\sqrt{X}}.$

172. $\displaystyle \int \frac{x^2\,dx}{\sqrt{X}} = \left(\frac{x}{2\,c} - \frac{3\,b}{4\,c^2}\right)\sqrt{X} + \frac{3\,b^2 - 4\,ac}{8\,c^2}\int \frac{dx}{\sqrt{X}}.$

173. $\displaystyle \int \frac{x^2\,dx}{X\sqrt{X}} = \frac{(2\,b^2 - 4\,ac)\,x + 2\,ab}{cq\,\sqrt{X}} + \frac{1}{c}\int \frac{dx}{\sqrt{X}}.$

174. $\int \dfrac{x^2\,dx}{X^n\sqrt{X}}$

$$= \dfrac{(2\,b^2 - 4\,ac)\,x + 2\,ab}{(2\,n - 1)\,cq\,X^{n-1}\sqrt{X}} + \dfrac{4\,ac + (2\,n - 3)\,b^2}{(2\,n - 1)\,cq} \int \dfrac{dx}{X^{n-1}\sqrt{X}}.$$

175. $\int \dfrac{x^3\,dx}{\sqrt{X}}$

$$= \left(\dfrac{x^2}{3\,c} - \dfrac{5\,bx}{12\,c^2} + \dfrac{5\,b^2}{8\,c^3} - \dfrac{2\,a}{3\,c^2}\right)\sqrt{X} + \left(\dfrac{3\,ab}{4\,c^2} - \dfrac{5\,b^3}{16\,c^3}\right)\int \dfrac{dx}{\sqrt{X}}.$$

176. $\int x\sqrt{X}\,dx = \dfrac{X\sqrt{X}}{3\,c} - \dfrac{b}{2\,c}\int \sqrt{X}\,dx.$

177. $\int xX\sqrt{X}\,dx = \dfrac{X^2\sqrt{X}}{5\,c} - \dfrac{b}{2\,c}\int X\sqrt{X}\,dx.$

178. $\int \dfrac{xX^n\,dx}{\sqrt{X}} = \dfrac{X^n\sqrt{X}}{(2\,n + 1)\,c} - \dfrac{b}{2\,c}\int \dfrac{X^n\,dx}{\sqrt{X}}.$

179. $\int x^2\sqrt{X}\,dx = \left(x - \dfrac{5\,b}{6\,c}\right)\dfrac{X\sqrt{X}}{4\,c} + \dfrac{5\,b^2 - 4\,ac}{16\,c^2}\int \sqrt{X}\,dx.$

180. $\int \dfrac{x^2X^n\,dx}{\sqrt{X}} = \dfrac{xX^n\sqrt{X}}{2\,(n + 1)\,c} - \dfrac{(2\,n + 3)\,b}{4\,(n + 1)\,c}\int \dfrac{xX^n\,dx}{\sqrt{X}}$

$$- \dfrac{a}{2\,(n + 1)\,c}\int \dfrac{X^n\,dx}{\sqrt{X}}.$$

181. $\int x^3\sqrt{X}\,dx = \left(x^2 - \dfrac{7\,bx}{8\,c} + \dfrac{35\,b^2}{48\,c^2} - \dfrac{2\,a}{3\,c}\right)\dfrac{X\sqrt{X}}{5\,c}$

$$+ \left(\dfrac{3\,ab}{8\,c^2} - \dfrac{7\,b^3}{32\,c^3}\right)\int \sqrt{X}\,dx.$$

182. $\int \dfrac{dx}{x\sqrt{X}} = -\dfrac{1}{\sqrt{a}}\log\left(\dfrac{\sqrt{X} + \sqrt{a}}{x} + \dfrac{b}{2\sqrt{a}}\right),$ if $a > 0.$

183. $\int \dfrac{dx}{x\sqrt{X}} = \dfrac{1}{\sqrt{-a}}\sin^{-1}\left(\dfrac{bx+2a}{x\sqrt{-q}}\right)$, or $\dfrac{-1}{\sqrt{a}}\sinh^{-1}\dfrac{2a+bx}{x\sqrt{q}}$.

184. $\int \dfrac{dx}{x\sqrt{X}} = -\dfrac{2\sqrt{X}}{bx}$, if $a = 0$.

185. $\int \dfrac{dx}{xX^n\sqrt{X}}$

$$= \dfrac{\sqrt{X}}{(2n-1)aX^n} + \dfrac{1}{a}\int \dfrac{dx}{xX^{n-1}\sqrt{X}} - \dfrac{b}{2a}\int \dfrac{dx}{X^n\sqrt{X}}.$$

186. $\int \dfrac{dx}{x^2\sqrt{X}} = -\dfrac{\sqrt{X}}{ax} - \dfrac{b}{2a}\int \dfrac{dx}{x\sqrt{X}}$.

187. $\int \dfrac{\sqrt{X}\,dx}{x} = \sqrt{X} + \dfrac{b}{2}\int \dfrac{dx}{\sqrt{X}} + a\int \dfrac{dx}{x\sqrt{X}}$.

188. $\int \dfrac{X^n\,dx}{x\sqrt{X}} = \dfrac{X^n}{(2n-1)\sqrt{X}} + a\int \dfrac{X^{n-1}\,dx}{x\sqrt{X}} + \dfrac{b}{2}\int \dfrac{X^{n-1}\,dx}{\sqrt{X}}$.

189. $\int \dfrac{\sqrt{X}\,dx}{x^2} = -\dfrac{\sqrt{X}}{x} + \dfrac{b}{2}\int \dfrac{dx}{x\sqrt{X}} + c\int \dfrac{dx}{\sqrt{X}}$.

190. $\int \dfrac{x^m\,dx}{X^n\sqrt{X}} = \dfrac{1}{c}\int \dfrac{x^{m-2}\,dx}{X^{n-1}\sqrt{X}} - \dfrac{b}{c}\int \dfrac{x^{m-1}\,dx}{X^n\sqrt{X}} - \dfrac{a}{c}\int \dfrac{x^{m-2}\,dx}{X^n\sqrt{X}}$.

191. $\int \dfrac{x^m X^n\,dx}{\sqrt{X}} = \dfrac{x^{m-1}X^n\sqrt{X}}{(2n+m)c} - \dfrac{(2n+2m-1)b}{2c(2n+m)}\int \dfrac{x^{m-1}X^n\,dx}{\sqrt{X}}$

$$- \dfrac{(m-1)a}{(2n+m)c}\int \dfrac{x^{m-2}X^n\,dx}{\sqrt{X}}.$$

192. $\int \dfrac{dx}{x^m X^n\sqrt{X}}$

$$= -\dfrac{\sqrt{X}}{(m-1)ax^{m-1}X^n} - \dfrac{(2n+2m-3)b}{2a(m-1)}\int \dfrac{dx}{x^{m-1}X^n\sqrt{X}}$$

$$- \dfrac{(2n+m-2)c}{(m-1)a}\int \dfrac{dx}{x^{m-2}X^n\sqrt{X}}.$$

193. $\displaystyle\int \frac{X^n\,dx}{x^m\sqrt{X}} = -\frac{X^{n-1}\sqrt{X}}{(m-1)\,x^{m-1}} + \frac{(2\,n-1)\,b}{2\,(m-1)}\int \frac{X^{n-1}\,dx}{x^{m-1}\sqrt{X}}$

$$+ \frac{(2\,n-1)\,c}{m-1}\int \frac{X^{n-1}\,dx}{x^{m-2}\sqrt{X}}.$$

194. $\displaystyle\int f(x,\ \sqrt{(x-a)(x-b)})\,dx$

$$= 2\,(a-b)\int f\left\{\frac{bu^2-a}{u^2-1},\ \frac{u(b-a)}{u^2-1}\right\}\frac{u\,du}{(u^2-1)^2},$$

where $u^2(x-b) = x-a$.

E. — Expressions Involving Products of Powers of $(a'+b'x)$ and $\sqrt{a+bx+cx^2}$.

Let $X = a + bx + cx^2$, $\quad v = a' + b'x$, $\quad q = 4\,ac - b^2$,
$\beta = bb' - 2\,a'c$, $\qquad k = ab'^2 - a'bb' + ca'^2$, then

195. $\displaystyle\int \frac{dx}{v\sqrt{X}} = \frac{1}{\sqrt{k}}\log \frac{2\,k + \beta v - 2\,b'\sqrt{kX}}{v}$

$$= \frac{1}{\sqrt{-k}}\tan^{-1}\frac{2\,k + \beta v}{2b'\sqrt{-kX}}$$

$$= \frac{1}{\sqrt{-k}}\sin^{-1}\frac{2\,k + \beta v}{b'v\sqrt{-q}},\ \text{if } k \gtrless 0.$$

196. $\displaystyle\int \frac{dx}{v\sqrt{X}} = -\frac{2\,b'\sqrt{X}}{\beta v},\ \text{if } k = 0:$

$$\text{thus, } \int \frac{dx}{(x\pm 1)\sqrt{x^2-1}} = \pm\sqrt{\frac{x\mp 1}{x\pm 1}}.$$

197. $\displaystyle\int \frac{dx}{v^2\sqrt{X}} = -\frac{b'\sqrt{X}}{kv} - \frac{\beta}{2\,k}\int \frac{dx}{v\sqrt{X}}.$

198. $\displaystyle\int \frac{dx}{v^2\sqrt{X}} = -\frac{2\,b'\sqrt{X}}{3\,\beta v^2} - \frac{2\,c}{3\,\beta}\int \frac{dx}{v\sqrt{X}},\ \text{if } k = 0.$

199. $\displaystyle\int \frac{dx}{v X \sqrt{X}} = \frac{1}{k}\left(\frac{b'}{\sqrt{X}} - \tfrac{1}{2}\beta \int \frac{dx}{X\sqrt{X}} + b'^2 \int \frac{dx}{v\sqrt{X}} \right).$

200. $\displaystyle\int \frac{v\,dx}{X\sqrt{X}} = -\frac{2\,(2\,k + \beta v)}{b'q\sqrt{X}}.$

201. $\displaystyle\int \frac{v\,dx}{\sqrt{X}} = \frac{b'\sqrt{X}}{c} - \frac{\beta}{2\,c}\int \frac{dx}{\sqrt{X}}.$

202. $\displaystyle\int v\sqrt{X}\,dx = \frac{b'X\sqrt{X}}{3\,c} - \frac{\beta}{2\,c}\int \sqrt{X}\,dx.$

203. $\displaystyle\int \frac{v\,dx}{X^n\sqrt{X}} = -\frac{b'\sqrt{X}}{(2\,n-1)\,cX^n} - \frac{\beta}{2\,c}\int \frac{dx}{X^n\sqrt{X}}.$

204. $\displaystyle\int \frac{v\,X^n\,dx}{\sqrt{X}} = \frac{b'X^n\sqrt{X}}{(2\,n+1)\,c} - \frac{\beta}{2\,c}\int \frac{X^n\,dx}{\sqrt{X}}.$

205. $\displaystyle\int \frac{dx}{v^m\sqrt{X}} = -\frac{b'\sqrt{X}}{(m-1)\,kv^{m-1}} - \frac{(2\,m-3)\,\beta}{2\,(m-1)\,k}\int \frac{dx}{v^{m-1}\sqrt{X}}$
$$\qquad\qquad -\frac{(m-2)\,c}{(m-1)\,k}\int \frac{dx}{v^{m-2}\sqrt{X}}, \text{ if } k \neq 0.$$

206. $\displaystyle\int \frac{dx}{v^m\sqrt{X}} = -\frac{2\,b'\sqrt{X}}{(2\,m-1)\,\beta v^m}$
$$\qquad\qquad -\frac{2\,(m-1)\,c}{(2\,m-1)\beta}\int \frac{dx}{v^{m-1}\sqrt{X}}, \text{ if } k = 0.$$

207. $\displaystyle\int \frac{\sqrt{X}\,dx}{v^m} = -\frac{b'X\sqrt{X}}{(m-1)\,kv^{m-1}} - \frac{(2\,m-5)\,\beta}{2\,(m-1)\,k}\int \frac{\sqrt{X}\,dx}{v^{m-1}}$
$$\qquad\qquad -\frac{(m-4)\,c}{(m-1)k}\int \frac{\sqrt{X}\,dx}{v^{m-2}}$$
$$= \frac{1}{(m-1)\,b'^2}\left(-\frac{b'\sqrt{X}}{v^{m-1}} + \tfrac{1}{2}\beta \int \frac{dx}{v^{m-1}\sqrt{X}} + c\int \frac{dx}{v^{m-2}\sqrt{X}} \right)$$
$$= \frac{1}{(m-2)\,b'^2}\left(-\frac{b'\sqrt{X}}{v^{m-1}} - k\int \frac{dx}{v^m\sqrt{X}} - \tfrac{1}{2}\beta \int \frac{dx}{v^{m-1}\sqrt{X}} \right).$$

208. $\displaystyle\int v^m \sqrt{X}\, dx = \frac{1}{(m+2)\,c}\bigg(b'\,v^{m-1}X\sqrt{X}$

$$- (m+\tfrac{1}{2})\,\beta \int v^{m-1}\sqrt{X}\, dx - (m-1)\,k \int v^{m-2}\sqrt{X}\, dx \bigg).$$

209. $\displaystyle\int \frac{dx}{v^m X^n \sqrt{X}}$

$$= -\frac{1}{(m-1)\,k}\bigg(\frac{b'\sqrt{X}}{v^{m-1}X^n} + (m+n-\tfrac{3}{2})\,\beta \int \frac{dx}{v^{m-1}X^n\sqrt{X}}$$

$$+ (m+2n-2)\,c \int \frac{dx}{v^{m-2}X^n\sqrt{X}} \bigg), \ \text{if } k \neq 0.$$

210. $\displaystyle\int \frac{dx}{v^m X^n \sqrt{X}} = \frac{-2}{(2m+2n-1)\,\beta}\bigg(\frac{b'\sqrt{X}}{v^m X^n}$

$$+ (m+2n-1)\,c \int \frac{dx}{v^{m-1}X^n\sqrt{X}} \bigg), \ \text{if } k = 0.$$

211. $\displaystyle\int \frac{X^n\, dx}{v^m \sqrt{X}}$

$$= -\frac{1}{(m-1)\,k}\bigg(\frac{b'X^n\sqrt{X}}{v^{m-1}} + (m-n-\tfrac{3}{2})\,\beta \int \frac{X^n\, dx}{v^{m-1}\sqrt{X}}$$

$$+ (m-2n-2)\,c \int \frac{X^n\, dx}{v^{m-2}\sqrt{X}} \bigg)$$

$$= -\frac{1}{(m-2n)\,b'^2}\bigg(\frac{b'X^{n-1}\sqrt{X}}{v^{m-1}} + (2n-1)\,k \int \frac{X^{n-1}\,dx}{v^m\sqrt{X}}$$

$$+ (n-\tfrac{1}{2})\,\beta \int \frac{X^{n-1}\, dx}{v^{m-1}\sqrt{X}} \bigg)$$

$$= \frac{1}{(m-1)\,b'^2}\bigg(-\frac{b'X^{n-1}\sqrt{X}}{v^{m-1}} + (n-\tfrac{1}{2})\,\beta \int \frac{X^{n-1}\, dx}{v^{m-1}\sqrt{X}}$$

$$+ (2n-1)\,c \int \frac{X^{n-1}\, dx}{v^{m-2}\sqrt{X}} \bigg).$$

212. $\displaystyle\int \frac{v^m X^n\, dx}{\sqrt{X}} = \frac{1}{(m+2n)\,c}\left(b'v^{m-1}X^n\sqrt{X} \right.$

$$\left. -\,(m+n-\tfrac{1}{2})\,\beta \int \frac{v^{m-1}X^n\, dx}{\sqrt{X}} - (m-1)\,k \int \frac{v^{m-2}X^n\, dx}{\sqrt{X}} \right).$$

213. $\displaystyle\int \frac{v^m\, dx}{X^n\sqrt{X}} = \frac{1}{(m-2n)\,c}\left(\frac{b'v^{m-1}\sqrt{X}}{X^n} \right.$

$$\left. -\,(m-n-\tfrac{1}{2})\,\beta \int \frac{v^{m-1}\, dx}{X^n\sqrt{X}} - (m-1)\,k \int \frac{v^{m-2}\, dx}{X^n\sqrt{X}} \right).$$

$$\frac{1}{(x+a)(x+b)\sqrt{X}} = \frac{1}{(b-a)(x+a)\sqrt{X}} + \frac{1}{(a-b)(x+b)\sqrt{X}}$$

$$\frac{1}{\sqrt{a+bx+cx^2} \pm \sqrt{a'+b'x+c'x^2}}$$

$$= \frac{\sqrt{a+bx+cx^2} \mp \sqrt{a'+b'x+c'x^2}}{a-a' + (b-b')\,x + (c-c')\,x^2}.$$

$$\frac{\sqrt{X}}{(x+a)(x+b)} = \frac{\sqrt{X}}{(b-a)(x+a)} + \frac{\sqrt{X}}{(a-b)(x+b)}.$$

$$\frac{(x+a)\sqrt{X}}{x+b} = \sqrt{X} + \frac{(a-b)\sqrt{X}}{x+b}.$$

$\displaystyle\int \sqrt{\frac{ax^2+b}{a'x^2+b'}}\, dx$ is an elliptic integral.

$$\int \frac{x\sqrt{a+bx^2}}{\sqrt{a'+b'x^2}}\, dx = \frac{1}{b'\sqrt{b'}} \int \sqrt{ab' - a'b + by^2}\cdot dy,$$

where $\qquad\qquad y^2 = a' + b'x^2.$

IV. MISCELLANEOUS ALGEBRAIC EXPRESSIONS.

214. $\displaystyle\int \sqrt{2\,ax-x^2}\cdot dx = \frac{x-a}{2}\sqrt{2\,ax-x^2} + \frac{a^2}{2}\sin^{-1}\frac{x-a}{a}$

215. $\displaystyle\int \frac{dx}{\sqrt{2\,ax-x^2}} = \text{versin}^{-1}\frac{x}{a} = \cos^{-1}\left(1-\frac{x}{a}\right)$

$$= 2\sin^{-1}\sqrt{\frac{x}{2\,a}}.$$

216. $\displaystyle\int \frac{x^n\,dx}{\sqrt{2\,ax-x^2}} = -\frac{x^{n-1}\sqrt{2\,ax-x^2}}{n}$

$$-\frac{a\,(1-2\,n)}{n}\int \frac{x^{n-1}\,dx}{\sqrt{2\,ax-x^2}}.$$

217. $\displaystyle\int \frac{dx}{x^n\sqrt{2\,ax-x^2}} = \frac{\sqrt{2\,ax-x^2}}{a\,(1-2\,n)\,x^n}$

$$+\frac{n-1}{(2\,n-1)\,a}\int \frac{dx}{x^{n-1}\sqrt{2\,ax-x^2}}.$$

218. $\displaystyle\int x^n\sqrt{2\,ax-x^2}\cdot dx = -\frac{x^{n-1}\sqrt{(2\,ax-x^2)^3}}{n+2}$

$$+\frac{(2\,n+1)\,a}{n+2}\int x^{n-1}\sqrt{2\,ax-x^2}\cdot dx$$

219. $\displaystyle\int \frac{\sqrt{2\,ax-x^2}\cdot dx}{x^n} = \frac{\sqrt{(2\,ax-x^2)^3}}{(3-2\,n)\,ax^n}$

$$+\frac{n-3}{(2\,n-3)\,a}\int \frac{\sqrt{2\,ax-x^2}\cdot dx}{x^{n-1}}.$$

220. $\displaystyle\int \frac{dx}{x\sqrt{x^n-a^2}} = \frac{2}{an}\cos^{-1}\frac{a}{x^{\frac{n}{2}}}.$

221. $\int \dfrac{dx}{x\sqrt{x^n + a^2}} = \dfrac{1}{an} \log \dfrac{\sqrt{a^2 + x^n} - a}{\sqrt{a^2 + x^n} + a}$.

222. $\int \dfrac{x^{\frac{1}{2}}\, dx}{\sqrt{a^3 - x^3}} = \frac{2}{3} \sin^{-1}\left(\dfrac{x}{a}\right)^{\frac{3}{2}}$.

223. $\int \dfrac{dx}{(a + bx^2)\sqrt{x}} = \dfrac{1}{b\delta^3\sqrt{2}} \Big\{ \log\left(\dfrac{x + \delta^2 + \sqrt{2\,\delta^2 x}}{\sqrt{a + bx^2}}\right)$

$\qquad + \tan^{-1}\left(1 + \dfrac{\sqrt{2}\,x}{\delta}\right) - \tan^{-1}\left(1 - \dfrac{\sqrt{2}\,x}{\delta}\right)\Big\}$, where $b\delta^4 = a$.

224. $\int \dfrac{\sqrt{x}\cdot dx}{a + bx^2} = \dfrac{1}{b\delta\sqrt{2}} \Big\{ \tan^{-1}\left(1 + \dfrac{\sqrt{2}\,x}{\delta}\right) - \tan^{-1}\left(1 - \dfrac{\sqrt{2}\,x}{\delta}\right)$

$\qquad - \log\left(\dfrac{x + \delta^2 + \sqrt{2\,\delta^2 x}}{\sqrt{a + bx^2}}\right)\Big\}$, where $b\delta^4 = a$.

225. $\int \dfrac{x^{\frac{3}{2}}\cdot dx}{a + bx^2} = \dfrac{2\sqrt{x}}{b} - \dfrac{a}{b}\int \dfrac{dx}{(a + bx^2)\sqrt{x}}$.

226. $\int \dfrac{dx}{(a + bx^2)^2 \sqrt{x}} = \dfrac{\sqrt{x}}{2\,a\,(a + bx^2)} + \dfrac{3}{4\,a}\int \dfrac{dx}{(a + bx^2)\sqrt{x}}$.

227. $\int \dfrac{\sqrt{x}\cdot dx}{(a + bx^2)^2} = \dfrac{x^{\frac{3}{2}}}{2\,a\,(a + bx^2)} + \dfrac{1}{4\,a}\int \dfrac{\sqrt{x}\cdot dx}{(a + bx^2)}$.

If a_1, a_2, a_3, etc., are the roots of the equation

$$p_0 x^n + p_1 x^{n-1} + p_2 x^{n-2} + \cdots + p_n = 0,$$

the integrand in the expression

$$\int \dfrac{(q_0 x^m + q_1 x^{m-1} + \cdots + q_n)\, dx}{(p_0 x^n + p_1 x^{n-1} + \cdots + p_n)\sqrt{a + bx + cx^2}},$$

where $m < n$, may be expressed as the sum of a number of partial fractions of the form $-\dfrac{A}{(x - a_k)^r \sqrt{a + bx + cx^2}}$, and these can be integrated by the aid of equations given above. Thus,

228. $\displaystyle\int \frac{(px + q)\,dx}{(x - a')(x - b')\sqrt{a + bx + cx^2}}$

$$= \frac{q + a'p}{a' - b'} \int \frac{dx}{(x - a')\sqrt{a + bx + cx^2}}$$

$$- \frac{q + b'p}{a' - b'} \int \frac{dx}{(x - b')\sqrt{a + bx + cx^2}}.$$

229. $\displaystyle\int \frac{dx}{(a' + c'x^2)\sqrt{a + cx^2}}$

$$= \frac{1}{a'} \sqrt{\frac{a'}{ac' - a'c}} \tan^{-1} x \sqrt{\frac{ac' - a'c}{a'(a + cx^2)}},$$

$$\text{or } \frac{1}{2\,a'} \sqrt{\frac{a'}{a'c - ac'}} \log \frac{\sqrt{a + cx^2} + x\sqrt{(a'c - ac')/a'}}{\sqrt{a + cx^2} - x\sqrt{(a'c - ac')/a'}}$$

230. $\displaystyle\int \frac{x\,dx}{(a' + c'x^2)\sqrt{a + cx^2}}$

$$= \frac{1}{c'} \sqrt{\frac{c'}{a'c - ac'}} \tan^{-1} \sqrt{\frac{c'(a + cx^2)}{a'c - ac'}},$$

$$\text{or } \frac{1}{2\,c'} \sqrt{\frac{c'}{ac' - a'c}} \log \frac{\sqrt{a + cx^2} - \sqrt{(ac' - a'c)/c'}}{\sqrt{a + cx^2} + \sqrt{(ac' - a'c)/c'}}.$$

231. $\displaystyle\int f\left\{ x,\ \sqrt[n]{\frac{a + bx}{a' + b'x}} \right\} dx$

$$= n(a'b - ab') \int f\left(\frac{a - a'z^n}{b'z^n - b},\ z \right) \cdot \frac{z^{n-1}\,dz}{(b'z^n - b)^2},$$

where $z^n(a' + b'x) = a + bx$.

232. $\int f\left(x, \ \sqrt[n]{c + \sqrt[m]{a + bx}}\right) dx$

$$= \frac{mn}{b} \int f\left\{\frac{(z^n - c)^m - a}{b}, \ z\right\}(z^n - c)^{m-1} z^{n-1} dz,$$

where $z^n = c + \sqrt[m]{a + bx}$.

233. $\int f\left\{x, \ \left[\frac{a + bx}{a' + b'x}\right]^{\frac{m}{n}}, \ \left[\frac{a + bx}{a' + b'x}\right]^{\frac{p}{q}}, \ \cdots\right\} dx$

$$= s\,(a'b - ab') \int f\left\{\frac{a'y^s - a}{b - b'y^s}, \ y^{\frac{ms}{n}}, \ y^{\frac{ps}{q}}, \ \cdots\right\} \frac{y^{s-1} dy}{(b - b'y^s)^2},$$

where $y^s\,(a' + b'x) = a + bx$ and s is the least common multiple of n, q, etc.

234. $\int f\left(x, \ \sqrt{a + bx + x^2}\right) dx$

$$= 2 \int f\left(\frac{2\sqrt{a}\cdot z - b}{1 - z^2}, \ \frac{z^2\sqrt{a} - bz + \sqrt{a}}{1 - z^2}\right) \cdot \frac{(z^2\sqrt{a} - bz + \sqrt{a})\,dz}{(1 - z^2)^2},$$

where $xz + \sqrt{a} = \sqrt{a + bx + x^2}$.

235. $\int f\left(x, \ \sqrt{a + bx + x^2}\right) dx$

$$= \int f\left(\frac{u^2 - a}{b - 2u}, \ \frac{u^2 - bu + a}{2u - b}\right) \frac{2\,(bu - a - u^2)\,du}{(b - 2u)^2},$$

where $u = \sqrt{a + bx + x^2} - x$.

$$\int \frac{dx}{x^4 + a^4} = \frac{1}{4\,a^3\sqrt{2}}\left\{\log\left(\frac{x^2 + ax\sqrt{2} + a^2}{x^2 - ax\sqrt{2} + a^2}\right) + 2\tan^{-1}\left(\frac{ax\sqrt{2}}{a^2 - x^2}\right)\right\}.$$

$$\int \frac{dx}{x^4 - a^4} = \frac{1}{4\,a^3}\left\{\log\left(\frac{x - a}{x + a}\right) - 2\tan^{-1}\left(\frac{x}{a}\right)\right\}.$$

V. TRANSCENDENTAL FUNCTIONS.

236. $\int \sin x \cdot f(\cos x)\, dx = -\int f(\cos x)\, d\,\cos x.$

237. $\int \cos x \cdot f(\sin x)\, dx = \int f(\sin x)\, d\,\sin x.$

238. $\int \sin x \cdot f(\sin x,\ \cos x)\, dx = -\int f(\sqrt{1-z^2},\ z)\, dz,$

where $z = \cos x.$

239. $\int \dfrac{dx}{a + b\cos x} = \dfrac{1}{c(b-a)}\left\{ \int \dfrac{dz}{z+c} - \int \dfrac{dz}{z-c} \right\},$

where $z = \tan \frac{1}{2} x,$ and $c^2 = (b+a)/(b-a).$ [See 651.]

240. $\int \dfrac{dx}{a \pm b\sin x} = \int \dfrac{2\, dz}{a \pm 2\, bz + az^2},$ where $z = \tan \frac{1}{2} x.$

241. $\int f(\sin x)\, dx = -\int f\left(\cos\left(\dfrac{\pi}{2} - x \right) \right) d\left(\dfrac{\pi}{2} - x \right).$

242. $\int f(\tan x)\, dx = -\int f \operatorname{ctn}\left(\dfrac{\pi}{2} - x \right) d\left(\dfrac{\pi}{2} - x \right).$

243. $\int f(\sec x)\, dx = -\int f \csc\left(\dfrac{\pi}{2} - x \right) d\left(\dfrac{\pi}{2} - x \right).$

244. $\int \dfrac{\sin x \cdot f(\sin^2 x)\, dx}{\sqrt{1 - k^2 \sin^2 x}} = \int \dfrac{f(z)\, dz}{2\sqrt{(1-z)(1-k^2 z)}},$

where $z = \sin^2 x.$

245. $\int \dfrac{\cos x \cdot f(\cos^2 x)\, dx}{\sqrt{1 - k^2 \sin^2 x}} = \int \dfrac{f(1-z)\, dz}{2\sqrt{z(1-k^2 z)}},$ where $z = \sin^2 x.$

246. $\displaystyle\int \frac{\tan x \cdot f(\tan^2 x)\,dx}{\sqrt{1 - k^2 \sin^2 x}} = \int f\!\left(\frac{z}{1-z}\right) \frac{dz}{2\,(1-z)\,\sqrt{1 - k^2 z}},$

where $z = \sin^2 x$.

247. $\displaystyle\int f(ax + b)\,dx = \frac{1}{a}\int f(ax + b)\,d\,(ax + b).$

248. $\displaystyle\int \sec^{n+2} x \cdot f(\tan x)\,dx = \int (1 + z^2)^{\frac{n}{2}} f(z)\,dz;\ \ z = \tan x.$

249. $\displaystyle\int f(\sin x,\ \cos x)\,dx$

$$= -\int f\!\left(\cos\!\left(\frac{\pi}{2} - x\right),\ \sin\!\left(\frac{\pi}{2} - x\right)\right) d\!\left(\frac{\pi}{2} - x\right).$$

250. $\displaystyle\int f(x) \cdot \sin^{-1} x \cdot dx = \sin^{-1} x \cdot \phi(x) - \int \frac{\phi(x)\,dx}{\sqrt{1 - x^2}},\ dx,$

where $\phi(x) = \int f(x)\,dx.$

251. $\displaystyle\int f(x) \cdot \cos^{-1} x\,dx = \cos^{-1} x \cdot \phi(x) + \int \frac{\phi(x)\,dx}{\sqrt{1 - x^2}}.$

252. $\displaystyle\int f(x) \cdot \tan^{-1} x\,dx = \tan^{-1} x \cdot \phi(x) - \int \frac{\phi(x)\,dx}{1 + x^2}.$

253. $\displaystyle\int f(x) \cdot \operatorname{ctn}^{-1} x\,dx = \operatorname{ctn}^{-1} x \cdot \phi(x) + \int \frac{\phi(x)\,dx}{1 + x^2}.$

254. $\displaystyle\int f(x,\ \cos x)\,dx = -\int f\!\left(\frac{\pi}{2} - z,\ \sin z\right) dz,$

where $z = \dfrac{\pi}{2} - x.$

255. $\displaystyle\int \frac{\sin x \cdot f(\cos x)\,dx}{a + b \cos x} = -\frac{1}{b}\int f\!\left(\frac{z - a}{b}\right) \frac{dz}{z},$

where $z = a + b \cos x.$

256. $\int f(x, \log x)\, dx = \int f(e^z, z)\, e^z\, dz$, where $z = \log x$.

257. $\int \dfrac{f(\log x)\, dx}{x} = \int f(z)\, dz$, where $z = \log x$.

258. $\int x^m f(\log x)\, dx = \int e^{(m+1)z} f(z)\, dz$.

259. $\int f(\sin x,\ \cos x,\ \tan x,\ \operatorname{ctn} x,\ \sec x,\ \csc x)\, dx$

$$= \int f\left(\frac{2z}{1+z^2},\ \frac{1-z^2}{1+z^2},\ \frac{2z}{1-z^2},\ \frac{1-z^2}{2z},\ \frac{1+z^2}{1-z^2},\ \frac{1+z^2}{2z}\right)$$

$\dfrac{2\, dz}{1+z^2}$, where $z = \tan \dfrac{x}{2}$;

$$= \int f\left(z,\ \sqrt{1-z^2},\ \frac{z}{\sqrt{1-z^2}},\ \frac{\sqrt{1-z^2}}{z},\ \frac{1}{\sqrt{1-z^2}},\ \frac{1}{z}\right)$$

$\dfrac{dz}{\sqrt{1-z^2}}$, where $z = \sin x$;

$$= \int f\left(\frac{z}{\sqrt{1+z^2}},\ \frac{1}{\sqrt{1+z^2}},\ z,\ \frac{1}{z},\ \sqrt{1+z^2},\ \frac{\sqrt{1+z^2}}{z}\right)$$

$\dfrac{dz}{1+z^2}$, where $z = \tan x$;

$$= \int f\left(\sqrt{z},\ \sqrt{1-z},\ \sqrt{\frac{z}{1-z}},\ \sqrt{\frac{1-z}{z}},\ \frac{1}{\sqrt{1-z}},\ \frac{1}{\sqrt{z}}\right)$$

$\dfrac{dz}{2\sqrt{z(1-z)}}$, where $z = \sin^2 x$;

$$= \int f\left(\sqrt{\frac{z}{1+z}},\ \frac{1}{\sqrt{1+z}},\ \sqrt{z},\ \frac{1}{\sqrt{z}},\ \sqrt{1+z},\ \sqrt{\frac{1+z}{z}}\right)$$

$\dfrac{dz}{2(1+z)\sqrt{z}}$, where $z = \tan^2 x$.

260. $\int \sin x\, dx = -\cos x.$ [See 247.]

261. $\int \sin^2 x\, dx = -\frac{1}{2}\cos x \sin x + \frac{1}{2}x = \frac{1}{2}x - \frac{1}{4}\sin 2x.$

262. $\int \sin^3 x\, dx = -\frac{1}{3}\cos x\,(\sin^2 x + 2).$

263. $\int \sin^n x\, dx = -\frac{\sin^{n-1} x \cos x}{n} + \frac{n-1}{n}\int \sin^{n-2} x\, dx.$

264. $\int \cos x\, dx = \sin x.$ [See 247.]

265. $\int \cos^2 x\, dx = \frac{1}{2}\sin x \cos x + \frac{1}{2}x = \frac{1}{2}x + \frac{1}{4}\sin 2x.$

266. $\int \cos^3 x\, dx = \frac{1}{3}\sin x\,(\cos^2 x + 2).$

267. $\int \cos^n x\, dx = \frac{1}{n}\cos^{n-1} x \sin x + \frac{n-1}{n}\int \cos^{n-2} x\, dx.$

268. $\int \sin x \cos x\, dx = \frac{1}{2}\sin^2 x.$

269. $\int \sin^2 x \cos^2 x\, dx = -\frac{1}{8}\left(\frac{1}{4}\sin 4x - x\right).$

270. $\int \sin x \cos^m x\, dx = -\frac{\cos^{m+1} x}{m+1}.$

271. $\int \sin^m x \cos x\, dx = \frac{\sin^{m+1} x}{m+1}.$

272. $\int \cos^m x \sin^n x\, dx = \frac{\cos^{m-1} x \sin^{n+1} x}{m+n}$
$$+ \frac{m-1}{m+n}\int \cos^{m-2} x \sin^n x\, dx.$$

273. $\int \cos^m x \sin^n x\, dx = -\frac{\sin^{n-1} x \cos^{m+1} x}{m+n}$
$$+ \frac{n-1}{m+n}\int \cos^m x \sin^{n-2} x\, dx.$$

274. $\displaystyle\int\frac{\sin^n x\,dx}{\cos^m x} = \frac{1}{n-m}\left(-\frac{\sin^{n-1}x}{\cos^{m-1}x} + (n-1)\int\frac{\sin^{n-2}x\,dx}{\cos^m x}\right)$

$\displaystyle = \frac{1}{m-1}\left(\frac{\sin^{n+1}x}{\cos^{m-1}x} - (n-m+2)\int\frac{\sin^n x\,dx}{\cos^{m-2}x}\right)$

$\displaystyle = \frac{1}{m-1}\left(\frac{\sin^{n-1}x}{\cos^{m-1}x} - (n-1)\int\frac{\sin^{n-2}x\,dx}{\cos^{m-2}x}\right).$

275. $\displaystyle\int\frac{\cos^m x\,dx}{\sin^n x} = -\frac{\cos^{m+1}x}{(n-1)\sin^{n-1}x} - \frac{m-n+2}{n-1}\int\frac{\cos^m x\,dx}{\sin^{n-2}x}$

$\displaystyle = \frac{\cos^{m-1}x}{(m-n)\sin^{n-1}x} + \frac{m-1}{m-n}\int\frac{\cos^{m-2}x\,dx}{\sin^n x}$

$\displaystyle = -\frac{1}{n-1}\frac{\cos^{m-1}x}{\sin^{n-1}x} - \frac{m-1}{n-1}\int\frac{\cos^{m-2}x\,dx}{\sin^{n-2}x}.$

276. $\displaystyle\int\frac{\sin^m x\,dx}{\cos^n x} = -\int\frac{\cos^m\left(\dfrac{\pi}{2}-x\right)d\left(\dfrac{\pi}{2}-x\right)}{\sin^n\left(\dfrac{\pi}{2}-x\right)}.$

277. $\displaystyle\int\frac{dx}{\sin x\,\cos x} = \log\tan x.$

278. $\displaystyle\int\frac{dx}{\cos x\,\sin^2 x} = \log\tan\left(\frac{\pi}{4}+\frac{x}{2}\right) - \csc x.$

279. $\displaystyle\int\frac{dx}{\sin^m x\,\cos^n x}$

$\displaystyle = \frac{1}{n-1}\cdot\frac{1}{\sin^{m-1}x\cdot\cos^{n-1}x} + \frac{m+n-2}{n-1}\int\frac{dx}{\sin^m x\cdot\cos^{n-2}x}$

$\displaystyle = -\frac{1}{m-1}\cdot\frac{1}{\sin^{m-1}x\cdot\cos^{n-1}x} + \frac{m+n-2}{m-1}\int\frac{dx}{\sin^{m-2}x\cdot\cos^n x}.$

280. $\displaystyle\int\frac{dx}{\sin^m x} = -\frac{1}{m-1}\cdot\frac{\cos x}{\sin^{m-1}x} + \frac{m-2}{m-1}\int\frac{dx}{\sin^{m-2}x}.$

281. $\displaystyle\int \frac{dx}{\cos^n x} = \frac{1}{n-1} \cdot \frac{\sin x}{\cos^{n-1} x} + \frac{n-2}{n-1}\int \frac{dx}{\cos^{n-2} x}.$

282. $\displaystyle\int \tan x\, dx = -\log \cos x.$ [See 247.]

283. $\displaystyle\int \tan^2 x\, dx = \tan x - x.$

284. $\displaystyle\int \tan^n x\, dx = \frac{\tan^{n-1} x}{n-1} - \int \tan^{n-2} x\, dx.$

285. $\displaystyle\int \operatorname{ctn} x\, dx = \log \sin x.$ [See 247.]

286. $\displaystyle\int \operatorname{ctn}^2 x\, dx = -\operatorname{ctn} x - x.$

287. $\displaystyle\int \operatorname{ctn}^n x\, dx = -\frac{\operatorname{ctn}^{n-1} x}{n-1} - \int \operatorname{ctn}^{n-2} x\, dx.$

288. $\displaystyle\int \sec x\, dx = \log \tan\left(\frac{\pi}{4} + \frac{x}{2}\right) = \tfrac{1}{2} \log \frac{1 + \sin x}{1 - \sin x}.$

289. $\displaystyle\int \sec^2 x\, dx = \tan x.$

290. $\displaystyle\int \sec^n x\, dx = \int \frac{dx}{\cos^n x} = \frac{\sin x}{(n-1)\cos^{n-1} x} + \frac{n-2}{n-1}\int \frac{dx}{\cos^{n-2} x}$
$$= \frac{\sin x}{(n-1)\cos^{n-1} x} + \frac{n-2}{n-1}\int \sec^{n-2} x\, dx.$$

291. $\displaystyle\int \csc x\, dx = \log \tan \tfrac{1}{2} x.$

292. $\displaystyle\int \csc^2 x\, dx = -\operatorname{ctn} x.$

293. $\int \csc^n x \, dx = -\dfrac{\cos x}{(n-1)\sin^{n-1}x} + \dfrac{n-2}{n-1}\int \csc^{n-2}x \, dx.$

294. $\int \dfrac{dx}{1+\sin x} = -\tan\left(\tfrac{1}{4}\pi - \tfrac{1}{2}x\right).$

295. $\int \dfrac{dx}{1-\sin x} = \operatorname{ctn}\left(\tfrac{1}{4}\pi - \tfrac{1}{2}x\right) = \tan\left(\tfrac{1}{4}\pi + \tfrac{1}{2}x\right).$

296. $\int \dfrac{dx}{1+\cos x} = \tan\tfrac{1}{2}x, \quad \text{or} \quad \csc x - \operatorname{ctn}x.$

297. $\int \dfrac{dx}{1-\cos x} = -\operatorname{ctn}\tfrac{1}{2}x, \quad \text{or} \quad -\operatorname{ctn}x - \csc x.$

298. $\int \dfrac{dx}{a+b\sin x} = \dfrac{2}{\sqrt{a^2-b^2}}\tan^{-1}\dfrac{a\tan\frac{1}{2}x+b}{\sqrt{a^2-b^2}},$

$\qquad$ or $\quad \dfrac{1}{\sqrt{b^2-a^2}}\log\dfrac{a\tan\frac{1}{2}x+b-\sqrt{b^2-a^2}}{a\tan\frac{1}{2}x+b+\sqrt{b^2-a^2}},$

$\qquad$ or $\quad \dfrac{-2}{\sqrt{b^2-a^2}}\tanh^{-1}\dfrac{a\tan\frac{1}{2}x+b}{\sqrt{b^2-a^2}},$

$\qquad$ or $\quad \dfrac{-2}{\sqrt{b^2-a^2}}\operatorname{ctnh}^{-1}\dfrac{a\tan\frac{1}{2}x+b}{\sqrt{b^2-a^2}}.$

299. $\int \dfrac{dx}{a+b\sin x} = \dfrac{1}{b\cos a}\log\dfrac{\sin\frac{1}{2}(x+\alpha)}{\cos\frac{1}{2}(x-\alpha)},$

$\qquad a = b\sin a, \quad \sqrt{b^2-a^2} = b\cos a, \quad -\pi < x < \pi.$

300. $\int \dfrac{dx}{a+b\cos x} = \dfrac{2}{\sqrt{a^2-b^2}}\tan^{-1}\dfrac{\sqrt{a^2-b^2}\tan\frac{1}{2}x}{a+b},$

$\qquad$ or $\quad \dfrac{1}{\sqrt{b^2-a^2}}\log\dfrac{\sqrt{b^2-a^2}\tan\frac{1}{2}x+a+b}{\sqrt{b^2-a^2}\tan\frac{1}{2}x-a-b},$

$\qquad$ or $\quad \dfrac{2}{\sqrt{b^2-a^2}}\tanh^{-1}\dfrac{\sqrt{b^2-a^2}\tan\frac{1}{2}x}{a+b},$

$\qquad$ or $\quad \dfrac{2}{\sqrt{b^2-a^2}}\operatorname{ctnh}^{-1}\dfrac{\sqrt{b^2-a^2}\tan\frac{1}{2}x}{a+b}.$

301. $\int \dfrac{dx}{a + b \tan x} = \dfrac{1}{a^2 + b^2} \left[b \log (a \cos x + b \sin x) + ax \right].$

302. $\int \dfrac{dx}{\sin x + \cos x} = \dfrac{1}{\sqrt{2}} \log \tan (\tfrac{1}{2} x + \tfrac{1}{8} \pi).$

303. $\int \dfrac{\sin x\, dx}{a + b \cos x} = -\dfrac{1}{b} \log (a + b \cos x).$

304. $\int \dfrac{(a' + b' \cos x)\, dx}{a + b \cos x} = \dfrac{b'x}{b} + \dfrac{a'b - ab'}{b} \int \dfrac{dx}{a + b \cos x}.$

305. $\int \dfrac{(a' + b' \cos x)\, dx}{(a + b \cos x)^2} = \dfrac{ab' - a'b}{a^2 - b^2} \dfrac{\sin x}{a + b \cos x}$

$$+ \dfrac{aa' - bb'}{a^2 - b^2} \int \dfrac{dx}{a + b \cos x}. \quad [\text{See } 241.]$$

306. $\int \dfrac{(a' + b' \cos x)\, dx}{(a + b \cos x)^n} = \dfrac{1}{(n - 1)\,(a^2 - b^2)} \left[\dfrac{(ab' - a'b) \sin x}{(a + b \cos x)^{n-1}} \right.$

$$\left. + \int \dfrac{\left[(aa' - bb')\,(n - 1) + (n - 2)\,(ab' - a'b) \cos x \right] dx}{(a + b \cos x)^{n-1}} \right].$$

307. $\int \dfrac{(a' + b' \cos x)\, dx}{(1 + \cos x)^n} = \dfrac{(a' - b')\tan \frac{1}{2} x}{(2n - 1)\,(1 + \cos x)^{n-1}}$

$$+ \dfrac{n (a' + b') - a'}{2n - 1} \int \dfrac{dx}{(1 + \cos x)^{n-1}}.$$

308. $\int \dfrac{dx}{(a + b \cos x)^n} = \dfrac{1}{(n - 1)\,(a^2 - b^2)} \left[\dfrac{-b \sin x}{(a + b \cos x)^{n-1}} \right.$

$$\left. + (2n - 3)\, a \int \dfrac{dx}{(a + b \cos x)^{n-1}} - (n - 2) \int \dfrac{dx}{(a + b \cos x)^{n-2}} \right].$$

309. $\int \dfrac{dx}{(1+\cos x)^n} = \dfrac{\tan \frac{1}{2} x}{(2n-1)(1+\cos x)^{n-1}}$

$$+ \frac{n-1}{2n-1} \int \frac{dx}{(1+\cos x)^{n-1}}. \qquad \text{[See 241.]}$$

310. $\int \dfrac{(a'+b' \cos x)\,dx}{\sin x\,(a+b \cos x)} = \dfrac{a'b - ab'}{a^2 - b^2} \log (a+b \cos x)$

$$+ \frac{a'+b'}{a+b} \log \sin \tfrac{1}{2} x - \frac{a'-b'}{a-b} \log \cos \tfrac{1}{2} x.$$

311. $\int \dfrac{(a'+b' \cos x)\,dx}{\cos x\,(a+b \cos x)} = \dfrac{a'}{a} \log \tan \tfrac{1}{2}(\tfrac{1}{2}\pi + x)$

$$+ \frac{(ab' - a'b)}{a} \int \frac{dx}{a+b \cos x}.$$

312. $\int \dfrac{(a'+b' \cos x)\,dx}{\sin x\,(1 \pm \cos x)} = \pm \dfrac{\frac{1}{2}(a' \mp b')}{1 \pm \cos x} + \frac{1}{2}(a' \pm b') \log \tan \frac{1}{2} x.$

313. $\int \dfrac{dx}{(1-\cos x)^n} = \dfrac{-\operatorname{ctn} \frac{1}{2} x}{(2n-1)(1-\cos x)^{n-1}}$

$$+ \frac{n-1}{2n-1} \int \frac{dx}{(1-\cos x)^{n-1}}. \qquad \text{[See 241.]}$$

314. $\int \dfrac{dx}{a+b \sin^2 x} = \dfrac{1}{\sqrt{a^2 + ab}} \tan^{-1} \dfrac{\sqrt{a^2 + ab}\, \tan x}{a},$

$$\text{or } \frac{1}{2\sqrt{-a^2 - ab}} \log \frac{\sqrt{-a^2 - ab}\, \tan x + a}{\sqrt{-a^2 - ab}\, \tan x - a},$$

$$\genfrac{}{}{0pt}{}{\frac{\pi}{2}}{\bigvee} \ \genfrac{}{}{0pt}{}{8}{\bigvee} \ \genfrac{}{}{0pt}{}{\frac{\pi}{2}}{|} \quad \text{or } \frac{1}{\sqrt{-a^2 - ab}} \tanh^{-1} \frac{\sqrt{-a^2 - ab}\, \tan x}{a},$$

$$\text{or } \frac{1}{\sqrt{-a^2 - ab}} \operatorname{ctnh}^{-1} \frac{\sqrt{-a^2 - ab}\, \tan x}{a}.$$

315. $\displaystyle\int \frac{dx}{a + b \cos^2 x} = \frac{1}{\sqrt{a^2 + ab}} \tan^{-1} \frac{\sqrt{a^2 + ab}\,\tan x}{a + b},$

or $\displaystyle\frac{1}{2\sqrt{-a^2 - ab}} \log \frac{\sqrt{-a^2 - ab}\,\tan x + a + b}{\sqrt{-a^2 - ab}\,\tan x - a - b},$

or $\displaystyle\frac{1}{\sqrt{-a^2 - ab}} \tanh^{-1} \frac{\sqrt{-a^2 - ab}\,\tan x}{a + b},$

or $\displaystyle\frac{1}{\sqrt{-a^2 - ab}} \operatorname{ctnh}^{-1} \frac{\sqrt{-a^2 - ab}\,\tan x}{a + b}.$

316. $\displaystyle\int \frac{dx}{a \cos^2 x + b \sin^2 x} = \frac{1}{\sqrt{ab}} \tan^{-1} \frac{\sqrt{ab}\,\tan x}{a},$

or $\displaystyle\frac{1}{2\sqrt{-ab}} \log \frac{\sqrt{-ab}\,\tan x - a}{\sqrt{-ab}\,\tan x - a},$

or $\displaystyle\frac{1}{\sqrt{-ab}} \tanh^{-1} \frac{\sqrt{-ab}\,\tan x}{a},$

or $\displaystyle\frac{1}{\sqrt{-ab}} \operatorname{ctnh}^{-1} \frac{\sqrt{-ab}\,\tan x}{a}.$

317. $\displaystyle\int \frac{\sin x \cos x\, dx}{a \cos^2 x + b \sin^2 x} = \frac{1}{2(b - a)} \log(a \cos^2 x + b \sin^2 x).$

318. $\displaystyle\int \frac{dx}{(a + b \cos x + c \sin x)^n} = \int \frac{d(x - \alpha)}{[a + r \cos(x - \alpha)]^n},$

where $b = r \cos \alpha$ and $c = r \sin \alpha.$

319. $\displaystyle\int \frac{dx}{a + b \cos x + c \sin x}$

$\displaystyle= \frac{2}{\sqrt{a^2 - b^2 - c^2}} \tan^{-1} \frac{(a - b)\tan \frac{1}{2}x + c}{\sqrt{a^2 - b^2 - c^2}},$

or $\displaystyle\frac{1}{\sqrt{b^2 + c^2 - a^2}} \log \frac{(a - b)\tan \frac{1}{2}x + c - \sqrt{b^2 + c^2 - a^2}}{(a - b)\tan \frac{1}{2}x + c + \sqrt{b^2 + c^2 - a^2}},$

or $\displaystyle\frac{-2}{\sqrt{b^2 + c^2 - a^2}} \tanh^{-1} \frac{(a - b)\tan \frac{1}{2}x + c}{\sqrt{b^2 + c^2 - a^2}},$

or $\displaystyle\frac{-2}{\sqrt{b^2 + c^2 - a^2}} \operatorname{ctnh}^{-1} \frac{(a - b)\tan \frac{1}{2}x + c}{\sqrt{b^2 + c^2 - a^2}}.$

320. $\int \dfrac{dx}{a\,(1 + \cos x) + c\,\sin x} = \dfrac{1}{c}\,\log\,(a + c\,\tan\tfrac{1}{2}\,x).$

321. $\int \dfrac{dx}{(a\,[1 + \cos x] + c\,\sin x)^2}$

$$= \frac{1}{c^3}\left[\frac{c\,(a\,\sin x - c\,\cos x)}{a\,(1 + \cos x) + c\,\sin x} - a\,\log\,(a + c\,\tan\tfrac{1}{2}\,x)\right]$$

322. $\int \dfrac{(x + \sin x)\,dx}{1 + \cos x} = x\,\tan\tfrac{1}{2}\,x.$

323. $\int \cos x\,\sqrt{1 - k^2\,\sin^2 x}\,dx$

$$= \tfrac{1}{2}\,\sin x\,\sqrt{1 - k^2\,\sin^2 x} + \frac{1}{2\,k}\,\sin^{-1}(k\,\sin x).$$

324. $\int \sin x\,\sqrt{1 - k^2\,\sin^2 x}\,dx$

$$= -\tfrac{1}{2}\cos x\,\sqrt{1 - k^2\sin^2 x} - \frac{1 - k^2}{2\,k}\,\log\,(k\,\cos x + \sqrt{1 - k^2\sin^2 x}).$$

325. $\int \sin x\,(1 - k^2\,\sin^2 x)^{\frac{3}{2}}\,dx = -\tfrac{1}{4}\cos x\,(1 - k^2\,\sin^2 x)^{\frac{3}{2}}$

$$+ \tfrac{3}{4}\,(1 - k^2)\int \sin x\,\sqrt{1 - k^2\,\sin^2 x}\,dx.$$

326. $\int \dfrac{\cos x\,dx}{\sqrt{1 - k^2\,\sin^2 x}} = \dfrac{1}{k}\,\sin^{-1}(k\,\sin x),$

$$\text{or }\frac{1}{b}\,\log\,(b\,\sin x + \sqrt{1 + b^2\,\sin^2 x}),\ \ \text{where } b^2 = -\,k^2.$$

327. $\int \dfrac{\sin x\,dx}{\sqrt{1 - k^2\,\sin^2 x}} = -\dfrac{1}{k}\,\log\,(k\,\cos x + \sqrt{1 - k^2\,\sin^2 x}),$

$$\text{or } -\frac{1}{b}\,\sin^{-1}\frac{b\,\cos x}{\sqrt{1 + b^2}},\ \text{where } b^2 = -\,k^2$$

328. $\int \dfrac{\tan x\,dx}{\sqrt{1 - k^2\,\sin^2 x}}$

$$= \frac{1}{2\,\sqrt{1 - k^2}}\,\log\left(\frac{\sqrt{1 - k^2\,\sin^2 x} + \sqrt{1 - k^2}}{\sqrt{1 - k^2\,\sin^2 x} - \sqrt{1 - k^2}}\right).$$

329. $\int \dfrac{x\,dx}{1+\sin x} = -x \tan \tfrac{1}{2}\left(\tfrac{1}{2}\pi - x\right) + 2 \log \cos \tfrac{1}{2}\left(\tfrac{1}{2}\pi - x\right).$

330. $\int \dfrac{x\,dx}{1-\sin x} = x \operatorname{ctn} \tfrac{1}{2}\left(\tfrac{1}{2}\pi - x\right) + 2 \log \sin \tfrac{1}{2}\left(\tfrac{1}{2}\pi - x\right).$

331. $\int \dfrac{x\,dx}{1+\cos x} = x \tan \tfrac{1}{2}x + 2 \log \cos \tfrac{1}{2}x.$

332. $\int \dfrac{x\,dx}{1-\cos x} = -x \operatorname{ctn} \tfrac{1}{2}x + 2 \log \sin \tfrac{1}{2}x.$

333. $\int \dfrac{\tan x\,dx}{\sqrt{a+b\tan^2 x}} = \dfrac{1}{\sqrt{b-a}} \cos^{-1}\!\left(\dfrac{\sqrt{b-a}}{\sqrt{b}} \cdot \cos x\right)\!.$

334. $\int \dfrac{dx}{a+b\tan^2 x} = \dfrac{1}{a-b}\left[x - \sqrt{\dfrac{b}{a}} \cdot \tan^{-1}\!\left(\sqrt{\dfrac{b}{a}} \cdot \tan x\right)\right]\!.$

335. $\int \dfrac{\tan x\,dx}{a+b\tan x}$

$$= \dfrac{1}{a^2+b^2}\left\{ bx - a \log\left(a+b\tan x\right) + a \log \sec x \right\}$$

336. $\int x \sin x\,dx = \sin x - x \cos x.$

337. $\int x^2 \sin x\,dx = 2\,x \sin x - (x^2-2)\cos x.$

338. $\int x^3 \sin x\,dx = (3\,x^2-6)\sin x - (x^3-6\,x)\cos x.$

339. $\int x^m \sin x\,dx = -x^m \cos x + m \int x^{m-1}\cos x\,dx.$

340. $\int x \cos x\,dx = \cos x + x \sin x.$

341. $\int x^2 \cos x\,dx = 2\,x \cos x + (x^2-2)\sin x.$

342. $\int x^3 \cos x\,dx = (3\,x^2-6)\cos x + (x^3-6\,x)\sin x.$

343. $\int x^m \cos x \, dx = x^m \sin x - m \int x^{m-1} \sin x \, dx.$

344. $\int \dfrac{\sin x}{x^m} \, dx = -\dfrac{1}{m-1} \cdot \dfrac{\sin x}{x^{m-1}} + \dfrac{1}{m-1} \int \dfrac{\cos x}{x^{m-1}} \, dx.$

345. $\int \dfrac{\cos x}{x^m} \, dx = -\dfrac{1}{m-1} \cdot \dfrac{\cos x}{x^{m-1}} - \dfrac{1}{m-1} \int \dfrac{\sin x}{x^{m-1}} \, dx.$

346. $\int \dfrac{\sin x}{x} \, dx = x - \dfrac{x^3}{3 \cdot 3!} + \dfrac{x^5}{5 \cdot 5!} - \dfrac{x^7}{7 \cdot 7!} + \dfrac{x^9}{9 \cdot 9!} \cdots.$

347. $\int \dfrac{\cos x}{x} \, dx = \log x - \dfrac{x^2}{2 \cdot 2!} + \dfrac{x^4}{4 \cdot 4!} - \dfrac{x^6}{6 \cdot 6!} + \dfrac{x^8}{8 \cdot 8!} \cdots.$

348. $\int \dfrac{x \, dx}{\sin x} = x + \dfrac{x^3}{3 \cdot 3!} + \dfrac{7 \, x^5}{3 \cdot 5 \cdot 5!} + \dfrac{31 \, x^7}{3 \cdot 7 \cdot 7!} + \dfrac{127 \, x^9}{3 \cdot 5 \cdot 9!} + \cdots.$

349. $\int \dfrac{x \, dx}{\cos x} = \dfrac{x^2}{2} + \dfrac{x^4}{4 \cdot 2!} + \dfrac{5 \, x^6}{6 \cdot 4!} + \dfrac{61 \, x^8}{8 \cdot 6!} + \dfrac{1385 \, x^{10}}{10 \cdot 8!} + \cdots.$

350. $\int \dfrac{x \, dx}{\sin^2 x} = -x \operatorname{ctn} x + \log \sin x.$

351. $\int \dfrac{x \, dx}{\cos^2 x} = x \tan x + \log \cos x.$

352. $n^2 \int x^m \sin^n x \, dx$

$= x^{m-1} \sin^{n-1} x \, (m \sin x - n x \cos x)$

$+ n (n-1) \int x^m \sin^{n-2} x \, dx - m (m-1) \int x^{m-2} \sin^n x \, dx.$

353. $n^2 \int x^m \cos^n x \, dx$

$= x^{m-1} \cos^{n-1} x \, (m \cos x + n x \sin x)$

$+ n (n-1) \int x^m \cos^{n-2} x \, dx - m (m-1) \int x^{m-2} \cos^n x \, dx$

354. $\displaystyle\int \frac{x^m\,dx}{\sin^n x}$

$$= \frac{1}{(n-1)(n-2)}\left[-\frac{x^{m-1}(m\sin x + (n-2)x\cos x)}{\sin^{n-1} x}\right.$$
$$\left. + (n-2)^2 \int \frac{x^m\,dx}{\sin^{n-2} x} + m(m-1)\int \frac{x^{m-2}\,dx}{\sin^{n-2} x}\right].$$

355. $\displaystyle\int \frac{x^m\,dx}{\cos^n x}$

$$= \frac{1}{(n-1)(n-2)}\left[-\frac{x^{m-1}(m\cos x - (n-2)x\sin x)}{\cos^{n-1} x}\right.$$
$$\left. + (n-2)^2 \int \frac{x^m\,dx}{\cos^{n-2} x} + m(m-1)\int \frac{x^{m-2}\,dx}{\cos^{n-2} x}\right].$$

356. $\displaystyle\int \frac{\sin^n x\,dx}{x^m}$

$$= \frac{1}{(m-1)(m-2)}\left[-\frac{\sin^{n-1} x((m-2)\sin x + nx\cos x)}{x^{m-1}}\right.$$
$$\left. - n^2 \int \frac{\sin^n x\,dx}{x^{m-2}} + n(n-1)\int \frac{\sin^{n-2} x\,dx}{x^{m-2}}\right].$$

357. $\displaystyle\int \frac{\cos^n x\,dx}{x^m}$

$$= \frac{1}{(m-1)(m-2)}\left[\frac{\cos^{n-1} x(nx\sin x - (m-2)\cos x)}{x^{m-1}}\right.$$
$$\left. - n^2 \int \frac{\cos^n x\,dx}{x^{m-2}} + n(n-1)\int \frac{\cos^{n-2} x\,dx}{x^{m-2}}\right].$$

358. $\displaystyle\int x^p \sin^m x \cos^n x\,dx$

$$= \frac{1}{(m+n)^2}\left[x^{p-1}\sin^m x \cos^{n-1} x\,(p\cos x + (m+n)x\sin x)\right.$$
$$+ (n-1)(m+n)\int x^p \sin^m x \cos^{n-2} x\,dx$$

$$- mp \int x^{p-1} \sin^{m-1} x \, \cos^{n-1} x \, dx$$

$$- p(p-1) \int x^{p-2} \sin^m x \, \cos^n x \, dx \Bigg].$$

$$= \frac{1}{(m+n)^2} \Bigg[x^{p-1} \sin^{m-1} x \, \cos^n x \, (p \sin x - (m+n) x \cos x)$$

$$+ (m-1)(m+n) \int x^p \sin^{m-2} x \, \cos^n x \, dx$$

$$+ np \int x^{p-1} \sin^{m-1} x \, \cos^{n-1} x \, dx$$

$$- p(p-1) \int x^{p-2} \sin^m x \, \cos^n x \, dx \Bigg].$$

359. $\displaystyle \int \sin mx \sin nx \, dx = \frac{\sin (m-n) x}{2(m-n)} - \frac{\sin (m+n) x}{2(m+n)}.$

360. $\displaystyle \int \sin mx \cos nx \, dx = - \frac{\cos (m-n) x}{2(m-n)} - \frac{\cos (m+n) x}{2(m+n)}.$

361. $\displaystyle \int \cos mx \cos nx \, dx = \frac{\sin (m-n) x}{2(m-n)} + \frac{\sin (m+n) x}{2(m+n)}.$

See page 61.

362. $\displaystyle \int \sin^2 mx \, dx = \frac{1}{2\,m} (mx - \sin mx \cos mx).$

363. $\displaystyle \int \cos^2 mx \, dx = \frac{1}{2\,m} (mx + \sin mx \cos mx).$

364. $\displaystyle \int \sin mx \cos mx \, dx = - \frac{1}{4\,m} \cos 2 mx.$

365. $\displaystyle \int \sin nx \sin^m x \, dx = \frac{1}{m+n} \Bigg[- \cos nx \sin^m x$

$$+ m \int \cos (n-1) x \cdot \sin^{m-1} x \, dx \Bigg].$$

366. $\displaystyle\int \sin nx \cos^m x\, dx = \frac{1}{m+n}\left[-\cos nx \cos^m x \right.$

$$\left. + m \int \sin (n-1)\, x \cdot \cos^{m-1} x\, dx \right].$$

367. $\displaystyle\int \cos nx \sin^m x\, dx = \frac{1}{m+n}\left[\sin nx \sin^m x \right.$

$$\left. - m \int \sin (n-1)\, x \cdot \sin^{m-1} x\, dx \right].$$

368. $\displaystyle\int \cos nx \cos^m x\, dx = \frac{1}{m+n}\left[\sin nx \cos^m x \right.$

$$\left. + m \int \cos (n-1)\, x \cdot \cos^{m-1} x\, dx \right].$$

369. $\displaystyle\int \frac{\cos nx\, dx}{\cos^m x} = 2 \int \frac{\cos (n-1)\, x\, dx}{\cos^{m-1} x} - \int \frac{\cos (n-2)\, x\, dx}{\cos^m x}.$

370. $\displaystyle\int \frac{\cos nx\, dx}{\sin^m x} = -2 \int \frac{\sin (n-1)\, x\, dx}{\sin^{m-1} x} + \int \frac{\cos (n-2)\, x\, dx}{\sin^m x}.$

371. $\displaystyle\int \frac{\sin nx\, dx}{\sin^m x} = 2 \int \frac{\cos (n-1)\, x\, dx}{\sin^{m-1} x} + \int \frac{\sin (n-2)\, x\, dx}{\sin^m x}.$

372. $\displaystyle\int \frac{\sin nx\, dx}{\cos^m x} = 2 \int \frac{\sin (n-1)\, x\, dx}{\cos^{m-1} x} - \int \frac{\sin (n-2)\, x\, dx}{\cos^m x}.$

373. $\displaystyle\int \frac{(\cos px + i \sin px)\, dx}{\cos nx} = -2\,i \int \frac{z^{p+n-1} dz}{1 + z^{2n}},$

where $z = \cos x + i \sin x$. This yields two real integrals.

374. $\displaystyle\int \frac{(\cos px + i \sin px)\, dx}{\sin nx} = -2 \int \frac{z^{p+n-1} dz}{1 - z^{2n}},$

where $z = \cos x + i \sin x$. This yields two real integrals.

375. $\displaystyle\int \frac{(i \cos x - \sin x)\,dx}{\sqrt[n]{\cos nx}} = \int \frac{dy}{2 - y^n},$

where $y = \dfrac{\cos x + i \sin x}{\sqrt[n]{\cos nx}}.$ This yields two real integrals.

376. $\displaystyle\int \sin ax \sin bx \sin cx\,dx = -\tfrac{1}{4}\left\{\frac{\cos(a-b+c)x}{a-b+c}\right.$

$$+ \frac{\cos(b+c-a)x}{b+c-a} + \frac{\cos(a+b-c)x}{a+b-c} - \left.\frac{\cos(a+b+c)x}{a+b+c}\right\}.$$

377. $\displaystyle\int \cos ax \cos bx \cos cx\,dx = \tfrac{1}{4}\left\{\frac{\sin(a+b+c)x}{a+b+c}\right.$

$$+ \frac{\sin(b+c-a)x}{b+c-a} + \frac{\sin(a-b+c)x}{a-b+c} + \left.\frac{\sin(a+b-c)x}{a+b-c}\right\}.$$

378. $\displaystyle\int \sin ax \cos bx \cos cx\,dx = -\tfrac{1}{4}\left\{\frac{\cos(a+b+c)x}{a+b+c}\right.$

$$- \frac{\cos(b+c-a)x}{b+c-a} + \frac{\cos(a+b-c)x}{a+b-c} + \left.\frac{\cos(a+c-b)x}{a+c-b}\right\}.$$

379. $\displaystyle\int \cos ax \sin bx \sin cx\,dx = \tfrac{1}{4}\left\{\frac{\sin(a+b-c)x}{a+b-c}\right.$

$$+ \frac{\sin(a-b+c)x}{a-b+c} - \frac{\sin(a+b+c)x}{a+b+c} - \left.\frac{\sin(b+c-a)x}{b+c-a}\right\}.$$

380. $\displaystyle\int \sin^{-1} x\,dx = x \sin^{-1} x + \sqrt{1 - x^2}.$

381. $\displaystyle\int \cos^{-1} x\,dx = x \cos^{-1} x - \sqrt{1 - x^2}.$

382. $\displaystyle\int \tan^{-1} x\,dx = x \tan^{-1} x - \tfrac{1}{2}\log(1 + x^2).$

383. $\displaystyle\int \mathrm{ctn}^{-1} x\,dx = x\,\mathrm{ctn}^{-1} x + \tfrac{1}{2}\log(1 + x^2).$

384. $\int \sec^{-1} x \, dx = x \sec^{-1} x - \log(x + \sqrt{x^2 - 1})$.

385. $\int \csc^{-1} x \, dx = x \csc^{-1} x + \log(x + \sqrt{x^2 - 1})$.

386. $\int \mathrm{versin}^{-1} x \, dx = (x - 1)\,\mathrm{versin}^{-1} x + \sqrt{2\,x - x^2}$.

387. $\int (\sin^{-1} x)^2 \, dx = x(\sin^{-1} x)^2 - 2\,x + 2\sqrt{1 - x^2}\,\sin^{-1} x$.

388. $\int (\cos^{-1} x)^2 \, dx = x(\cos^{-1} x)^2 - 2\,x - 2\sqrt{1 - x^2}\,\cos^{-1} x$.

389. $\int x \sin^{-1} x \, dx = \frac{1}{4}\big[(2\,x^2 - 1)\sin^{-1} x + x\sqrt{1 - x^2}\big]$.

390. $\int x \cos^{-1} x \, dx = \frac{1}{4}\big[(2\,x^2 - 1)\cos^{-1} x - x\sqrt{1 - x^2}\big]$.

391. $\int x \tan^{-1} x \, dx = \frac{1}{2}\big[(x^2 + 1)\tan^{-1} x - x\big]$.

392. $\int x \operatorname{ctn}^{-1} x \, dx = \frac{1}{2}\big[(x^2 + 1)\operatorname{ctn}^{-1} x + x\big]$.

393. $\int x \sec^{-1} x \, dx = \frac{1}{2}\big[x^2 \sec^{-1} x - \sqrt{x^2 - 1}\big]$.

394. $\int x \csc^{-1} x \, dx = \frac{1}{2}\big[x^2 \csc^{-1} x + \sqrt{x^2 - 1}\big]$.

395. $\int x^n \sin^{-1} x \, dx = \frac{1}{n + 1}\left(x^{n+1}\sin^{-1} x - \int \frac{x^{n+1}\,dx}{\sqrt{1 - x^2}}\right)$.

396. $\int x^n \cos^{-1} x \, dx = \frac{1}{n + 1}\left(x^{n+1}\cos^{-1} x + \int \frac{x^{n+1}\,dx}{\sqrt{1 - x^2}}\right)$.

397. $\int x^n \tan^{-1}x\,dx = \dfrac{1}{n+1}\left(x^{n+1}\tan^{-1}x - \int \dfrac{x^{n+1}\,dx}{1+x^2} \right)$

398. $\int x^n \operatorname{ctn}^{-1}x\,dx = \dfrac{1}{n+1}\left(x^{n+1}\operatorname{ctn}^{-1}x + \int \dfrac{x^{n+1}\,dx}{1+x^2} \right).$

399. $\int \dfrac{\sin^{-1}x\,dx}{x^2} = \log\left(\dfrac{1-\sqrt{1-x^2}}{x} \right) - \dfrac{\sin^{-1}x}{x}.$

400. $\int \dfrac{\tan^{-1}x\,dx}{x^2} = \log x - \tfrac{1}{2}\log(1+x^2) - \dfrac{\tan^{-1}x}{x}.$

401. $\int e^{ax}\,dx = \dfrac{e^{ax}}{a}. \qquad \int f(e^{ax})\,dx = \int \dfrac{f(y)\,dy}{ay}, \; y = e^{ax}.$

402. $\int x\,e^{ax}\,dx = \dfrac{e^{ax}}{a^2}(ax-1).$

403. $\int x^m e^{ax}\,dx = \dfrac{x^m e^{ax}}{a} - \dfrac{m}{a}\int x^{m-1}e^{ax}\,dx.$

404. $\int \dfrac{e^{ax}}{x^m}\,dx = \dfrac{1}{m-1}\left[-\dfrac{e^{ax}}{x^{m-1}} + a\int \dfrac{e^{ax}\,dx}{x^{m-1}} \right].$

405. $\int a^{bx}\,dx = \dfrac{a^{bx}}{b\log a}. \qquad \int f(a^{bx})\,dx = \int \dfrac{f(y)\,dy}{b\cdot\log a\cdot y}, \; y = a^{bx}$

406. $\int x^n a^x\,dx = \dfrac{a^x x^n}{\log a} - \dfrac{na^x x^{n-1}}{(\log a)^2} + \dfrac{n(n-1)a^x x^{n-2}}{(\log a)^3}\cdots$
$$\pm \dfrac{n(n-1)(n-2)\cdots 2.1\,a^x}{(\log a)^{n+1}}.$$

407. $\int \dfrac{a^x\,dx}{x^n} = \dfrac{1}{n-1}\left[-\dfrac{a^x}{x^{n-1}} - \dfrac{a^x\cdot\log a}{(n-2)\,x^{n-2}} \right.$
$$\left. -\dfrac{a^x\cdot(\log a)^2}{(n-2)(n-3)\,x^{n-3}} - \cdots + \dfrac{(\log a)^{n-1}}{(n-2)(n-3)\cdots 2.1}\int \dfrac{a^x\,dx}{x} \right].$$

408. $\int \dfrac{a^x\,dx}{x} = \log x + x\log a + \dfrac{(x\log a)^2}{2\cdot 2!} + \dfrac{(x\log a)^3}{3\cdot 3!} + \cdots.$

409. $\int \dfrac{dx}{1 + e^x} = \log \dfrac{e^x}{1 + e^x}.$

410. $\int \dfrac{dx}{a + be^{mx}} = \dfrac{1}{am}[mx - \log(a + be^{mx})].$

411. $\int \dfrac{dx}{ae^{mx} + be^{-mx}} = \dfrac{1}{m\sqrt{ab}} \tan^{-1}\left(e^{mx}\sqrt{\dfrac{a}{b}}\right).$

412. $\int \dfrac{dx}{\sqrt{a + be^{mx}}} = \dfrac{-2}{m\sqrt{-a}} \sin^{-1}\sqrt{\dfrac{-a}{b}}\, e^{-\frac{1}{2}mx},$

$\qquad$ or $\dfrac{-2}{m\sqrt{a}} \log(\sqrt{a} + \sqrt{a + be^{mx}}) + \dfrac{x}{\sqrt{a}}.$

413. $\int \dfrac{xe^x\, dx}{(1 + x)^2} = \dfrac{e^x}{1 + x}, \quad \int x^n \cdot e^{ax^{n+1}}\, dx = \dfrac{e^{ax^{n+1}}}{a(n + 1)}$

414. $\int e^{ax} \sin px\, dx = \dfrac{e^{ax}(a \sin px - p \cos px)}{a^2 + p^2}.$

415. $\int e^{ax} \cos px\, dx = \dfrac{e^{ax}(a \cos px + p \sin px)}{a^2 + p^2}.$

416. $\int e^{ax} \log x\, dx = \dfrac{e^{ax} \log x}{a} - \dfrac{1}{a}\int \dfrac{e^{ax}\, dx}{x}.$

417. $\int e^{ax} \sin^2 x\, dx = \dfrac{e^{ax}}{4 + a^2}\left(\sin x (a \sin x - 2 \cos x) + \dfrac{2}{a}\right)$

418. $\int e^{ax} \cos^2 x\, dx = \dfrac{e^{ax}}{4 + a^2}\left(\cos x (2 \sin x + a \cos x) + \dfrac{2}{a}\right).$

419. $\int e^{ax} \sin^n bx\, dx = \dfrac{1}{a^2 + n^2 b^2}\Big((a \sin bx$

$\qquad - nb \cos bx)\, e^{ax} \sin^{n-1} bx + n(n-1)b^2 \int e^{ax} \sin^{n-2} bx \cdot dx\Big)$

420. $\int e^{ax} \cos^n bx\, dx = \dfrac{1}{a^2 + n^2 b^2} \Big((a \cos bx$

$+ nb \sin bx)\, e^{ax} \cos^{n-1} bx + n(n-1)\, b^2 \int e^{ax} \cos^{n-2} bx\, dx \Big).$

421. $\int e^{ax} \tan^n x\, dx$

$= \dfrac{e^{ax} \tan^{n-1} x}{n-1} - \dfrac{a}{n-1} \int e^{ax} \tan^{n-1} x\, dx - \int e^{ax} \tan^{n-2} x\, dx.$

422. $\int e^{ax} \operatorname{ctn}^n x\, dx$

$= - \dfrac{e^{ax} \operatorname{ctn}^{n-1} x}{n-1} + \dfrac{a}{n-1} \int e^{ax} \operatorname{ctn}^{n-1} x\, dx - \int e^{ax} \operatorname{ctn}^{n-2} x\, dx.$

423. $\int \dfrac{e^{ax}\, dx}{\sin^n x} = - e^{ax} \dfrac{a \sin x + (n-2) \cos x}{(n-1)(n-2) \sin^{n-1} x}$

$+ \dfrac{a^2 + (n-2)^2}{(n-1)(n-2)} \int \dfrac{e^{ax}\, dx}{\sin^{n-2} x}.$

424. $\int \dfrac{e^{ax}\, dx}{\cos^n x} = - e^{ax} \dfrac{a \cos x - (n-2) \sin x}{(n-1)(n-2) \cos^{n-1} x}$

$+ \dfrac{a^2 + (n-2)^2}{(n-1)(n-2)} \int \dfrac{e^{ax}\, dx}{\cos^{n-2} x}.$

425. $\int e^{ax} \sin^m x \cos^n x\, dx$

$= \dfrac{1}{(m+n)^2 + a^2} \Big\{ e^{ax} \sin^m x \cos^{n-1} x\, (a \cos x + (m+n) \sin x)$

$- ma \int e^{ax} \sin^{m-1} x \cos^{n-1} x\, dx$

$+ (n-1)(m+n) \int e^{ax} \sin^m x \cos^{n-2} x\, dx \Big\}$

$$= \frac{1}{(m+n)^2 + a^2} \left\{ e^{ax} \sin^{m-1} x \cos^n x \left(a \sin x - (m+n) \cos x \right) \right.$$

$$+ na \int e^{ax} \sin^{m-1} x \cos^{n-1} x \, dx$$

$$\left. + (m-1)(m+n) \int e^{ax} \sin^{m-2} x \cos^n x \, dx \right\}$$

$$= \frac{1}{(m+n)^2 + a^2} \left\{ \left[e^{ax} \cos^{n-1} x \sin^{m-1} x \left(a \sin x \cos x + n \sin^2 x \right. \right. \right.$$

$$\left. \left. - m \cos^2 x \right) \right] + n(n-1) \int e^{ax} \sin^m x \cos^{n-2} x \, dx$$

$$\left. + m(m-1) \int e^{ax} \sin^{m-2} x \cos^n x \, dx \right\}$$

$$= \frac{1}{(m+n)^2 + a^2} \left\{ \left[e^{ax} \sin^{m-1} x \cos^{n-1} x \left(a \sin x \cos x + n \sin^2 x \right. \right. \right.$$

$$\left. \left. - m \cos^2 x \right) \right] + n(n-1) \int e^{ax} \sin^{m-2} x \cos^{n-2} x \, dx$$

$$\left. + (m-n)(m+n-1) \int e^{ax} \sin^{m-2} x \cos^n x \, dx \right\}$$

$$= \frac{1}{(m+n)^2 + a^2} \left\{ \left[e^{ax} \sin^{m-1} x \cos^{n-1} x \left(a \sin x \cos x + n \sin^2 x \right. \right. \right.$$

$$\left. \left. - m \cos^2 x \right) \right] + m(m-1) \int e^{ax} \sin^{m-2} x \cos^{n-2} x \, dx$$

$$\left. - (m-n)(m+n-1) \int e^{ax} \sin^m x \cos^{n-2} x \, dx \right\}.$$

426. $\int \log x \, dx = x \log x - x.$

427. $\int x^m \log x \, dx = x^{m+1} \left[\dfrac{\log x}{m+1} - \dfrac{1}{(m+1)^2} \right].$

428. $\int (\log x)^n \, dx = x (\log x)^n - n \int (\log x)^{n-1} \, dx.$

429. $\int x^m (\log x)^n \, dx = \dfrac{x^{m+1} (\log x)^n}{m+1} - \dfrac{n}{m+1} \int x^m (\log x)^{n-1} \, dx.$

430. $\int \dfrac{(\log x)^n\, dx}{x} = \dfrac{(\log x)^{n+1}}{n+1}.$

431. $\int \dfrac{dx}{\log x} = \log(\log x) + \log x + \dfrac{(\log x)^2}{2\cdot 2!} + \dfrac{(\log x)^3}{3\cdot 3!} + \cdots.$

432. $\int \dfrac{dx}{(\log x)^n} = -\dfrac{x}{(n-1)(\log x)^{n-1}} + \dfrac{1}{n-1}\int \dfrac{dx}{(\log x)^{n-1}}.$

433. $\int \dfrac{x^m\, dx}{(\log x)^n} = -\dfrac{x^{m+1}}{(n-1)(\log x)^{n-1}} + \dfrac{m+1}{n-1}\int \dfrac{x^m\, dx}{(\log x)^{n-1}}.$

434. $\int \dfrac{x^m\, dx}{\log x} = \int \dfrac{e^{-y}}{y}\, dy,$ where $y = -(m+1)\log x.$

435. $\int \dfrac{dx}{x \log x} = \log(\log x),$ and $\int \dfrac{(n-1)\, dx}{x (\log x)^n} = \dfrac{-1}{(\log x)^{n-1}}.$

436. $\int \log(a^2 + x^2)\, dx = x\cdot \log(a^2 + x^2) - 2x + 2a\cdot \tan^{-1}\left(\dfrac{x}{a}\right)$

437. $\int (a + bx)^m \log x\, dx$

$$= \dfrac{1}{b(m+1)}\left[(a+bx)^{m+1}\log x - \int \dfrac{(a+bx)^{m+1}\, dx}{x}\right].$$

438. $\int x^m \log(a + bx)\, dx$

$$= \dfrac{1}{m+1}\left[x^{m+1}\log(a+bx) - b\int \dfrac{x^{m+1}\, dx}{a+bx}\right].$$

439. $\int \dfrac{\log(a + bx)\, dx}{x}$

$$= \log a \cdot \log x + \dfrac{bx}{a} - \dfrac{1}{2^2}\left(\dfrac{bx}{a}\right)^2 + \dfrac{1}{3^2}\left(\dfrac{bx}{a}\right)^3 - \cdots.$$

$$= \tfrac{1}{2}(\log bx)^2 - \dfrac{a}{bx} + \dfrac{1}{2^2}\left(\dfrac{a}{bx}\right)^2 - \dfrac{1}{3^2}\left(\dfrac{a}{bx}\right)^3 + \cdots.$$

440. $\displaystyle\int \frac{\log x\,dx}{(a+bx)^m}$

$$= \frac{1}{b\,(m-1)}\left[-\frac{\log x}{(a+bx)^{m-1}} + \int \frac{dx}{x\,(a+bx)^{m-1}}\right].$$

441. $\displaystyle\int \frac{\log x\,dx}{a+bx} = \frac{1}{b}\log x\cdot\log(a+bx) - \frac{1}{b}\int \frac{\log(a+bx)\,dx}{x}.$

442. $\displaystyle\int (a+bx)\log x\,dx = \frac{(a+bx)^2}{2\,b}\log x - \frac{a^2\log x}{2\,b} - ax - \tfrac{1}{4}bx^2.$

443. $\displaystyle\int \frac{\log x\,dx}{\sqrt{a+bx}}$

$$= \frac{2}{b}\left[(\log x - 2)\sqrt{a+bx} + \sqrt{a}\,\log(\sqrt{a+bx}+\sqrt{a})\right.$$

$$\left. -\sqrt{a}\,\log(\sqrt{a+bx}-\sqrt{a})\right],\ \text{if } a>0$$

$$= \frac{2}{b}\left[(\log x - 2)\sqrt{a+bx} + 2\sqrt{-a}\,\tan^{-1}\sqrt{\frac{a+bx}{-a}}\right],\ \text{if } a<0.$$

444. $\displaystyle\int \sin\log x\,dx = \tfrac{1}{2}x\,[\sin\log x - \cos\log x].$

445. $\displaystyle\int \cos\log x\,dx = \tfrac{1}{2}x\,[\sin\log x + \cos\log x].$

446. $\displaystyle\int \sinh x\,dx = \cosh x.$

447. $\displaystyle\int \cosh x\,dx = \sinh x.$

448. $\displaystyle\int \tanh x\,dx = \log\cosh x.$

449. $\displaystyle\int \operatorname{ctnh} x\,dx = \log\sinh x.$

450. $\int \operatorname{sech} x \, dx = 2 \tan^{-1} e^x.$

451. $\int \operatorname{csch} x \, dx = \log \tanh \dfrac{x}{2}.$

452. $\int \sinh^n x \, dx = \dfrac{1}{n} \sinh^{n-1} x \cdot \cosh x - \dfrac{n-1}{n} \int \sinh^{n-2} x \, dx$

$\qquad = \dfrac{1}{n+1} \sinh^{n+1} x \cosh x - \dfrac{n+2}{n+1} \int \sinh^{n+2} x \, dx.$

453. $\int \cosh^n x \, dx = \dfrac{1}{n} \sinh x \cdot \cosh^{n-1} x + \dfrac{n-1}{n} \int \cosh^{n-2} x \, dx$

$\qquad = -\dfrac{1}{n+1} \sinh x \cosh^{n+1} x + \dfrac{n+2}{n+1} \int \cosh^{n+2} x \, dx$

454. $\int x \sinh x \, dx = x \cosh x - \sinh x.$

455. $\int x \cosh x \, dx = x \sinh x - \cosh x.$

456. $\int x^2 \sinh x \, dx = (x^2 + 2) \cosh x - 2 x \sinh x.$

457. $\int x^n \sinh x \, dx = x^n \cosh x - n x^{n-1} \sinh x$

$\qquad\qquad + n(n-1) \int x^{n-2} \sinh x \, dx.$

458. $\int \sinh^2 x \, dx = \frac{1}{2} (\sinh x \cosh x - x).$

459. $\int \sinh x \cdot \cosh x \, dx = \frac{1}{4} \cosh (2 x).$

460. $\int \cosh^2 x \, dx = \frac{1}{2} (\sinh x \cosh x + x).$

461. $\int \tanh^2 x \, dx = x - \tanh x.$

462. $\int \operatorname{ctnh}^2 x \, dx = x - \operatorname{ctnh} x.$

463. $\int \operatorname{sech}^2 x \, dx = \tanh x.$

464. $\int \operatorname{csch}^2 x \, dx = - \operatorname{ctnh} x.$

465. $\int \sinh^{-1} x \, dx = x \sinh^{-1} x - \sqrt{1 + x^2}.$

466. $\int \cosh^{-1} x \, dx = x \cosh^{-1} x - \sqrt{x^2 - 1}.$

467. $\int \tanh^{-1} x \, dx = x \tanh^{-1} x + \frac{1}{2} \log(1 - x^2).$

468. $\int x \sinh^{-1} x \, dx = \frac{1}{4} \left[(2\,x^2 + 1) \sinh^{-1} x - x \sqrt{1 + x^2} \right].$

469. $\int x \cosh^{-1} x \, dx = \frac{1}{4} \left[(2\,x^2 - 1) \cosh^{-1} x - x \sqrt{x^2 - 1} \right].$

470. $\int \dfrac{dx}{\cosh a + \cosh x}$

$\qquad = \operatorname{csch} a \left[\log \cosh \tfrac{1}{2}(x + a) - \log \cosh \tfrac{1}{2}(x - a) \right],$

$\qquad = 2 \operatorname{csch} a \cdot \tanh^{-1} (\tanh \tfrac{1}{2} x \cdot \tanh \tfrac{1}{2} a).$

471. $\int \dfrac{dx}{\cos a + \cosh x} = 2 \csc a \cdot \tan^{-1} (\tanh \tfrac{1}{2} x \cdot \tan \tfrac{1}{2} a).$

472. $\int \dfrac{dx}{1 + \cos a \cdot \cosh x} = 2 \csc a \cdot \tanh^{-1} (\tanh \tfrac{1}{2} x \cdot \tan \tfrac{1}{2} a).$

473. $\int \sinh x \cdot \cos x \, dx = \frac{1}{2} (\cosh x \cdot \cos x + \sinh x \cdot \sin x).$

474 $\int \cosh x \cdot \cos x \, dx = \frac{1}{2} (\sinh x \cdot \cos x + \cosh x \cdot \sin x).$

475. $\int \sinh x \cdot \sin x \, dx = \frac{1}{2} (\cosh x \cdot \sin x - \sinh x \cdot \cos x).$

476. $\int \cosh x \cdot \sin x \, dx = \frac{1}{2}(\sinh x \cdot \sin x - \cosh x \cdot \cos x).$

477. $\int \sinh(mx) \sinh(nx) \, dx$

$$= \frac{1}{m^2 - n^2}\Big[m \sinh(nx) \cosh(mx) - n \cosh(nx) \sinh(mx) \Big].$$

478. $\int \cosh(mx) \sinh(nx) \, dx$

$$= \frac{1}{m^2 - n^2}\Big[m \sinh(nx) \sinh(mx) - n \cosh(nx) \cosh(mx) \Big].$$

479. $\int \cosh(mx) \cosh(nx) \, dx$

$$= \frac{1}{m^2 - n^2}\Big[m \sinh(mx) \cosh(nx) - n \sinh(nx) \cosh(mx) \Big].$$

$$\int \frac{dx}{a \cos^2 x + c \sin x \cdot \cos x + b \sin^2 x} = \int \frac{d(\tan x)}{a + c \tan x + b \tan^2 x}.$$

$$\int \frac{(l + m \cos x + n \sin x)\, dx}{a + b \cos x + c \sin x} = \int \frac{(m \cos \delta + n \sin \delta) \cos z \cdot dz}{Z}$$

$$+ \int \frac{l \cdot dz}{Z} - \int \frac{(m \sin \delta - n \cos \delta) \sin z \cdot dz}{Z},$$

where $b = q \cdot \cos \delta$, $c = q \cdot \sin \delta$, $z = x - \delta$, $Z = a + q \cdot \cos z.$

[See 303 and 304.]

$$\int \sin(mx + a) \cdot \sin(nx + b) \, dx$$

$$= \frac{\sin[mx - nx + a - b]}{2(m - n)} - \frac{\sin[mx + nx + a + b]}{2(m + n)}.$$

$$\int \cos(mx + a) \cdot \cos(nx + b) \, dx$$

$$= \frac{\sin[mx + nx + a + b]}{2(m + n)} + \frac{\sin[mx - nx + a - b]}{2(m - n)}.$$

$$\int \sin(mx + a) \cdot \cos(nx + b) \, dx$$

$$= -\frac{\cos[mx + nx + a + b]}{2(m + n)} - \frac{\cos[mx - nx + a - b]}{2(m - n)}.$$

VI. MISCELLANEOUS DEFINITE INTEGRALS.*

480. $\int_0^\infty \dfrac{a\,dx}{a^2 + x^2} = \dfrac{\pi}{2}$, if $a > 0$; 0, if $a = 0$; $-\dfrac{\pi}{2}$, if $a < 0$.

481. $\int_0^\infty x^{n-1} e^{-x}\,dx = \int_0^1 \left[\log \dfrac{1}{x}\right]^{n-1} dx \equiv \Gamma(n)$.

$$\Gamma(z+1) = z \cdot \Gamma(z), \text{ if } z > 0.$$

$$\Gamma(y) \cdot \Gamma(1-y) = \dfrac{\pi}{\sin \pi y}, \text{ if } 1 > y > 0. \quad \Gamma(2) = \Gamma(1) = 1.$$

$$\Gamma(n+1) = n!, \text{ if } n \text{ is an integer.} \qquad \Gamma(z) = \Pi(z-1).$$

$$\Gamma(\tfrac{1}{2}) = \sqrt{\pi}. \qquad Z(y) = D_y[\log \Gamma(y)]. \quad Z(1) = -0.577216$$

482. $\int_0^1 x^{m-1}(1-x)^{n-1}\,dx = \int_0^\infty \dfrac{x^{m-1}\,dx}{(1+x)^{m+n}} = \dfrac{\Gamma(m)\,\Gamma(n)}{\Gamma(m+n)}$.

483. $\int_0^{\frac{\pi}{2}} \sin^n x\,dx = \int_0^{\frac{\pi}{2}} \cos^n x\,dx$

$$= \dfrac{1 \cdot 3 \cdot 5 \cdots (n-1)}{2 \cdot 4 \cdot 6 \cdots (n)} \cdot \dfrac{\pi}{2}, \text{ if } n \text{ is an even integer,}$$

$$= \dfrac{2 \cdot 4 \cdot 6 \cdots (n-1)}{1 \cdot 3 \cdot 5 \cdot 7 \cdots n}, \text{ if } n \text{ is an odd integer,}$$

$$= \tfrac{1}{2} \sqrt{\pi}\, \dfrac{\Gamma\left(\dfrac{n+1}{2}\right)}{\Gamma\left(\dfrac{n}{2}+1\right)}, \text{ for any value of } n \text{ greater than } -1.$$

484. $\int_0^\infty \dfrac{\sin mx\,dx}{x} = \dfrac{\pi}{2}$, if $m > 0$; 0, if $m = 0$; $-\dfrac{\pi}{2}$, if $m < 0$.

* For very complete lists of definite integrals, see Bierens de Haan, *Tables d'inté-grales définies*, Amsterdam, 1858-64, and *Nouv. Tables d'intégrales définies*, Leyden, 1867.

485. $\int_0^\infty \frac{\sin x \cdot \cos mx\, dx}{x} = 0$, if $m < -1$ or $m > 1$;

$\frac{\pi}{4}$, if $m = -1$ or $m = 1$; $\frac{\pi}{2}$, if $-1 < m < 1$.

486. $\int_0^\infty \frac{\sin^2 x\, dx}{x^2} = \frac{\pi}{2}$.

487. $\int_0^\infty \cos(x^2)\, dx = \int_0^\infty \sin(x^2)\, dx = \frac{1}{2} \sqrt{\frac{\pi}{2}}$.

488. $\int_0^\pi \sin kx \cdot \sin mx\, dx = \int_0^\pi \cos kx \cdot \cos mx\, dx = 0$,

if k is different from m.

489. $\int_0^\pi \sin^2 mx\, dx = \int_0^\pi \cos^2 mx\, dx = \frac{\pi}{2}$.

490. $\int_0^\infty \frac{\cos mx\, dx}{1 + x^2} = \frac{\pi}{2} \cdot e^{-|m|}$. $\qquad m > 0.$

491. $\int_0^\infty \frac{\cos x\, dx}{\sqrt{x}} = \int_0^\infty \frac{\sin x\, dx}{\sqrt{x}} = \sqrt{\frac{\pi}{2}}$.

492. $\int_0^\infty e^{-a^2 x^2}\, dx = \frac{1}{2a} \sqrt{\pi} = \frac{1}{2a} \Gamma(\tfrac{1}{2})$. $\qquad a > 0.$

493. $\int_0^\infty x^n e^{-ax}\, dx = \frac{\Gamma(n+1)}{a^{n+1}} = \frac{n!}{a^{n+1}}$. $\qquad n > -1,\ a > 0.$

494. $\int_0^\infty x^{2n} e^{-ax^2}\, dx = \frac{1 \cdot 3 \cdot 5 \cdots (2n-1)}{2^{n+1} a^n} \sqrt{\frac{\pi}{a}}$.

495. $\int_0^\infty e^{-x^2 - \frac{a^2}{x^2}}\, dx = \frac{e^{-2a} \sqrt{\pi}}{2}$. $\qquad a > 0.$

496. $\int_0^\infty e^{-nx} \sqrt{x}\, dx = \frac{1}{2n} \sqrt{\frac{\pi}{n}}$.

497. $\int_0^\infty \frac{e^{-nx}}{\sqrt{x}}\, dx = \sqrt{\frac{\pi}{n}}$.

498. $\displaystyle\int_0^\infty \frac{dx}{e^{nx} + e^{-nx}} = \frac{\pi}{4\,n}.$

499. $\displaystyle\int_0^\infty \frac{x\,dx}{e^{nx} - e^{-nx}} = \frac{\pi^2}{8\,n^2}.$

500. $\displaystyle\int_0^{\pi i} \sinh(mx)\cdot\sinh(nx)\,dx = \int_0^{\pi i} \cosh(mx)\cdot\cosh(nx)\,dx$

$\qquad\qquad\qquad = 0,$ if m is different from n.

501. $\displaystyle\int_0^{\pi i} \cosh^2(mx)\,dx = -\int_0^{\pi i} \sinh^2(mx)\,dx = \frac{\pi i}{2}.$

502. $\displaystyle\int_{-\pi i}^{+\pi i} \sinh(mx)\,dx = 0.$

503. $\displaystyle\int_0^{\pi i} \cosh(mx)\,dx = 0.$

504. $\displaystyle\int_{-\pi i}^{\pi i} \sinh(mx)\cosh(nx)\,dx = 0.$

505. $\displaystyle\int_0^{\pi i} \sinh(mx)\cosh(mx)\,dx = 0.$

506. $\displaystyle\int_0^\infty e^{-ax}\cos mx\,dx = \frac{a}{a^2 + m^2},$ if $a > 0.$

507. $\displaystyle\int_0^\infty e^{-ax}\sin mx\,dx = \frac{m}{a^2 + m^2},$ if $a > 0.$

508. $\displaystyle\int_0^\infty e^{-a^2x^2}\cos bx\,dx = \frac{\sqrt{\pi}\cdot e^{-\frac{b^2}{4a^2}}}{2\,a}.$ $\qquad\qquad a > 0.$

509. $\displaystyle\int_0^1 \frac{\log x}{1-x}\,dx = -\frac{\pi^2}{6}.$

510. $\displaystyle\int_0^1 \frac{\log x}{1+x}\,dx = -\frac{\pi^2}{12}.$

511. $\displaystyle\int_0^1 \frac{\log x}{1-x^2}\,dx = -\frac{\pi^2}{8}.$

512. $\int_0^1 \log\left(\frac{1+x}{1-x}\right) \cdot \frac{dx}{x} = \frac{\pi^2}{4}$.

513. $\int_0^1 \frac{\log x\, dx}{\sqrt{1-x^2}} = -\frac{\pi}{2} \log 2$.

514. $\int_0^1 \frac{(x^p - x^q)\, dx}{\log x} = \log \frac{p+1}{q+1}$, if $p+1 > 0$, $q+1 > 0$.

515. $\int_0^1 (\log x)^n\, dx = (-1)^n \cdot n!$.

516. $\int_0^1 \left(\log \frac{1}{x}\right)^{\frac{1}{2}} dx = \frac{\sqrt{\pi}}{2}$.

517. $\int_0^1 \left(\log \frac{1}{x}\right)^n dx = n!$.

518. $\int_0^1 \frac{dx}{\sqrt{\log\left(\frac{1}{x}\right)}} = \sqrt{\pi}$.

519. $\int_0^1 x^m \left(\log \frac{1}{x}\right)^n dx = \frac{\Gamma(n+1)}{(m+1)^{n+1}}$, if $m+1 > 0$, $n+1 > 0$.

520. $\int_0^\infty \log\left(\frac{e^x+1}{e^x-1}\right) dx = \frac{\pi^2}{4}$.

521. $\int_0^{\frac{\pi}{2}} \log \sin x\, dx = \int_0^{\frac{\pi}{2}} \log \cos x\, dx = -\frac{\pi}{2} \cdot \log 2$.

522. $\int_0^\pi x \cdot \log \sin x\, dx = -\frac{\pi^2}{2} \log 2$.

523. $\int_0^\pi \log(a \pm b \cos x)\, dx = \pi \log\left(\frac{a + \sqrt{a^2 - b^2}}{2}\right)$. $a \geqq b$

VII. ELLIPTIC INTEGRALS.

$$F(\phi, k) \equiv \int_0^\phi \frac{d\theta}{\sqrt{1 - k^2 \sin^2 \theta}} \equiv \int_0^x \frac{dz}{\sqrt{1 - z^2} \sqrt{1 - k^2 z^2}} \equiv u,$$

where $k^2 < 1$, $x = \sin \phi$.

$$E(\phi, k) \equiv \int_0^\phi \sqrt{1 - k^2 \sin^2 \theta} \cdot d\theta.$$

$$\Pi(\phi, n, k) \equiv \int_0^\phi \frac{d\theta}{(1 + n \sin^2 \theta) \sqrt{1 - k^2 \sin^2 \theta}}.$$

$\phi \equiv \operatorname{am} u,\ \sin \phi \equiv x \equiv \operatorname{sn} u,\ \cos \phi \equiv \sqrt{1 - x^2} \equiv \operatorname{cn} u,\ \tan \phi \equiv \operatorname{tn} u,$
$\Delta \phi \equiv \sqrt{1 - k^2 \sin^2 \phi} \equiv \sqrt{1 - k^2 x^2} \equiv \operatorname{dn} u,\ k'^2 \equiv 1 - k^2.$

$$u \equiv \operatorname{am}^{-1}(\phi, k) \equiv \operatorname{sn}^{-1}(x, k) \equiv \operatorname{cn}^{-1}(\sqrt{1 - x^2}, k)$$
$$\equiv \operatorname{dn}^{-1}(\sqrt{1 - k^2 x^2}, k).$$

$K \equiv F(\tfrac{1}{2}\pi, k),\ K' \equiv F(\tfrac{1}{2}\pi, k'),\ E \equiv E(\tfrac{1}{2}\pi, k),\ E' \equiv E(\tfrac{1}{2}\pi, k')$

If $k_0 = \dfrac{2 k^{\frac{1}{2}}}{1 + k}$ and $\tan \phi \equiv \dfrac{\sin 2\omega}{k + \cos 2\omega}$,

$$F(\phi, k) \equiv \frac{2}{1 + k} F(\omega, k_0).$$

524. $\displaystyle \int_0^{\frac{\pi}{2}} \frac{d\theta}{\sqrt{1 - k^2 \sin^2 \theta}}$

$= \dfrac{\pi}{2} \left[1 + (\tfrac{1}{2})^2 k^2 + \left(\dfrac{1 \cdot 3}{2 \cdot 4} \right)^2 k^4 + \left(\dfrac{1 \cdot 3 \cdot 5}{2 \cdot 4 \cdot 6} \right)^2 k^6 + \cdots \right]$, if $k^2 < 1$,

$= K.$

525. $\displaystyle \int_0^{\frac{\pi}{2}} \sqrt{1 - k^2 \sin^2 \theta} \cdot d\theta$

$= \dfrac{\pi}{2} \left[1 - (\tfrac{1}{2})^2 k^2 - \left(\dfrac{1 \cdot 3}{2 \cdot 4} \right)^2 \dfrac{k^4}{3} - \left(\dfrac{1 \cdot 3 \cdot 5}{2 \cdot 4 \cdot 6} \right)^2 \dfrac{k^6}{5} - \cdots \right]$, if $k^2 < 1$,

$= E.$

526. $\displaystyle\int_0^\phi \frac{d\theta}{\sqrt{1-k^2\sin^2\theta}} = \frac{2}{\pi}\,\phi\cdot K - \sin\phi\,\cos\phi\left[\frac{1\cdot1}{2\cdot2}\,k^2\right.$

$$+ \frac{1\cdot3}{2\cdot4}\,A_4 k^4 + \frac{1\cdot3\cdot5}{2\cdot4\cdot6}\,A_6 k^6 + \cdots\Bigg]$$

$$= F(\phi,\,k),$$

where $A_4 \equiv \tfrac14\sin^2\phi + \dfrac{3}{2\cdot4}$, $A_6 \equiv \tfrac16\sin^4\phi + \dfrac{5}{6\cdot4}\sin^2\phi + \dfrac{5\cdot3}{6\cdot4\cdot2}$,

$A_8 \equiv \tfrac18\sin^6\phi + \dfrac{7}{8\cdot6}\sin^4\phi + \dfrac{7\cdot5}{8\cdot6\cdot4}\sin^2\phi + \dfrac{7\cdot5\cdot3}{8\cdot6\cdot4\cdot2}$, etc.

527. $\displaystyle\int_0^\phi \sqrt{1-k^2\sin^2\theta}\cdot d\theta = \frac{2}{\pi}\,\phi\cdot E + \sin\phi\,\cos\phi\left[\frac{1\cdot1}{2\cdot2}\,k^2\right.$

$$+ \frac{1}{2\cdot4}\,k^4 A_4 + \frac{1\cdot3}{2\cdot4\cdot6}\,k^6 A_6 + \cdots\Bigg]$$

$$= E(\phi,\,k).$$

528.[*] $\displaystyle\int_0^x \frac{dx}{\sqrt{(1-x^2)(1-k^2x^2)}} = \operatorname{sn}^{-1}(x,\,k)$

$$= F(\sin^{-1}x,\,k). \quad 0 < x < 1.$$

529. $\displaystyle\int_x^1 \frac{dx}{\sqrt{(1-x^2)(k'^2+k^2x^2)}} = \operatorname{cn}^{-1}(x,\,k)$

$$= F(\cos^{-1}x,\,k) = \operatorname{sn}^{-1}(\sqrt{1-x^2},\,k). \quad 0 < x < 1.$$

530. $\displaystyle\int_x^1 \frac{dx}{\sqrt{(1-x^2)(x^2-k'^2)}} = \operatorname{dn}^{-1}(x,\,k)$

$$= F(\Delta^{-1}x,\,k) = \operatorname{sn}^{-1}\!\left(\frac{1}{k}\sqrt{1-x^2},\,k\right)\!. \quad 0 < x < 1.$$

531. $\displaystyle\int_0^x \frac{dx}{\sqrt{(1+x^2)(1+k'^2x^2)}} = \operatorname{tn}^{-1}(x,\,k)$

$$= F(\tan^{-1}x,\,k) = \operatorname{sn}^{-1}\!\left(\frac{x}{\sqrt{1+x^2}},\,k\right)\!. \quad 0 < x < 1.$$

---

[*] The next forty-two integrals are copied in order from a class-room list of Prof. W. E. Byerly.

532. $\int_0^x \dfrac{dx}{\sqrt{x(1-x)(1-k^2x)}}$ $= 2\operatorname{sn}^{-1}(\sqrt{x},\, k)$
$$= 2\,F(\sin^{-1}\sqrt{x},\, k).\ \ 0 < x < 1.$$

533. $\int_x^1 \dfrac{dx}{\sqrt{x(1-x)(k'^2+k^2x)}} = 2\operatorname{cn}^{-1}(\sqrt{x},\, k)$
$$= 2\,F(\cos^{-1}\sqrt{x},\, k) = 2\operatorname{sn}^{-1}(\sqrt{1-x},\, k).\ \ 0 < x < 1.$$

534. $\int_x^1 \dfrac{dx}{\sqrt{x(1-x)(x-k'^2)}} = 2\operatorname{dn}^{-1}(\sqrt{x},\, k)$
$$= 2\,F(\Delta^{-1}\sqrt{x},\, k) = 2\operatorname{sn}^{-1}\!\left(\frac{1}{k}\sqrt{1-x},\, k\right)\cdot\ 0 < x < 1.$$

535. $\int_0^x \dfrac{dx}{\sqrt{x(1+x)(1+k'^2x)}} = 2\operatorname{tn}^{-1}(\sqrt{x},\, k)$
$$= 2\,F(\tan^{-1}\sqrt{x},\, k) = 2\operatorname{sn}^{-1}\!\left(\sqrt{\frac{x}{1+x}},\, k\right)\cdot\ 0 < x < 1.$$

536. $\int_0^x \dfrac{dx}{\sqrt{(a^2-x^2)(b^2-x^2)}} = \dfrac{1}{a}\operatorname{sn}^{-1}\!\left(\dfrac{x}{b},\, \dfrac{b}{a}\right)\cdot\quad a > b > x > 0.$

537. $\int_x^\infty \dfrac{dx}{\sqrt{(x^2-a^2)(x^2-b^2)}} = \dfrac{1}{a}\operatorname{sn}^{-1}\!\left(\dfrac{a}{x},\, \dfrac{b}{a}\right)\cdot\quad x > a > b.$

538. $\int_x^b \dfrac{dx}{\sqrt{(a^2+x^2)(b^2-x^2)}}$
$$= \frac{1}{\sqrt{a^2+b^2}}\operatorname{cn}^{-1}\!\left(\frac{x}{b},\, \frac{b}{\sqrt{a^2+b^2}}\right)\cdot\qquad b > x > 0.$$

539. $\int_b^x \dfrac{dx}{\sqrt{(a^2+x^2)(x^2-b^2)}}$
$$= \frac{1}{\sqrt{a^2+b^2}}\operatorname{cn}^{-1}\!\left(\frac{b}{x},\, \frac{a}{\sqrt{a^2+b^2}}\right)\cdot\qquad x > b > 0.$$

540. $\displaystyle\int_x^a \frac{dx}{\sqrt{(a^2 - x^2)(x^2 - b^2)}}$

$$= \frac{1}{a}\,\mathrm{sn}^{-1}\left(\sqrt{\frac{a^2 - x^2}{a^2 - b^2}},\ \sqrt{\frac{a^2 - b^2}{a^2}}\right). \qquad a > x > b.$$

541. $\displaystyle\int_0^x \frac{dx}{\sqrt{(x^2 + a^2)(x^2 + b^2)}}$

$$= \frac{1}{a}\,\mathrm{tn}^{-1}\left(\frac{x}{b},\ \sqrt{\frac{a^2 - b^2}{a^2}}\right). \qquad x > 0.$$

$$a > \beta > \gamma.$$

542. $\displaystyle\int_x^x \frac{dx}{\sqrt{(x - a)(x - \beta)(x - \gamma)}}$

$$= \frac{2}{\sqrt{a - \gamma}}\,\mathrm{sn}^{-1}\left(\sqrt{\frac{a - \gamma}{x - \gamma}},\ \sqrt{\frac{\beta - \gamma}{a - \gamma}}\right). \qquad x > a.$$

543. $\displaystyle\int_a^x \frac{dx}{\sqrt{(x - a)(x - \beta)(x - \gamma)}}$

$$= \frac{2}{\sqrt{a - \gamma}}\,\mathrm{sn}^{-1}\left(\sqrt{\frac{x - a}{x - \beta}},\ \sqrt{\frac{\beta - \gamma}{a - \gamma}}\right). \qquad x > a.$$

544. $\displaystyle\int_x^a \frac{dx}{\sqrt{(a - x)(x - \beta)(x - \gamma)}}$

$$= \frac{2}{\sqrt{a - \gamma}}\,\mathrm{sn}^{-1}\left(\sqrt{\frac{a - x}{a - \beta}},\ \sqrt{\frac{a - \beta}{a - \gamma}}\right). \qquad a > x > \beta.$$

545. $\displaystyle\int_\beta^x \frac{dx}{\sqrt{(a - x)(x - \beta)(x - \gamma)}}$

$$= \frac{2}{\sqrt{a - \gamma}}\,\mathrm{sn}^{-1}\left(\sqrt{\frac{a - \gamma}{a - \beta}\cdot\frac{x - \beta}{x - \gamma}},\ \sqrt{\frac{a - \beta}{a - \gamma}}\right). \qquad a > x > \beta.$$

546. $\displaystyle\int_x^\beta \frac{dx}{\sqrt{(a - x)(\beta - x)(x - \gamma)}}$

$$= \frac{2}{\sqrt{a - \gamma}}\,\mathrm{sn}^{-1}\left(\sqrt{\frac{a - \gamma}{\beta - \gamma}\cdot\frac{\beta - x}{a - x}},\ \sqrt{\frac{\beta - \gamma}{a - \gamma}}\right). \qquad \beta > x > \gamma.$$

547. $\displaystyle\int_{\gamma}^{x} \frac{dx}{\sqrt{(a-x)(\beta-x)(x-\gamma)}}$

$$= \frac{2}{\sqrt{a-\gamma}} \operatorname{sn}^{-1}\left(\sqrt{\frac{x-\gamma}{\beta-\gamma}}, \ \sqrt{\frac{\beta-\gamma}{a-\gamma}}\right). \qquad \beta > x > \gamma.$$

548. $\displaystyle\int_{x}^{\gamma} \frac{dx}{\sqrt{(a-x)(\beta-x)(\gamma-x)}}$

$$= \frac{2}{\sqrt{a-\gamma}} \operatorname{sn}^{-1}\left(\sqrt{\frac{\gamma-x}{\beta-x}}, \ \sqrt{\frac{a-\beta}{a-\gamma}}\right). \qquad \gamma > x.$$

549. $\displaystyle\int_{-\infty}^{x} \frac{dx}{\sqrt{(a-x)(\beta-x)(\gamma-x)}}$

$$= \frac{2}{\sqrt{a-\gamma}} \operatorname{sn}^{-1}\left(\sqrt{\frac{a-\gamma}{a-x}}, \ \sqrt{\frac{a-\beta}{a-\gamma}}\right). \qquad \gamma > x.$$

$$a > \beta > \gamma > \delta.$$

550. $\displaystyle\int_{a}^{x} \frac{dx}{\sqrt{(x-a)(x-\beta)(x-\gamma)(x-\delta)}}$

$$= \frac{2}{\sqrt{(a-\gamma)(\beta-\delta)}} \operatorname{sn}^{-1}\left(\sqrt{\frac{\beta-\delta}{a-\delta}\cdot\frac{x-a}{x-\beta}}, \ \sqrt{\frac{\beta-\gamma}{a-\gamma}\cdot\frac{a-\delta}{\beta-\delta}}\right).$$
$$x > a.$$

551. $\displaystyle\int_{x}^{a} \frac{dx}{\sqrt{(a-x)(x-\beta)(x-\gamma)(x-\delta)}}$

$$= \frac{2}{\sqrt{(a-\gamma)(\beta-\delta)}} \operatorname{sn}^{-1}\left(\sqrt{\frac{\beta-\delta}{a-\beta}\cdot\frac{a-x}{x-\delta}}, \ \sqrt{\frac{a-\beta}{a-\gamma}\cdot\frac{\gamma-\delta}{\beta-\delta}}\right).$$
$$a > x > \beta$$

552. $\displaystyle\int_{\beta}^{x} \frac{dx}{\sqrt{(a-x)(x-\beta)(x-\gamma)(x-\delta)}}$

$$= \frac{2}{\sqrt{(a-\gamma)(\beta-\delta)}} \operatorname{sn}^{-1}\left(\sqrt{\frac{a-\gamma}{a-\beta}\cdot\frac{x-\beta}{x-\gamma}}, \ \sqrt{\frac{a-\beta}{a-\gamma}\cdot\frac{\gamma-\delta}{\beta-\delta}}\right).$$
$$a > x > \beta.$$

553. $\displaystyle\int_x^\beta \frac{dx}{\sqrt{(a-x)(\beta-x)(x-\gamma)(x-\delta)}}$

$$= \frac{2}{\sqrt{(a-\gamma)(\beta-\delta)}} \, \mathrm{sn}^{-1}\left(\sqrt{\frac{a-\gamma}{\beta-\gamma}\cdot\frac{\beta-x}{a-x}}, \ \sqrt{\frac{\beta-\gamma}{a-\gamma}\cdot\frac{a-\delta}{\beta-\delta}}\right).$$
$$\beta > x > \gamma$$

554. $\displaystyle\int_\gamma^x \frac{dx}{\sqrt{(a-x)(\beta-x)(x-\gamma)(x-\delta)}}$

$$= \frac{2}{\sqrt{(a-\gamma)(\beta-\delta)}} \, \mathrm{sn}^{-1}\left(\sqrt{\frac{\beta-\delta}{\beta-\gamma}\cdot\frac{x-\gamma}{x-\delta}}, \ \sqrt{\frac{\beta-\gamma}{a-\gamma}\cdot\frac{a-\delta}{\beta-\delta}}\right).$$
$$\beta > x > \gamma.$$

555. $\displaystyle\int_x^\gamma \frac{dx}{\sqrt{(a-x)(\beta-x)(\gamma-x)(x-\delta)}}$

$$= \frac{2}{\sqrt{(a-\gamma)(\beta-\delta)}} \, \mathrm{sn}^{-1}\left(\sqrt{\frac{\beta-\delta}{\gamma-\delta}\cdot\frac{\gamma-x}{\beta-x}}, \ \sqrt{\frac{a-\beta}{a-\gamma}\cdot\frac{\gamma-\delta}{\beta-\delta}}\right).$$
$$\gamma > x > \delta.$$

556. $\displaystyle\int_\delta^x \frac{dx}{\sqrt{(a-x)(\beta-x)(\gamma-x)(x-\delta)}}$

$$= \frac{2}{\sqrt{(a-\gamma)(\beta-\delta)}} \, \mathrm{sn}^{-1}\left(\sqrt{\frac{a-\gamma}{\gamma-\delta}\cdot\frac{x-\delta}{a-x}}, \ \sqrt{\frac{a-\beta}{a-\gamma}\cdot\frac{\gamma-\delta}{\beta-\delta}}\right).$$
$$\gamma > x > \delta.$$

557. $\displaystyle\int_x^\delta \frac{dx}{\sqrt{(a-x)(\beta-x)(\gamma-x)(\delta-x)}}$

$$= \frac{2}{\sqrt{(a-\gamma)(\beta-\delta)}} \, \mathrm{sn}^{-1}\left(\sqrt{\frac{a-\gamma}{a-\delta}\cdot\frac{\delta-x}{\gamma-x}}, \ \sqrt{\frac{\beta-\gamma}{a-\gamma}\cdot\frac{a-\delta}{\beta-\delta}}\right).$$
$$\delta > x.$$

558. $\displaystyle\int \mathrm{sn}\, x\, dx = -\frac{1}{k}\cosh^{-1}\left(\frac{\mathrm{dn}\, x}{k'}\right).$

559. $\displaystyle\int \mathrm{cn}\, x\, dx = \frac{1}{k}\cos^{-1}(\mathrm{dn}\, x).$

560. $\int \mathrm{dn}\, x\, dx = \sin^{-1}(\mathrm{sn}\, x) = \mathrm{am}\, x.$

561. $\int \dfrac{dx}{\mathrm{sn}\, x} = \log\left[\dfrac{\mathrm{sn}\, x}{\mathrm{cn}\, x + \mathrm{dn}\, x}\right].$

562. $\int \dfrac{dx}{\mathrm{cn}\, x} = \dfrac{1}{k'}\log\left[\dfrac{k'\,\mathrm{sn}\, x + \mathrm{dn}\, x}{\mathrm{cn}\, x}\right].$

563. $\int \dfrac{dx}{\mathrm{dn}\, x} = \dfrac{1}{k'}\tan^{-1}\left[\dfrac{k'\,\mathrm{sn}\, x - \mathrm{cn}\, x}{k'\,\mathrm{sn}\, x + \mathrm{cn}\, x}\right].$

564. $\int_0^x \mathrm{sn}^2 x\, dx = \dfrac{1}{k^2}[x - E(\mathrm{am}\, x, k)].$

565. $\int_0^x \mathrm{cn}^2 x\, dx = \dfrac{1}{k^2}[E(\mathrm{am}\, x, k) - k'^2 x].$

566. $\int_0^x \mathrm{dn}^2 x\, dx = E(\mathrm{am}\, x, k).$

567. $(m+1)\displaystyle\int \mathrm{sn}^m x\, dx = (m+2)(1+k^2)\int \mathrm{sn}^{m+2} x\, dx$

$$- (m+3)k^2 \int \mathrm{sn}^{m+4} x\, dx + \mathrm{sn}^{m+1} x\ \mathrm{cn}\, x\ \mathrm{dn}\, x.$$

568. $(m+1)k'^2\displaystyle\int \mathrm{cn}^m x\, dx = (m+2)(1-2k^2)\int \mathrm{cn}^{m+2} x\, dx$

$$+ (m+3)k^2 \int \mathrm{cn}^{m+4} x\, dx - \mathrm{cn}^{m+1} x\ \mathrm{sn}\, x\ \mathrm{dn}\, x.$$

569. $(m+1)k'^2\displaystyle\int \mathrm{dn}^m x\, dx = (m+2)(2-k^2)\int \mathrm{dn}^{m+2} x\, dx$

$$- (m+3)\int \mathrm{dn}^{m+4} x\, dx + k^2\,\mathrm{dn}^{m+1} x\ \mathrm{sn}\, x\ \mathrm{cn}\, x.$$

Since $\sin^2\theta \equiv \dfrac{1}{k^2} - \dfrac{1}{k^2}(1 - k^2 \cdot \sin^2\theta),$

$$\int_0^{\frac{\pi}{2}} \dfrac{\sin^2\theta \cdot d\theta}{\sqrt{1 - k^2\sin^2\theta}} = \dfrac{1}{k^2}\int_0^{\frac{\pi}{2}} \dfrac{d\theta}{\sqrt{1 - k^2\sin^2\theta}} - \dfrac{1}{k^2}\int_0^{\frac{\pi}{2}}\sqrt{1 - k^2\sin^2\theta}\ d\theta.$$

VIII. AUXILIARY FORMULAS.

A. — Trigonometric Functions.

570. $\tan a \cdot \operatorname{ctn} a = \sin a \cdot \csc a = \cos a \cdot \sec a = 1.$

$\tan a = \sin a \div \cos a, \quad \sec^2 a = 1 + \tan^2 a,$

$\csc^2 a = 1 + \operatorname{ctn}^2 a, \qquad \sin^2 a + \cos^2 a = 1.$

571. $\sin a = \sqrt{1 - \cos^2 a} = 2 \sin \tfrac{1}{2} a \cdot \cos \tfrac{1}{2} a = \cos a \cdot \tan a$

$$= \frac{1}{\sqrt{1 + \operatorname{ctn}^2 a}} = \frac{\tan a}{\sqrt{1 + \tan^2 a}} = \sqrt{\frac{1 - \cos 2a}{2}} = \frac{2 \tan \tfrac{1}{2} a}{1 + \tan^2 \tfrac{1}{2} a}$$

$$= \sqrt{\frac{\sec^2 a - 1}{\sec^2 a}} = \operatorname{ctn} \tfrac{1}{2} a \cdot (1 - \cos a) = \tan \tfrac{1}{2} a \cdot (1 + \cos a).$$

572. $\cos a = \sqrt{1 - \sin^2 a} = \dfrac{1}{\sqrt{1 + \tan^2 a}} = \dfrac{\operatorname{ctn} a}{\sqrt{1 + \operatorname{ctn}^2 a}}$

$$= \sqrt{\frac{1 + \cos 2a}{2}} = \frac{1 - \tan^2 \tfrac{1}{2} a}{1 + \tan^2 \tfrac{1}{2} a} = \cos^2 \tfrac{1}{2} a - \sin^2 \tfrac{1}{2} a$$

$$= 1 - 2 \sin^2 \tfrac{1}{2} a = 2 \cos^2 \tfrac{1}{2} a - 1 = \sin a \cdot \operatorname{ctn} a$$

$$= \frac{\sin 2a}{2 \sin a} = \sqrt{\frac{\csc^2 a - 1}{\csc^2 a}} = \frac{\operatorname{ctn} \tfrac{1}{2} a - \tan \tfrac{1}{2} a}{\operatorname{ctn} \tfrac{1}{2} a + \tan \tfrac{1}{2} a}.$$

573. $\tan a = \dfrac{\sin a}{\sqrt{1 - \sin^2 a}} = \dfrac{\sqrt{1 - \cos^2 a}}{\cos a} = \dfrac{\sin 2a}{1 + \cos 2a}$

$$= \frac{1 - \cos 2a}{\sin 2a} = \sqrt{\frac{1 - \cos 2a}{1 + \cos 2a}} = \frac{2 \tan \tfrac{1}{2} a}{1 - \tan^2 \tfrac{1}{2} a}$$

$$= \frac{\sec a}{\csc a} = \frac{2}{\operatorname{ctn} \tfrac{1}{2} a - \tan \tfrac{1}{2} a} = \frac{2 \operatorname{ctn} \tfrac{1}{2} a}{\operatorname{ctn}^2 \tfrac{1}{2} a - 1}.$$

574.

	$-\alpha.$	$90° \pm \alpha.$	$180° \pm \alpha.$	$270° \pm \alpha.$	$360° \pm \alpha.$
sin	$-\sin\alpha$	$+\cos\alpha$	$\mp\sin\alpha$	$-\cos\alpha$	$\pm\sin\alpha$
cos	$+\cos\alpha$	$\mp\sin\alpha$	$-\cos\alpha$	$\pm\sin\alpha$	$+\cos\alpha$
tan	$-\tan\alpha$	$\mp\operatorname{ctn}\alpha$	$\pm\tan\alpha$	$\mp\operatorname{ctn}\alpha$	$\pm\tan\alpha$
ctn	$-\operatorname{ctn}\alpha$	$\mp\tan\alpha$	$\pm\operatorname{ctn}\alpha$	$\mp\tan\alpha$	$\pm\operatorname{ctn}\alpha$
sec	$+\sec\alpha$	$\mp\csc\alpha$	$-\sec\alpha$	$\pm\csc\alpha$	$+\sec\alpha$
csc	$-\csc\alpha$	$+\sec\alpha$	$\mp\csc\alpha$	$-\sec\alpha$	$\pm\csc\alpha$

575.

	0°.	30°.	45°.	60°.	90°.	120°.	135°.	150°.	180°.
sin	0	$\frac{1}{2}$	$\frac{1}{2}\sqrt{2}$	$\frac{1}{2}\sqrt{3}$	1	$\frac{1}{2}\sqrt{3}$	$\frac{1}{2}\sqrt{2}$	$\frac{1}{2}$	0
cos	1	$\frac{1}{2}\sqrt{3}$	$\frac{1}{2}\sqrt{2}$	$\frac{1}{2}$	0	$-\frac{1}{2}$	$-\frac{1}{2}\sqrt{2}$	$-\frac{1}{2}\sqrt{3}$	-1
tan	0	$\dfrac{1}{\sqrt{3}}$	1	$\sqrt{3}$	∞	$-\sqrt{3}$	-1	$-\dfrac{1}{\sqrt{3}}$	0
ctn	∞	$\sqrt{3}$	1	$\dfrac{1}{\sqrt{3}}$	0	$-\dfrac{1}{\sqrt{3}}$	-1	$-\sqrt{3}$	∞
sec	1	$\dfrac{2}{\sqrt{3}}$	$\sqrt{2}$	2	∞	-2	$-\sqrt{2}$	$-\dfrac{2}{\sqrt{3}}$	-1
csc	∞	2	$\sqrt{2}$	$\dfrac{2}{\sqrt{3}}$	1	$\dfrac{2}{\sqrt{3}}$	$\sqrt{2}$	2	∞

576. $\sin\frac{1}{2}a = \sqrt{\frac{1}{2}(1-\cos a)}.$

577. $\cos\frac{1}{2}a = \sqrt{\frac{1}{2}(1+\cos a)}.$

578. $\tan\frac{1}{2}a = \sqrt{\dfrac{1-\cos a}{1+\cos a}} = \dfrac{1-\cos a}{\sin a} = \dfrac{\sin a}{1+\cos a}.$

579. $\sin 2a = 2\sin a \cos a.$

580. $\sin 3a = 3\sin a - 4\sin^3 a.$

581. $\sin 4a = 8\cos^3 a \cdot \sin a - 4\cos a \sin a.$

582. $\sin 5\,a = 5 \sin a - 20 \sin^3 a + 16 \sin^5 a.$

583. $\sin 6\,a = 32 \cos^5 a \sin a - 32 \cos^3 a \sin a + 6 \cos a \sin a.$

584. $\cos 2\,a = \cos^2 a - \sin^2 a = 1 - 2 \sin^2 a = 2 \cos^2 a - 1.$

585. $\cos 3\,a = 4 \cos^3 a - 3 \cos a.$

586. $\cos 4\,a = 8 \cos^4 a - 8 \cos^2 a + 1.$

587. $\cos 5\,a = 16 \cos^5 a - 20 \cos^3 a + 5 \cos a.$

588. $\cos 6\,a = 32 \cos^6 a - 48 \cos^4 a + 18 \cos^2 a - 1.$

589. $\tan 2\,a = \dfrac{2 \tan a}{1 - \tan^2 a}.$

590. $\operatorname{ctn} 2\,a = \dfrac{\operatorname{ctn}^2 a - 1}{2 \operatorname{ctn} a}.$

591. $\sin(a \pm \beta) = \sin a \cdot \cos \beta \pm \cos a \cdot \sin \beta.$

592. $\cos(a \pm \beta) = \cos a \cdot \cos \beta \mp \sin a \cdot \sin \beta.$

593. $\tan(a \pm \beta) = \dfrac{\tan a \pm \tan \beta}{1 \mp \tan a \cdot \tan \beta}.$

594. $\operatorname{ctn}(a \pm \beta) = \dfrac{\operatorname{ctn} a \cdot \operatorname{ctn} \beta \mp 1}{\operatorname{ctn} \beta \pm \operatorname{ctn} a}.$

595. $\sin a \pm \sin \beta = 2 \sin \tfrac{1}{2}(a \pm \beta) \cdot \cos \tfrac{1}{2}(a \mp \beta).$

596. $\cos a + \cos \beta = 2 \cos \tfrac{1}{2}(a + \beta) \cdot \cos \tfrac{1}{2}(a - \beta).$

597. $\cos a - \cos \beta = -2 \sin \tfrac{1}{2}(a + \beta) \cdot \sin \tfrac{1}{2}(a - \beta).$

598. $\tan a \pm \tan \beta = \dfrac{\sin(a \pm \beta)}{\cos a \cdot \cos \beta}.$

599. $\operatorname{ctn} a \pm \operatorname{ctn} \beta = \pm \dfrac{\sin(a \pm \beta)}{\sin a \cdot \sin \beta}.$

600. $\dfrac{\sin a \pm \sin \beta}{\cos a + \cos \beta} = \tan \frac{1}{2}(a \pm \beta).$

601. $\dfrac{\sin a \pm \sin \beta}{\cos a - \cos \beta} = -\operatorname{ctn} \frac{1}{2}(a \mp \beta).$

602. $\dfrac{\sin a + \sin \beta}{\sin a - \sin \beta} = \dfrac{\tan \frac{1}{2}(a + \beta)}{\tan \frac{1}{2}(a - \beta)}.$

603. $\sin^2 a - \sin^2 \beta = \sin(a + \beta) \cdot \sin(a - \beta).$

604. $\cos^2 a - \cos^2 \beta = -\sin(a + \beta) \cdot \sin(a - \beta).$

605. $\cos^2 a - \sin^2 \beta = \cos(a + \beta) \cdot \cos(a - \beta).$

606. $\sin xi = \frac{1}{2} i (e^x - e^{-x}) = i \sinh x.$

607. $\cos xi = \frac{1}{2} (e^x + e^{-x}) = \cosh x.$

608. $\tan xi = \dfrac{i(e^x - e^{-x})}{e^x + e^{-x}} = i \tanh x.$

609. $e^{x + yi} = e^x \cos y + i e^x \sin y.$

610. $a^{x + yi} = a^x \cos(y \cdot \log a) + i a^x \sin(y \cdot \log a).$

611. $(\cos \theta \pm i \cdot \sin \theta)^n = \cos n\theta \pm i \cdot \sin n\theta.$

612. $\sin x = -\frac{1}{2} i (e^{xi} - e^{-xi}).$

613. $\cos x = \frac{1}{2} (e^{xi} + e^{-xi}).$

614. $\tan x = -i \dfrac{e^{2xi} - 1}{e^{2xi} + 1}.$

615. $\sin(x \pm yi) = \sin x \cos yi \pm \cos x \sin yi$
$$= \sin x \cosh y \pm i \cos x \sinh y.$$

616. $\cos(x \pm yi) = \cos x \cos yi \mp \sin x \sin yi$
$$= \cos x \cosh y \mp i \sin x \sinh y.$$

In any plane triangle,

617. $\dfrac{a}{\sin A} = \dfrac{b}{\sin B} = \dfrac{c}{\sin C}.$

618. $a^2 = b^2 + c^2 - 2\,bc \cos A.$

619. $\dfrac{a+b}{a-b} = \dfrac{\sin A + \sin B}{\sin A - \sin B} = \dfrac{\tan \frac{1}{2}(A+B)}{\tan \frac{1}{2}(A-B)} = \dfrac{\operatorname{ctn} \frac{1}{2}C}{\tan \frac{1}{2}(A-B)}.$

620. $\sin \frac{1}{2} A = \sqrt{\dfrac{(s-b)(s-c)}{bc}},$ where $2\,s = a + b + c.$

621. $\cos \frac{1}{2} A = \sqrt{\dfrac{s(s-a)}{bc}}.$

622. $\tan \frac{1}{2} A = \sqrt{\dfrac{(s-b)(s-c)}{s(s-a)}}.$

623. $\text{Area} = \frac{1}{2} bc \sin A = \sqrt{s(s-a)(s-b)(s-c)}.$

In any spherical triangle,

624. $\dfrac{\sin A}{\sin a} = \dfrac{\sin B}{\sin b} = \dfrac{\sin C}{\sin c}.$

625. $\cos a = \cos b \cos c + \sin b \sin c \cos A.$

626. $-\cos A = \cos B \cos C - \sin B \sin C \cos a.$

627. $\sin a \operatorname{ctn} b = \sin C \operatorname{ctn} B + \cos a \cos C.$

628. $\cos \frac{1}{2} A = \sqrt{\dfrac{\sin s \cdot \sin (s-a)}{\sin b \cdot \sin c}}.$

629. $\sin \frac{1}{2} A = \sqrt{\dfrac{\sin (s-b) \cdot \sin (s-c)}{\sin b \cdot \sin c}}.$

630. $\tan \frac{1}{2} A = \sqrt{\dfrac{\sin (s-b) \cdot \sin (s-c)}{\sin s \cdot \sin (s-a)}}$

631. $\cos \frac{1}{2} a = \sqrt{\dfrac{\cos (S - B) \cdot \cos (S - C)}{\sin B \cdot \sin C}}.$

632. $\sin \frac{1}{2} a = \sqrt{\dfrac{- \cos S \cdot \cos (S - A)}{\sin B \sin C}}.$

633. $\tan \frac{1}{2} a = \sqrt{\dfrac{- \cos S \cdot \cos (S - A)}{\cos (S - B) \cdot \cos (S - C)}}.$

$$2 s = a + b + c. \qquad 2 S = A + B + C.$$

634. $\cos \frac{1}{2} (A + B) = \dfrac{\cos \frac{1}{2} (a + b)}{\cos \frac{1}{2} c} \sin \frac{1}{2} C.$

635. $\cos \frac{1}{2} (A - B) = \dfrac{\sin \frac{1}{2} (a + b)}{\sin \frac{1}{2} c} \sin \frac{1}{2} C.$

636. $\sin \frac{1}{2} (A + B) = \dfrac{\cos \frac{1}{2} (a - b)}{\cos \frac{1}{2} c} \cos \frac{1}{2} C.$

637. $\sin \frac{1}{2} (A - B) = \dfrac{\sin \frac{1}{2} (a - b)}{\sin \frac{1}{2} c} \cos \frac{1}{2} C.$

638. $\tan \frac{1}{2} (A + B) = \dfrac{\cos \frac{1}{2} (a - b)}{\cos \frac{1}{2} (a + b)} \operatorname{ctn} \frac{1}{2} C.$

639. $\tan \frac{1}{2} (A - B) = \dfrac{\sin \frac{1}{2} (a - b)}{\sin \frac{1}{2} (a + b)} \operatorname{ctn} \frac{1}{2} C.$

640. $\tan \frac{1}{2} (a + b) = \dfrac{\cos \frac{1}{2} (A - B)}{\cos \frac{1}{2} (A + B)} \tan \frac{1}{2} c.$

641. $\tan \frac{1}{2} (a - b) = \dfrac{\sin \frac{1}{2} (A - B)}{\sin \frac{1}{2} (A + B)} \tan \frac{1}{2} c.$

642. $\dfrac{\cos \frac{1}{2} (a + b)}{\cos \frac{1}{2} (a - b)} = \dfrac{\operatorname{ctn} \frac{1}{2} C}{\tan \frac{1}{2} (A + B)}.$

In interpreting equations which involve logarithmic and anti-trigonometric functions, it is necessary to remember that these functions are multiple valued. To save space the formulas on this page and the next are printed in contracted form.

643. $\sin^{-1}x = \cos^{-1}\sqrt{1-x^2} = \tan^{-1}\dfrac{x}{\sqrt{1-x^2}} = \sec^{-1}\dfrac{1}{\sqrt{1-x^2}}$

$= \csc^{-1}\dfrac{1}{x} = 2\sin^{-1}[\frac{1}{2} - \frac{1}{2}\sqrt{1-x^2}]^{\frac{1}{2}}$

$= \frac{1}{2}\sin^{-1}(2x\sqrt{1-x^2}) = 2\tan^{-1}\left[\dfrac{1-\sqrt{1-x^2}}{x}\right]$

$= \frac{1}{2}\tan^{-1}\left[\dfrac{2x\sqrt{1-x^2}}{1-2x^2}\right] = \frac{1}{2}\pi - \cos^{-1}x$

$= \frac{1}{2}\pi - \sin^{-1}\sqrt{1-x^2} = -\sin^{-1}(-x)$

$= \operatorname{ctn}^{-1}\dfrac{\sqrt{1-x^2}}{x} = (2n+\frac{1}{2})\pi - i\log(x+\sqrt{x^2-1})$

$= \frac{1}{4}\pi + \frac{1}{2}\sin^{-1}(2x^2-1) = \frac{1}{2}\cos^{-1}(1-2x^2).$

644. $\cos^{-1}x = \sin^{-1}\sqrt{1-x^2} = \tan^{-1}\dfrac{\sqrt{1-x^2}}{x} = \sec^{-1}\dfrac{1}{x}$

$= \frac{1}{2}\pi - \sin^{-1}x = 2\cos^{-1}\sqrt{\dfrac{1+x}{2}}$

$= \frac{1}{2}\cos^{-1}(2x^2-1)$

$= 2\tan^{-1}\sqrt{\dfrac{1-x}{1+x}} = \frac{1}{2}\tan^{-1}\left[\dfrac{2x\sqrt{1-x^2}}{2x^2-1}\right]$

$= \csc^{-1}\dfrac{1}{\sqrt{1-x^2}} = \pi - \cos^{-1}(-x)$

$= \operatorname{ctn}^{-1}\dfrac{x}{\sqrt{1-x^2}}$

$= i\log(x+\sqrt{x^2-1}) = \pi - i\log(\sqrt{x^2-1}-x).$

645. $\tan^{-1}x = \sin^{-1}\dfrac{x}{\sqrt{1+x^2}} = \cos^{-1}\dfrac{1}{\sqrt{1+x^2}} = \tfrac{1}{2}\sin^{-1}\dfrac{2x}{1+x^2}$

$$= \operatorname{ctn}^{-1}\dfrac{1}{x} = \tfrac{1}{2}\pi - \operatorname{ctn}^{-1}x = \sec^{-1}\sqrt{1+x^2}$$

$$= \tfrac{1}{2}\pi - \tan^{-1}\dfrac{1}{x}$$

$$= \csc^{-1}\dfrac{\sqrt{1+x^2}}{x} = \tfrac{1}{2}\cos^{-1}\left[\dfrac{1-x^2}{1+x^2}\right]$$

$$= 2\cos^{-1}\left[\dfrac{1+\sqrt{1+x^2}}{2\sqrt{1+x^2}}\right]^{\frac{1}{2}} = 2\sin^{-1}\left[\dfrac{\sqrt{1+x^2}-1}{2\sqrt{1+x^2}}\right]^{\frac{1}{2}}$$

$$= \tfrac{1}{2}\tan^{-1}\dfrac{2x}{1-x^2} = 2\tan^{-1}\left[\dfrac{\sqrt{1+x^2}-1}{x}\right]$$

$$= -\tan^{-1}c + \tan^{-1}\left[\dfrac{x+c}{1-cx}\right] = -\tan^{-1}(-x)$$

$$= \tfrac{1}{2}i\log\dfrac{1-xi}{1+xi} = \tfrac{1}{2}i\log\dfrac{i+x}{i-x}$$

$$= -\tfrac{1}{2}i\log\dfrac{1+xi}{1-xi}.$$

646. $\sin^{-1}x \pm \sin^{-1}y = \sin^{-1}[x\sqrt{1-y^2} \pm y\sqrt{1-x^2}].$

647. $\cos^{-1}x \pm \cos^{-1}y = \cos^{-1}[xy \mp \sqrt{(1-x^2)(1-y^2)}].$

648. $\tan^{-1}x \pm \tan^{-1}y = \tan^{-1}\left[\dfrac{x \pm y}{1 \mp xy}\right].$

649. $\sin^{-1}x \pm \cos^{-1}y = \sin^{-1}[xy \pm \sqrt{(1-x^2)(1-y^2)}]$
$$= \cos^{-1}[y\sqrt{1-x^2} \mp x\sqrt{1-y^2}].$$

650. $\tan^{-1}x \pm \operatorname{ctn}^{-1}y = \tan^{-1}\left[\dfrac{xy \pm 1}{y \mp x}\right] = \operatorname{ctn}^{-1}\left[\dfrac{y \mp x}{xy \pm 1}\right]$

651. $\log(x+yi) = \tfrac{1}{2}\log(x^2+y^2) + i\tan^{-1}(y/x).$

B. — HYPERBOLIC FUNCTIONS.

652. $\sinh x = \frac{1}{2}(e^x - e^{-x}) = -\sinh(-x) = -i\sin(ix)$
$= (\operatorname{csch} x)^{-1} = 2\tanh \frac{1}{2}x \div (1 - \tanh^2 \frac{1}{2}x).$

653. $\cosh x = \frac{1}{2}(e^x + e^{-x}) = \cosh(-x) = \cos(ix) = (\operatorname{sech} x)^{-1}$
$= (1 + \tanh^2 \frac{1}{2}x) \div (1 - \tanh^2 \frac{1}{2}x).$

654. $\tanh x = (e^x - e^{-x}) \div (e^x + e^{-x}) = -\tanh(-x)$
$= -i\tan(ix) = (\operatorname{ctnh} x)^{-1} = \sinh x \div \cosh x.$

655. $\cosh xi = \cos x.$

656. $\sinh xi = i\sin x.$

657. $\cosh^2 x - \sinh^2 x = 1.$

658. $1 - \tanh^2 x = \operatorname{sech}^2 x.$

659. $1 - \operatorname{ctnh}^2 x = -\operatorname{csch}^2 x.$

660. $\sinh(x \pm y) = \sinh x \cdot \cosh y \pm \cosh x \cdot \sinh y.$

661. $\cosh(x \pm y) = \cosh x \cdot \cosh y \pm \sinh x \cdot \sinh y.$

662. $\tanh(x \pm y) = (\tanh x \pm \tanh y) \div (1 \pm \tanh x \cdot \tanh y).$

663. $\sinh(2x) = 2\sinh x \cosh x.$

664. $\cosh(2x) = \cosh^2 x + \sinh^2 x = 2\cosh^2 x - 1 = 1 + 2\sinh^2 x.$

665. $\tanh(2x) = 2\tanh x \div (1 + \tanh^2 x).$

666. $\sinh(\frac{1}{2}x) = \sqrt{\frac{1}{2}(\cosh x - 1)}.$

667. $\cosh(\frac{1}{2}x) = \sqrt{\frac{1}{2}(\cosh x + 1)}.$

668. $\tanh(\frac{1}{2}x) = (\cosh x - 1) \div \sinh x = \sinh x \div (\cosh x + 1).$

669. $\sinh x + \sinh y = 2\sinh \frac{1}{2}(x+y) \cdot \cosh \frac{1}{2}(x-y).$

670. $\sinh x - \sinh y = 2\cosh \frac{1}{2}(x+y) \cdot \sinh \frac{1}{2}(x-y).$

671. $\cosh x + \cosh y = 2 \cosh \tfrac{1}{2}(x+y) \cdot \cosh \tfrac{1}{2}(x-y).$

672. $\cosh x - \cosh y = 2 \sinh \tfrac{1}{2}(x+y) \cdot \sinh \tfrac{1}{2}(x-y).$

673. $d \sinh x = \cosh x \cdot dx.$

674. $d \cosh x = \sinh x \cdot dx.$

675. $d \tanh x = \operatorname{sech}^2 x \cdot dx.$

676. $d \operatorname{ctnh} x = - \operatorname{csch}^2 x \cdot dx.$

677. $d \operatorname{sech} x = - \operatorname{sech} x \cdot \tanh x \cdot dx.$

678. $d \operatorname{csch} x = - \operatorname{csch} x \cdot \operatorname{ctnh} x \cdot dx.$

679. $\sinh^{-1} x = \log(x + \sqrt{x^2+1}) = \displaystyle\int \frac{dx}{\sqrt{x^2+1}}$
$$= \cosh^{-1} \sqrt{x^2+1}.$$

680. $\cosh^{-1} x = \log(x + \sqrt{x^2-1}) = \displaystyle\int \frac{dx}{\sqrt{x^2-1}}$
$$= \sinh^{-1} \sqrt{x^2-1}.$$

681. $\tanh^{-1} x = \tfrac{1}{2} \log(1+x) - \tfrac{1}{2} \log(1-x) = \displaystyle\int \frac{dx}{1-x^2}.$

682. $\operatorname{ctnh}^{-1} x = \tfrac{1}{2} \log(1+x) - \tfrac{1}{2} \log(x-1) = \displaystyle\int \frac{dx}{1-x^2}.$

683. $\operatorname{sech}^{-1} x = \log\left(\dfrac{1}{x} + \sqrt{\dfrac{1}{x^2} - 1}\right) = - \displaystyle\int \frac{dx}{x\sqrt{1-x^2}}.$

684. $\operatorname{csch}^{-1} x = \log\left(\dfrac{1}{x} + \sqrt{\dfrac{1}{x^2} + 1}\right) = - \displaystyle\int \frac{dx}{x\sqrt{x^2+1}}.$

685. $d \sinh^{-1} x = \dfrac{dx}{\sqrt{1+x^2}}.$

686. $d \cosh^{-1} x = \dfrac{dx}{\sqrt{x^2-1}}.$

687. $d \tanh^{-1} x = \dfrac{dx}{1 - x^2}.$

688. $d \operatorname{ctnh}^{-1} x = -\dfrac{dx}{x^2 - 1}.$

689. $d \operatorname{sech}^{-1} x = -\dfrac{dx}{x\sqrt{1 - x^2}}.$

690. $d \operatorname{csch}^{-1} x = -\dfrac{dx}{x\sqrt{x^2 + 1}}.$

If m is an integer,

691. $\sinh(m\pi i) = 0.$

692. $\cosh(m\pi i) = \cos m\pi = (-1)^m.$

693. $\tanh(m\pi i) = 0.$

694. $\sinh(x + m\pi i) = (-1)^m \sinh x.$

695. $\cosh(x + m\pi i) = (-1)^m \cosh(x).$

696. $\sinh(2m+1)\tfrac{1}{2}\pi i = i \sin(2m+1)\tfrac{1}{2}\pi = \pm i$

697. $\cosh(2m+1)\tfrac{1}{2}\pi i = 0.$

698. $\sinh\left(\dfrac{\pi i}{2} \pm x\right) = i \cosh x.$

799. $\cosh\left(\dfrac{\pi i}{2} \pm x\right) = \pm i \sinh x.$

700. $\sinh u = \tan \operatorname{gd} u.$

701. $\cosh u = \sec \operatorname{gd} u.$

702. $\tanh u = \sin \operatorname{gd} u.$

703. $\tanh \tfrac{1}{2} u = \tan \tfrac{1}{2} \operatorname{gd} u.$

704. $u = \log \tan(\tfrac{1}{4}\pi + \tfrac{1}{2}\operatorname{gd} u).$ $\displaystyle\int \sec x \, dx = \operatorname{gd}^{-1} x.$

C. — Elliptic Functions.

If $u \equiv F(\phi, k) \equiv \int_0^x \dfrac{dz}{\sqrt{(1 - z^2)(1 - k^2 z^2)}} \equiv \int_0^\phi \dfrac{d\theta}{\sqrt{1 - k^2 \sin^2 \theta}}$,

where $k < 1$, and $x \equiv \sin \phi$, ϕ is called the *amplitude* of u and is written $\text{am}(u, \bmod k)$, or, more simply, $\text{am}\, u$; $x \equiv \sin \phi \equiv \text{sn}\, u$,

$$\sqrt{1 - x^2} \equiv \cos \phi \equiv \text{cn}\, u, \quad \sqrt{1 - k^2 x^2} \equiv \Delta\phi \equiv \Delta\text{n}\, u \equiv \text{dn}\, u,$$

$$K \equiv F(\tfrac{1}{2}\pi, k), \qquad K' \equiv F(\tfrac{1}{2}\pi, k').$$

Hence, $\text{am}(0) = 0, \quad \text{sn}(0) = 0, \quad \text{cn}(0) = 1, \quad \text{dn}(0) = 1,$

$$\text{am}(-u) = -\text{am}\, u, \qquad \text{sn}(-u) = -\text{sn}\, u,$$

$$\text{cn}(-u) = \text{cn}\, u, \qquad \text{dn}(-u) = \text{dn}\, u.$$

705. $\text{sn}^2 u + \text{cn}^2 u = 1.$

706. $\text{dn}^2 u + k^2 \text{sn}^2 u = 1.$

707. $\text{dn}^2 u - k^2 \text{cn}^2 u = 1 - k^2 = k'^2.$

708. $\text{sn}\, 2u = \dfrac{2\, \text{sn}\, u \cdot \text{cn}\, u \cdot \text{dn}\, u}{1 - k^2 \text{sn}^4 u}.$

709. $\text{cn}\, 2u = \dfrac{\text{cn}^2 u - \text{sn}^2 u \cdot \text{dn}^2 u}{1 - k^2 \text{sn}^4 u} = \dfrac{1 - 2\, \text{sn}^2 u + k^2 \text{sn}^4 u}{1 - k^2 \text{sn}^4 u}$

$$= 1 - \dfrac{2\, \text{sn}^2 u \cdot \text{dn}^2 u}{1 - k^2 \text{sn}^4 u} = \dfrac{2\, \text{cn}^2 u}{1 - k^2 \text{sn}^4 u} - 1.$$

710. $\text{dn}\, 2u = \dfrac{\text{dn}^2 u - k^2 \text{sn}^2 u \cdot \text{cn}^2 u}{1 - k^2 \text{sn}^4 u} = \dfrac{1 - 2 k^2 \text{sn}^2 u + k^2 \text{sn}^4 u}{1 - k^2 \text{sn}^4 u}$

$$= 1 - \dfrac{2 k^2 \text{sn}^2 u \cdot \text{cn}^2 u}{1 - k^2 \text{sn}^4 u} = \dfrac{2\, \text{dn}^2 u}{1 - k^2 \text{sn}^4 u} - 1.$$

711. $\text{sn}^2\left(\dfrac{u}{2}\right) = \dfrac{1 - \text{cn}\, u}{1 + \text{dn}\, u} = \dfrac{1 - \text{dn}\, u}{k^2(1 + \text{cn}\, u)} = \dfrac{\text{dn}\, u - \text{cn}\, u}{k'^2 + \text{dn}\, u - k^2 \text{cn}\, u}.$

712. $\text{cn}^2\left(\dfrac{u}{2}\right) = \dfrac{\text{dn}\, u + \text{cn}\, u}{1 + \text{dn}\, u} = \dfrac{k^2 \text{cn}\, u - k'^2 + \text{dn}\, u}{k^2(1 + \text{cn}\, u)}$

$$= \dfrac{k'^2(1 + \text{cn}\, u)}{k'^2 + \text{dn}\, u - k^2 \text{cn}\, u}.$$

713. $\mathrm{dn}^2 \left(\dfrac{u}{2} \right) = \dfrac{k'^2 + \mathrm{dn}\, u + k^2\, \mathrm{cn}\, u}{1 + \mathrm{dn}\, u} = \dfrac{k^2 (\mathrm{cn}\, u + \mathrm{dn}\, u)}{k^2 (1 + \mathrm{cn}\, u)}$

$$= \dfrac{k'^2 (1 + \mathrm{dn}\, u)}{k'^2 + \mathrm{dn}\, u - k^2\, \mathrm{cn}\, u}.$$

If, moreover, $v = \displaystyle\int_0^y \dfrac{dz}{\sqrt{(1 - z^2)(1 - k^2 z^2)}}$,

714. $\mathrm{sn}^2\, u - \mathrm{sn}^2\, v = \mathrm{cn}^2\, v - \mathrm{cn}^2\, u.$

715. $\mathrm{sn}\, (u \pm v) = \dfrac{\mathrm{sn}\, u \cdot \mathrm{cn}\, v \cdot \mathrm{dn}\, v \pm \mathrm{cn}\, u \cdot \mathrm{sn}\, v \cdot \mathrm{dn}\, u}{1 - k^2\, \mathrm{sn}^2\, u \cdot \mathrm{sn}^2\, v}.$

716. $\mathrm{cn}\, (u \pm v) = \dfrac{\mathrm{cn}\, u \cdot \mathrm{cn}\, v \mp \mathrm{sn}\, u \cdot \mathrm{sn}\, v \cdot \mathrm{dn}\, u \cdot \mathrm{dn}\, v}{1 - k^2\, \mathrm{sn}^2\, u \cdot \mathrm{sn}^2\, v}$

$$= \mathrm{cn}\, u \cdot \mathrm{cn}\, v \mp \mathrm{sn}\, u \cdot \mathrm{sn}\, v \cdot \mathrm{dn}\, (u \pm v).$$

717. $\mathrm{dn}\, (u \pm v) = \dfrac{\mathrm{dn}\, u \cdot \mathrm{dn}\, v \mp k^2\, \mathrm{sn}\, u \cdot \mathrm{sn}\, v \cdot \mathrm{cn}\, u \cdot \mathrm{cn}\, v}{1 - k^2\, \mathrm{sn}^2\, u \cdot \mathrm{sn}^2\, v}$

$$= \mathrm{dn}\, u \cdot \mathrm{dn}\, v \mp k^2\, \mathrm{sn}\, u \cdot \mathrm{sn}\, v \cdot \mathrm{cn}\, (u \pm v).$$

718. $\mathrm{tn}\, (u \pm v) = \dfrac{\mathrm{tn}\, u \cdot \mathrm{dn}\, v \pm \mathrm{tn}\, v \cdot \mathrm{dn}\, u}{1 \mp \mathrm{tn}\, u \cdot \mathrm{tn}\, v \cdot \mathrm{dn}\, u \cdot \mathrm{dn}\, v}.$

719. $\mathrm{sn}\, (u + v) + \mathrm{sn}\, (u - v) = \dfrac{2\, \mathrm{sn}\, u \cdot \mathrm{cn}\, v \cdot \mathrm{dn}\, v}{1 - k^2\, \mathrm{sn}^2\, u \cdot \mathrm{sn}^2\, v}.$

720. $\mathrm{sn}\, (u + v) - \mathrm{sn}\, (u - v) = \dfrac{2\, \mathrm{sn}\, v \cdot \mathrm{cn}\, u \cdot \mathrm{dn}\, u}{1 - k^2\, \mathrm{sn}^2\, u \cdot \mathrm{sn}^2\, v}.$

721. $\mathrm{cn}\, (u + v) + \mathrm{cn}\, (u - v) = \dfrac{2\, \mathrm{cn}\, u \cdot \mathrm{cn}\, v}{1 - k^2\, \mathrm{sn}^2\, u \cdot \mathrm{sn}^2\, v}.$

722. $\mathrm{cn}\, (u + v) - \mathrm{cn}\, (u - v) = - \dfrac{2\, \mathrm{sn}\, u \cdot \mathrm{sn}\, v \cdot \mathrm{dn}\, u \cdot \mathrm{dn}\, v}{1 - k^2\, \mathrm{sn}^2\, u \cdot \mathrm{sn}^2\, v}.$

723. $\mathrm{dn}\, (u + v) + \mathrm{dn}\, (u - v) = \dfrac{2\, \mathrm{dn}\, u \cdot \mathrm{dn}\, v}{1 - k^2\, \mathrm{sn}^2\, u \cdot \mathrm{sn}^2\, v}.$

724. $\operatorname{dn}(u+v) - \operatorname{dn}(u-v) = -\dfrac{2\,k^2\operatorname{sn}u\cdot\operatorname{sn}v\cdot\operatorname{cn}u\cdot\operatorname{cn}v}{1-k^2\operatorname{sn}^2u\cdot\operatorname{sn}^2v}.$

725. $\operatorname{sn}(u+v)\cdot\operatorname{sn}(u-v) = \dfrac{\operatorname{sn}^2u - \operatorname{sn}^2v}{1-k^2\operatorname{sn}^2u\cdot\operatorname{sn}^2v}$

$= \dfrac{\operatorname{cn}^2v + \operatorname{sn}^2u\cdot\operatorname{dn}^2v}{1-k^2\operatorname{sn}^2u\cdot\operatorname{sn}^2v} - 1 = \dfrac{1}{k^2}\left[\dfrac{\operatorname{dn}^2v + k^2\operatorname{sn}^2u\cdot\operatorname{cn}^2v}{1-k^2\operatorname{sn}^2u\cdot\operatorname{sn}^2v} - 1\right].$

726. $\operatorname{cn}(u+v)\cdot\operatorname{cn}(u-v) = \dfrac{\operatorname{cn}^2u - \operatorname{sn}^2v + k^2\operatorname{sn}^2u\cdot\operatorname{sn}^2v}{1-k^2\operatorname{sn}^2u\cdot\operatorname{sn}^2v}$

$= \dfrac{\operatorname{cn}^2u + \operatorname{cn}^2v}{1-k^2\operatorname{sn}^2u\cdot\operatorname{sn}^2v} - 1 = 1 - \dfrac{\operatorname{sn}^2u\cdot\operatorname{dn}^2v + \operatorname{sn}^2v\cdot\operatorname{dn}^2u}{1-k^2\operatorname{sn}^2u\cdot\operatorname{sn}^2v}.$

727. $\operatorname{dn}(u+v)\cdot\operatorname{dn}(u-v)$

$$= \dfrac{1 - k^2\operatorname{sn}^2u - k^2\operatorname{sn}^2v + k^2\operatorname{sn}^2u\cdot\operatorname{sn}^2v}{1-k^2\operatorname{sn}^2u\cdot\operatorname{sn}^2v}$$

$$= \dfrac{\operatorname{dn}^2u + \operatorname{dn}^2v}{1-k^2\operatorname{sn}^2u\cdot\operatorname{sn}^2v} - 1.$$

728. $\operatorname{sn}(u\pm v)\operatorname{cn}(u\mp v) = \dfrac{\operatorname{sn}u\cdot\operatorname{cn}u\cdot\operatorname{dn}v \pm \operatorname{sn}v\cdot\operatorname{cn}v\cdot\operatorname{dn}u}{1-k^2\operatorname{sn}^2u\cdot\operatorname{sn}^2v}.$

729. $\operatorname{sn}(u\pm v)\operatorname{dn}(u\mp v) = \dfrac{\operatorname{sn}u\cdot\operatorname{dn}u\cdot\operatorname{cn}v \pm \operatorname{sn}v\cdot\operatorname{dn}v\cdot\operatorname{cn}u}{1-k^2\operatorname{sn}^2u\cdot\operatorname{sn}^2v}.$

730. $\operatorname{cn}(u\pm v)\operatorname{dn}(u\mp v) = \dfrac{\operatorname{cn}u\cdot\operatorname{dn}u\cdot\operatorname{cn}v\cdot\operatorname{dn}v \mp k'^2\operatorname{sn}u\cdot\operatorname{sn}v}{1-k^2\operatorname{sn}^2u\cdot\operatorname{sn}^2v}.$

731. $\left[1\pm\operatorname{sn}(u+v)\right]\left[1\pm\operatorname{sn}(u-v)\right] = \dfrac{(\operatorname{cn}v \pm \operatorname{sn}u\cdot\operatorname{dn}v)^2}{1-k^2\operatorname{sn}^2u\cdot\operatorname{sn}^2v}.$

732. $\operatorname{sn}(ui,\,k) = i\operatorname{sn}(u,\,k')/\operatorname{cn}(u,\,k').$

733. $\operatorname{cn}(ui,\,k) = 1/\operatorname{cn}(u,\,k').$

734. $\operatorname{dn}(ui,\,k) = \operatorname{dn}(u,\,k')/\operatorname{cn}(u,\,k').$

D. — BESSEL'S FUNCTIONS.

735. $J_0(x) = 1 - \dfrac{x^2}{2^2} + \dfrac{x^4}{2^2 \cdot 4^2} - \dfrac{x^6}{2^2 \cdot 4^2 \cdot 6^2} + \cdots$

736. $K_0(x) = J_0(x) \cdot \log x + \dfrac{x^2}{2^2} - \dfrac{x^4 \cdot \Omega_2}{2^2 \cdot 4^2} + \dfrac{x^6 \cdot \Omega_3}{2^2 \cdot 4^2 \cdot 6^2} - \cdots$

$$[\Omega_k = 1 + \tfrac{1}{2} + \tfrac{1}{3} + \cdots + 1/k.]$$

737. $J_n(x) = \displaystyle\sum_{k=0}^{\infty} \dfrac{(-1)^k x^{n+2k}}{2^{n+2k} \cdot k! \, \Gamma(n+k+1)}.$ [When n is an integer, 819 may be used.]

738. $K_n(x) = J_n(x) \cdot \log x - \dfrac{x^{-n}}{2^{1-n}} \displaystyle\sum_0^{n-1} \dfrac{(n-k-1)! \, x^{2k}}{2^{2k} \cdot k!}$

$$- \dfrac{x^n}{2^{1+n}} \sum_0^{\infty} \dfrac{(-1)^k}{(n+k)! \, k!} \left[\Omega_k + \Omega_{k+n} \left(\dfrac{x}{2} \right)^{2k} \right].$$

739. According as n is or is not an integer, $A \cdot J_n(x) + B \cdot K_n(x)$, or $A \cdot J_n(x) + B \cdot J_{-n}(x)$ is a particular solution of Bessel's equation,

$$\dfrac{d^2 z}{dx^2} + \dfrac{1}{x} \cdot \dfrac{dz}{dx} + \left(1 - \dfrac{n^2}{x^2} \right) z = 0.$$

740. $dJ_0(x)/dx = -J_1(x); \; d[x^n \cdot J_n(x)]/dx = x^n \cdot J_{n-1}(x),$
if $n > \tfrac{1}{2}; \; d[x^{-n} \cdot J_n(x)]/dx = -x^{-n} \cdot J_{n+1}(x),$ if $n > -\tfrac{1}{2}.$

741. $J_{n-1}(x) - J_{n+1}(x) = 2 \cdot dJ_n(x)/dx;$
$2n \cdot J_n(x) = x \cdot J_{n-1}(x) + x \cdot J_{n+1}(x).$

When x is large it is sometimes convenient to compute approximate numerical values of $J_n(x)$ by means of the semi-convergent series,

742. $J_n(x) = \sqrt{\dfrac{2}{\pi x}} \left[P_n \cdot \cos \left\{ \dfrac{(2n+1)\pi}{4} - x \right\} \right.$

$$\left. + Q_n \cdot \sin \left\{ \dfrac{(2n+1)\pi}{4} - x \right\} \right].$$

743. $P_n = 1 - \dfrac{(4n^2 - 1)(4n^2 - 9)}{2! \, (8x)^2}$

$$+ \dfrac{(4n^2 - 1)(4n^2 - 9)(4n^2 - 25)(4n^2 - 49)}{4! \, (8x)^4} - \cdots$$

744. $Q_n = \dfrac{4n^2 - 1}{8x} - \dfrac{(4n^2 - 1)(4n^2 - 9)(4n^2 - 25)}{3! \, (8x)^3} + \cdots$

E. — SERIES AND PRODUCTS.

[The expression in brackets attached to an infinite series shows values of the variable which lie within the interval of convergence. If a series is convergent for all finite values of x, the expression $[x^2 < \infty]$ is used.]

745. $(a + b)^n = a^n + na^{n-1}b$

$$+ \frac{n(n-1)}{2!} a^{n-2}b^2 + \cdots + \frac{n! \, a^{n-k}b^k}{(n-k)! \, k!} + \cdots \quad [b^2 < a^2.]$$

746. $(a - bx)^{-1} = \frac{1}{a} \left[1 + \frac{bx}{a} + \frac{b^2x^2}{a^2} + \frac{b^3x^3}{a^3} + \cdots \right] \cdot \quad [b^2x^2 < a^2.]$

747. $(1 \pm x)^n = 1 \pm nx + \frac{n(n-1)}{2!} x^2$

$$\pm \frac{n(n-1)(n-2) x^3}{3!} + \cdots + \frac{(\pm 1)^k n! \, x^k}{(n-k)! \, k!} + \cdots$$
$$[x^2 < 1.]$$

748. $(1 \pm x)^{-n} = 1 \mp nx + \frac{n(n+1)}{2!} x^2$

$$\mp \frac{n(n+1)(n+2) x^3}{3!} + \cdots (\mp)^k \frac{(n+k-1)! \, x^k}{(n-1)! \, k!} + \cdots$$
$$[x^2 < 1.]$$

749. $(1 \pm x)^{\frac{1}{2}} = 1 \pm \frac{1}{2} x - \frac{1 \cdot 1}{2 \cdot 4} x^2 \pm \frac{1 \cdot 1 \cdot 3}{2 \cdot 4 \cdot 6} x^3$

$$- \frac{1 \cdot 1 \cdot 3 \cdot 5}{2 \cdot 4 \cdot 6 \cdot 8} x^4 \pm \cdots. \quad [x^2 < 1.]$$

750. $(1 \pm x)^{-\frac{1}{2}} = 1 \mp \frac{1}{2} x + \frac{1 \cdot 3}{2 \cdot 4} x^2 \mp \frac{1 \cdot 3 \cdot 5}{2 \cdot 4 \cdot 6} x^3$

$$+ \frac{1 \cdot 3 \cdot 5 \cdot 7}{2 \cdot 4 \cdot 6 \cdot 8} x^4 \mp \cdots. \quad [x^2 < 1.]$$

751. $(1 \pm x)^{\frac{1}{3}} = 1 \pm \frac{1}{3} x - \frac{1 \cdot 2}{3 \cdot 6} x^2 \pm \frac{1 \cdot 2 \cdot 5}{3 \cdot 6 \cdot 9} x^3$

$$- \frac{1 \cdot 2 \cdot 5 \cdot 8}{3 \cdot 6 \cdot 9 \cdot 12} x^4 \pm \cdots. \quad [x^2 < 1.]$$

752. $(1 \pm x)^{-\frac{1}{3}} = 1 \mp \frac{1}{3} x + \frac{1 \cdot 4}{3 \cdot 6} x^2 \mp \frac{1 \cdot 4 \cdot 7}{3 \cdot 6 \cdot 9} x^3$

$$+ \frac{1 \cdot 4 \cdot 7 \cdot 10}{3 \cdot 6 \cdot 9 \cdot 12} x^4 \mp \cdots . \qquad [x^3 < 1.]$$

753. $(1 \pm x^2)^{\frac{1}{2}} = 1 \pm \frac{1}{2} x^2 - \frac{x^4}{2 \cdot 4} \pm \frac{1 \cdot 3 \, x^6}{2 \cdot 4 \cdot 6} - \frac{1 \cdot 3 \cdot 5 \, x^8}{2 \cdot 4 \cdot 6 \cdot 8} \pm \cdots$

$$[x^2 < 1.]$$

754. $(1 \pm x^2)^{-\frac{1}{2}} = 1 \mp \frac{1}{2} x^2 + \frac{1 \cdot 3}{2 \cdot 4} x^4 \mp \frac{1 \cdot 3 \cdot 5}{2 \cdot 4 \cdot 6} x^6 + \cdots$

$$[x^2 < 1.]$$

755. $(1 \pm x)^{-1} = 1 \mp x + x^2 \mp x^3 + x^4 \mp x^5 + \cdots . \qquad [x^2 < 1.]$

756. $(1 \pm x)^{\frac{1}{2}} = 1 \pm \frac{3}{2} x + \frac{3 \cdot 1}{2 \cdot 4} x^2 \mp \frac{3 \cdot 1 \cdot 1}{2 \cdot 4 \cdot 6} x^3$

$$+ \frac{3 \cdot 1 \cdot 1 \cdot 3}{2 \cdot 4 \cdot 6 \cdot 8} x^4 \mp \frac{3 \cdot 1 \cdot 1 \cdot 3 \cdot 5}{2 \cdot 4 \cdot 6 \cdot 8 \cdot 10} x^5 + \cdots . \qquad [x^2 < 1.]$$

757. $(1 \pm x)^{-\frac{1}{2}} = 1 \mp \frac{3}{2} x + \frac{3 \cdot 5}{2 \cdot 4} x^2 \mp \frac{3 \cdot 5 \cdot 7}{2 \cdot 4 \cdot 6} x^3 + \cdots . \quad [x^2 < 1.]$

758. $(1 \pm x)^{-2} = 1 \mp 2 \, x + 3 \, x^2 \mp 4 \, x^3 + 5 \, x^4 \mp 6 \, x^5 + \cdots$

$$[x^2 < 1.]$$

———————

759. $e^x = 1 + x + \frac{x^2}{2!} + \frac{x^3}{3!} + \cdots . \qquad [x^2 < \infty.]$

760. $a^x = 1 + x \log a + \frac{(x \log a)^2}{2!} + \frac{(x \log a)^3}{3!} + \cdots . \, [x^2 < \infty.]$

761. $\frac{1}{2} (e^x + e^{-x}) = 1 + \frac{x^2}{2!} + \frac{x^4}{4!} + \frac{x^6}{6!} + \cdots . \qquad [x^2 < \infty.]$

762. $\frac{1}{2} (e^x - e^{-x}) = x + \frac{x^3}{3!} + \frac{x^5}{5!} + \frac{x^7}{7!} + \cdots . \qquad [x^2 < \infty.]$

763. $e^{-x^2} = 1 - x^2 + \frac{x^4}{2!} - \frac{x^6}{3!} + \frac{x^8}{4!} - \cdots . \qquad [x^2 < \infty.]$

A series of numbers, B_1, B_2, $B_3 \cdots$, of odd and even orders, which appear in the developments of many functions, may be computed by means of the equations,

$$B_{2n} - \frac{2n(2n-1)}{2!} B_{2n-2}$$

$$+ \frac{2n(2n-1)(2n-2)(2n-3)}{4!} B_{2n-4} - \cdots + (-1)^n = 0.$$

$$\frac{2^{2n}(2^{2n}-1)}{2n} B_{2n-1} = (2n-1) B_{2n-2}$$

$$- \frac{(2n-1)(2n-2)(2n-3)}{3!} B_{2n-4} + \cdots + (-1)^{n-1}.$$

Whence $B_1 = \frac{1}{6}$, $B_2 = 1$, $B_3 = \frac{1}{30}$, $B_4 = 5$, $B_5 = \frac{1}{42}$, $B_6 = 61$, $B_7 = \frac{1}{30}$, $B_8 = 1385$, $B_9 = \frac{5}{66}$, $B_{10} = 50521$, $B_{11} = \frac{691}{2730}$, $B_{12} = 2702765$, $B_{13} = \frac{7}{6}$, etc. The B's of odd orders are called Bernoulli's Numbers; those of even orders, Euler's Numbers. What are here denoted by B_{2n-1} and B_{2n} are sometimes represented by B_n and E_n, respectively,

$$\frac{B_{2n-1}}{(2n)!} = \frac{2}{(2^{2n}-1)\pi^{2n}} \left[1 + \frac{1}{3^{2n}} + \frac{1}{5^{2n}} + \frac{1}{7^{2n}} + \cdots \right],$$

$$\frac{B_{2n}}{(2n)!} = \frac{2^{2n+2}}{\pi^{2n+1}} \left[1 - \frac{1}{3^{2n+1}} + \frac{1}{5^{2n+1}} - \frac{1}{7^{2n+1}} + \cdots \right].$$

764. $\dfrac{x}{e^x - 1} = 1 - \dfrac{x}{2} + \dfrac{B_1 x^2}{2!} - \dfrac{B_3 x^4}{4!} + \dfrac{B_5 x^6}{6!} - \dfrac{B_7 x^8}{8!} + \cdots.$

$$[x < 2\pi.]$$

765. $\log x = (x-1) - \frac{1}{2}(x-1)^2 + \frac{1}{3}(x-1)^3 - \cdots.$

$$[2 > x > 0.]$$

766. $\log x = \dfrac{x-1}{x} + \frac{1}{2}\left(\dfrac{x-1}{x}\right)^2 + \frac{1}{3}\left(\dfrac{x-1}{x}\right)^3 + \cdots.$

$$[x > \tfrac{1}{2}.]$$

767. $\log x = 2\left[\dfrac{x-1}{x+1} + \tfrac{1}{3}\left(\dfrac{x-1}{x+1}\right)^3 + \tfrac{1}{5}\left(\dfrac{x-1}{x+1}\right)^5 + \cdots\right].$

$[x > 0.]$

768. $\log(1+x) = x - \tfrac{1}{2}x^2 + \tfrac{1}{3}x^3 - \tfrac{1}{4}x^4 + \cdots.$ $[x^2 < 1.]$

769. $\log\left(\dfrac{1+x}{1-x}\right) = 2\left[x + \tfrac{1}{3}x^3 + \tfrac{1}{5}x^5 + \tfrac{1}{7}x^7 + \cdots\right].$ $[x^2 < 1.]$

770. $\log\left(\dfrac{x+1}{x-1}\right) = 2\left[\dfrac{1}{x} + \tfrac{1}{3}\left(\dfrac{1}{x}\right)^3 + \tfrac{1}{5}\left(\dfrac{1}{x}\right)^5 + \cdots\right].$ $[x^2 > 1.]$

771. $\log(x + \sqrt{1+x^2}) = x - \dfrac{1}{6}x^3 + \dfrac{1\cdot 3\,x^5}{2\cdot 4\cdot 5} - \dfrac{1\cdot 3\cdot 5\,x^7}{2\cdot 4\cdot 6\cdot 7} + \cdots.$

$[x^2 < 1.]$

Series for denary and other logarithms can be obtained from the foregoing developments by aid of the equations,

$$\log_a x = \log_e x \cdot \log_a e, \quad \log_e x = \log_a x \cdot \log_e a,$$
$$\log_e(-z) = (2n+1)\pi i + \log_e z.$$

772. $\sin x = x - \dfrac{x^3}{3!} + \dfrac{x^5}{5!} - \dfrac{x^7}{7!} + \cdots.$ $[x^2 < \infty.]$

773. $\cos x = 1 - \dfrac{x^2}{2!} + \dfrac{x^4}{4!} - \dfrac{x^6}{6!} + \cdots = 1 - \operatorname{versin} x.$ $[x^2 < \infty.]$

774. $\tan x = x + \dfrac{x^3}{3} + \dfrac{2\,x^5}{15} + \dfrac{17\,x^7}{315} + \dfrac{62\,x^9}{2835}$

$+ \cdots + \dfrac{2^{2n}(2^{2n}-1)\,B_{2n-1}\,x^{2n-1}}{(2n)!} + \cdots.$ $\left[x^2 < \tfrac{1}{4}\pi^2.\right]$

775. $\operatorname{ctn} x = \dfrac{1}{x} - \dfrac{x}{3} - \dfrac{x^3}{45} - \dfrac{2\,x^5}{945} - \dfrac{x^7}{4725}$

$- \cdots - \dfrac{B_{2n-1}(2x)^{2n}}{x(2n)!} - \cdots.$ $[x^2 < \pi^2.]$

776. $\sec x = 1 + \dfrac{x^2}{2!} + \dfrac{5\,x^4}{4!} + \dfrac{61\,x^6}{6!} + \cdots + \dfrac{B_{2n}x^{2n}}{(2n)!} + \cdots \left[x^2 < \dfrac{\pi^2}{4}. \right]$

777. $\csc x = \dfrac{1}{x} + \dfrac{x}{3!} + \dfrac{7\,x^3}{3 \cdot 5!} + \dfrac{31\,x^5}{3 \cdot 7!}$

$$+ \cdots + \dfrac{2\,(2^{2n+1} - 1)}{(2n+2)!}\, B_{2n+1}x^{2n+1} + \cdots . \qquad [x^2 < \pi^2.]$$

778. $\sin^{-1}x = x + \dfrac{x^3}{6} + \dfrac{1 \cdot 3}{2 \cdot 4} \cdot \dfrac{x^5}{5} + \dfrac{1 \cdot 3 \cdot 5}{2 \cdot 4 \cdot 6} \cdot \dfrac{x^7}{7}$

$$+ \cdots = \tfrac{1}{2}\,\pi - \cos^{-1}x. \qquad [x^2 < 1.]$$

779. $\tan^{-1}x = x - \tfrac{1}{3}x^3 + \tfrac{1}{5}x^5 - \tfrac{1}{7}x^7 + \cdots = \tfrac{1}{2}\,\pi - \operatorname{ctn}^{-1}x.$
$$[x^2 < 1.]$$

780. $\tan^{-1}x = \dfrac{\pi}{2} - \dfrac{1}{x} + \dfrac{1}{3\,x^3} - \dfrac{1}{5\,x^5} + \cdots . \qquad [x^2 > 1.]$

781. $\sec^{-1}x = \dfrac{\pi}{2} - \dfrac{1}{x} - \dfrac{1}{6x^3} - \dfrac{1 \cdot 3}{2 \cdot 4 \cdot 5\,x^5} - \dfrac{1 \cdot 3 \cdot 5}{2 \cdot 4 \cdot 6 \cdot 7\,x^7} - \cdots$
$$= \tfrac{1}{2}\,\pi - \csc^{-1}x. \qquad [x^2 > 1.]$$

782. $\log \sin x = \log x - \tfrac{1}{6}x^2 - \tfrac{1}{180}x^4 - \tfrac{1}{2835}x^6$

$$- \cdots - \dfrac{2^{2n-1}B_{2n-1}x^{2n}}{n\,(2n)!} - \cdots . \qquad [x^2 < \pi^2.]$$

783. $\log \cos x = - \tfrac{1}{2}x^2 - \tfrac{1}{12}x^4 - \tfrac{1}{45}x^6 - \tfrac{17}{2520}x^8$

$$- \cdots - \dfrac{2^{2n-1}(2^{2n} - 1)\,B_{2n-1}x^{2n}}{n\,(2n)!} - \cdots . \qquad [x^2 < \tfrac{1}{4}\,\pi^2.]$$

784. $\log \tan x = \log x + \tfrac{1}{3}x^2 + \tfrac{7}{90}x^4 + \tfrac{62}{2835}x^6$

$$+ \cdots + \dfrac{(2^{2n-1} - 1)\,2^{2n}B_{2n-1}x^{2n}}{n\,(2n)!} + \cdots . \qquad [x^2 < \tfrac{1}{4}\,\pi^2.]$$

785. $e^{\sin x} = 1 + x + \dfrac{x^2}{2!} - \dfrac{3\,x^4}{4!} - \dfrac{8\,x^5}{5!} - \dfrac{3\,x^6}{6!} + \dfrac{56\,x^7}{7!} + \cdots .$
$$[x^2 < \infty.]$$

786. $e^{\cos x} = e\left(1 - \dfrac{x^2}{2!} + \dfrac{4\,x^4}{4!} - \dfrac{31\,x^6}{6!} + \cdots\right).$ $[x^2 < \infty.]$

787. $e^{\tan x} = 1 + x + \dfrac{x^2}{2!} + \dfrac{3\,x^3}{3!} + \dfrac{9\,x^4}{4!} + \dfrac{37\,x^5}{5!} + \cdots.$ $[x^2 < \tfrac{1}{4}\pi^2.]$

788. $e^{\sin^{-1} x} = 1 + x + \dfrac{x^2}{2!} + \dfrac{2\,x^3}{3!} + \dfrac{5\,x^4}{4!} + \cdots.$ $[x^2 < 1.]$

789. $e^{\tan^{-1} x} = 1 + x + \dfrac{x^2}{2} - \dfrac{x^3}{6} - \dfrac{7\,x^4}{24} - \cdots.$ $[x^2 < 1.]$

---

790. $\sinh x = x + \dfrac{x^3}{3!} + \dfrac{x^5}{5!} + \dfrac{x^7}{7!} + \cdots.$ $[x^2 < \infty.]$

791. $\cosh x = 1 + \dfrac{x^2}{2!} + \dfrac{x^4}{4!} + \dfrac{x^6}{6!} + \dfrac{x^8}{8!} + \cdots.$ $[x^2 < \infty.]$

792. $\tanh x = (2^2 - 1)\,2^2\,B_1\dfrac{x}{2!} - (2^4 - 1)\,2^4\,B_3\dfrac{x^3}{4!} + \cdots$

$$= \Sigma\left[(-1)^{n-1}\,2^{2n}(2^{2n} - 1)\,B_{2n-1}\,x^{2n-1}/(2\,n)!\right].$$
$$[x^2 < \tfrac{1}{4}\pi^2.]$$

793. $\operatorname{ctnh} x = \dfrac{1}{x}\left(1 + \Sigma\left[(-1)^{n-1}\,2^{2n}\,B_{2n-1}\,x^{2n}/(2\,n)!\right]\right).$
$$[x^2 < \pi^2.]$$

794. $\operatorname{sech} x = 1 + \Sigma\left[(-1)^n\,B_{2n}\,x^{2n}/(2\,n)!\right].$ $[x^2 < \tfrac{1}{4}\pi^2.]$

795. $\operatorname{csch} x = \dfrac{1}{x} - (2 - 1)\,2\,B_1\dfrac{x}{2!} + (2^3 - 1)\,2\,B_3\dfrac{x^3}{4!} - \cdots$

$$= \dfrac{1}{x}\left(1 + 2\,\Sigma\left[(-1)^n\,(2^{2n-1} - 1)\,B_{2n-1}\,x^{2n}/(2\,n)!\right]\right).$$
$$[x^2 < \pi^2.]$$

796. $\sinh^{-1} x = x - \tfrac{1}{6}x^3 + \dfrac{1\cdot 3\cdot x^5}{2\cdot 4\cdot 5} - \dfrac{1\cdot 3\cdot 5\cdot x^7}{2\cdot 4\cdot 6\cdot 7} + \cdots.$ $[x^2 < 1.]$

797. $\tanh^{-1} x = x + \dfrac{x^3}{3} + \dfrac{x^5}{5} + \dfrac{x^7}{7} + \cdots.$ $\qquad [x^2 < 1.]$

798. $\operatorname{ctnh}^{-1} x = \dfrac{1}{x} + \dfrac{1}{3\,x^3} + \dfrac{1}{5\,x^5} + \cdots.$ $\qquad [x^2 > 1.]$

799. $\operatorname{csch}^{-1} x = \dfrac{1}{x} - \dfrac{1}{2\cdot 3 \cdot x^3} + \dfrac{1\cdot 3}{2\cdot 4} \dfrac{1}{5\cdot x^5} - \dfrac{1\cdot 3\cdot 5}{2\cdot 4\cdot 6\cdot 7\cdot x^7} + \cdots.$
$$[x^2 > 1.]$$

800. $\displaystyle\int_0^x e^{-x^2}\, dx = x - \tfrac{1}{3} x^3 + \dfrac{x^5}{5\cdot 2!} - \dfrac{x^7}{7\cdot 3!} + \cdots. \qquad [x^2 < \infty.]$

801. $\displaystyle\int_0^x \cos(x^2)\, dx = x - \dfrac{x^5}{5\cdot 2!} + \dfrac{x^9}{9\cdot 4!} - \dfrac{x^{13}}{13\cdot 6!} + \cdots. \quad [x^2 < \infty.]$

802. $\displaystyle\int_0^1 \dfrac{x^{a-1}\, dx}{1 + x^b} = \dfrac{1}{a} - \dfrac{1}{a + b} + \dfrac{1}{a + 2\,b} - \dfrac{1}{a + 3\,b} + \cdots.$

---

803. $f(x + h) = f(x) + h \cdot f'(x + \theta h).$

804. $f(x + h) = f(x) + h \cdot f'(x) + \dfrac{h^2}{2!} f''(x)$
$$+ \cdots + \dfrac{h^n}{n!} \cdot f^n(x + \theta h).$$

805. $f(x + h) = f(x) + h \cdot f'(x) + \dfrac{h^2}{2!} f''(x)$
$$+ \cdots + \dfrac{h^n}{(n-1)!} \cdot (1 - \theta)^{n-1} \cdot f^n(x + \theta h)$$

806. $f(x + h, y + k) = f(x, y) + h f'_x(x + \theta h, y + \theta k)$
$$+ k f'_y(x + \theta h, y + \theta k).$$

807. $f(x + h, y + k) = f(x, y) + \left(h \dfrac{\partial f(x, y)}{\partial x} + k \dfrac{\partial f(x, y)}{\partial y} \right)$
$$+ \dfrac{1}{2!}\left(h^2 \dfrac{\partial^2 f(x, y)}{\partial x^2} + 2\,hk \dfrac{\partial^2 f(x, y)}{\partial x \cdot \partial y} + k^2 \dfrac{\partial^2 f(x, y)}{\partial y^2} \right)$$

$$+ \frac{1}{3!}\left(h^3 \frac{\partial^3 f(x, y)}{\partial x^3} + 3\, h^2 k\, \frac{\partial^3 f(x, y)}{\partial y \cdot \partial x^2} + 3\, hk^2\, \frac{\partial^3 f(x, y)}{\partial x \cdot \partial y^2} \right.$$

$$\left. + k^3 \frac{\partial f(x, y)}{\partial y^3} \right) + \cdots + R_n$$

$$= f(x, y) + (hD_x + kD_y) f(x, y) + \frac{1}{2!}(hD_x + kD_y)^2 f(x, y)$$

$$+ \cdots + \frac{1}{(n-1)!}(hD_x + kD_y)^{n-1} f(x, y)$$

$$+ \frac{1}{n!}(hD_x + kD_y)^n f(x + \theta h, \, y + \theta k).$$

---

808. $1 = \dfrac{4}{\pi}\left[\sin \dfrac{\pi x}{c} + \tfrac{1}{3} \sin \dfrac{3\,\pi x}{c} + \tfrac{1}{5} \sin \dfrac{5\,\pi x}{c} + \cdots \right].$
$$[0 < x < c.]$$

809. $x = \dfrac{2\,c}{\pi}\left[\sin \dfrac{\pi x}{c} - \tfrac{1}{2} \sin \dfrac{2\,\pi x}{c} + \tfrac{1}{3} \sin \dfrac{3\,\pi x}{c} - \cdots \right].$
$$[-c < x < c.]$$

810. $x = \dfrac{c}{2} - \dfrac{4\,c}{\pi^2}\left[\cos \dfrac{\pi x}{c} + \dfrac{1}{3^2} \cos \dfrac{3\,\pi x}{c} + \dfrac{1}{5^2} \cos \dfrac{5\,\pi x}{c} + \cdots \right].$
$$[0 < x < c.]$$

811. $x^2 = \dfrac{2\,c^2}{\pi^3}\left[\left(\dfrac{\pi^2}{1} - \dfrac{4}{1} \right) \sin \dfrac{\pi x}{c} - \dfrac{\pi^2}{2} \sin \dfrac{2\,\pi x}{c} \right.$

$$+ \left(\dfrac{\pi^2}{3} - \dfrac{4}{3^3} \right) \sin \dfrac{3\,\pi x}{c} - \dfrac{\pi^2}{4} \sin \dfrac{4\,\pi x}{c}$$

$$\left. + \left(\dfrac{\pi^2}{5} - \dfrac{4}{5^3} \right) \sin \dfrac{5\,\pi x}{c} + \cdots \right]. \qquad [0 < x < c.]$$

812. $x^2 = \dfrac{c^2}{3} - \dfrac{4\,c^2}{\pi^2}\left[\cos \dfrac{\pi x}{c} - \dfrac{1}{2^2} \cos \dfrac{2\,\pi x}{c} + \dfrac{1}{3^2} \cos \dfrac{3\,\pi x}{c} \right.$

$$\left. - \dfrac{1}{4^2} \cos \dfrac{4\,\pi x}{c} + \cdots \right]. \qquad [-c < x < c.]$$

813. $\log \sin \frac{1}{2} x = - \log 2 - \cos x - \frac{1}{2} \cos 2x - \frac{1}{3} \cos 3x - \cdots.$
$$[0 < x < \tfrac{1}{2}\pi.]$$

814. $\log \cos \frac{1}{2} x = - \log 2 + \cos x - \frac{1}{2} \cos 2x + \frac{1}{3} \cos 3x - \cdots.$
$$[0 < x < \tfrac{1}{2}\pi.]$$

815. $f(x) = \frac{1}{2} b_0 + b_1 \cos \dfrac{\pi x}{c} + b_2 \cos \dfrac{2\pi x}{c} + \cdots$

$$+ a_1 \sin \dfrac{\pi x}{c} + a_2 \sin \dfrac{2\pi x}{c} + \cdots, \quad [-c < x < c.]$$

where $b_m = \dfrac{1}{c} \displaystyle\int_{-c}^{+c} f(a) \cos \dfrac{m\pi a}{c}\, da,$

$$a_m = \dfrac{1}{c} \displaystyle\int_{-c}^{+c} f(a) \sin \dfrac{m\pi a}{c}\, da.$$

---

816. $\sin \theta = \theta \left[1 - \left(\dfrac{\theta}{\pi} \right)^2 \right]\left[1 - \left(\dfrac{\theta}{2\pi} \right)^2 \right]\left[1 - \left(\dfrac{\theta}{3\pi} \right)^2 \right]\cdots.$
$$[\theta^2 < \infty.]$$

817. $\cos \theta = \left[1 - \left(\dfrac{2\theta}{\pi} \right)^2 \right]\left[1 - \left(\dfrac{2\theta}{3\pi} \right)^2 \right]\left[1 - \left(\dfrac{2\theta}{5\pi} \right)^2 \right]\cdots.$
$$[\theta^2 < \infty.]$$

818. $\dfrac{2^2 \cdot 4^2 \cdot 6^2 \cdots (2m)^2 (2m+2)}{1^2 \cdot 3^2 \cdot 5^2 \cdots (2m+1)^2} > \dfrac{\pi}{2}$

$$> \dfrac{2^2 \cdot 4^2 \cdot 6^2 \cdots (2m)^2 (2m+1)}{1^2 \cdot 3^2 \cdot 5^2 \cdots (2m+1)^2}.$$

819. $J_n(x) = \dfrac{x^n}{2^n n!} \left\{ 1 - \dfrac{x^2}{2(2n+2)} + \dfrac{x^4}{2 \cdot 4 (2n+2)(2n+4)} \right.$

$$\left. - \dfrac{x^6}{2 \cdot 4 \cdot 6 (2n+2)(2n+4)(2n+6)} + \cdots \right\}.$$

F. — Derivatives.

820. $\dfrac{d\,(au)}{dx} = \dfrac{a\,du}{dx}$.

821. $\dfrac{d\,(u+v)}{dx} = \dfrac{du}{dx} + \dfrac{dv}{dx}$.

822. $\dfrac{d\,(uv)}{dx} = v\,\dfrac{du}{dx} + u\,\dfrac{dv}{dx}$.

823. $\dfrac{d\left(\dfrac{u}{v}\right)}{dx} = \dfrac{v\,\dfrac{du}{dx} - u\,\dfrac{dv}{dx}}{v^2}$.

824. $\dfrac{d\,f(u)}{dx} = \dfrac{d\,f(u)}{du} \cdot \dfrac{du}{dx}$.

825. $\dfrac{d^2 f(u)}{dx^2} = \dfrac{df}{du} \cdot \dfrac{d^2 u}{dx^2} + \dfrac{d^2 f}{du^2} \cdot \dfrac{du^2}{dx^2}$.

826. $\dfrac{dx^n}{dx} = nx^{n-1}$.

827. $\dfrac{de^x}{dx} = e^x$.

828. $\dfrac{da^u}{dx} = a^u \cdot \dfrac{du}{dx} \cdot \log_e a$.

829. $\dfrac{dx^x}{dx} = x^x\,(1 + \log_e x)$.

830. $\dfrac{d\,(\log_a x)}{dx} = \dfrac{1}{x \cdot \log_e a} = \dfrac{\log_a e}{x}$.

831. $\dfrac{d\,\sin x}{dx} = \cos x$.

832. $\dfrac{d\,\cos x}{dx} = -\sin x$.

833. $\dfrac{d \tan x}{dx} = \sec^2 x.$

834. $\dfrac{d \operatorname{ctn} x}{dx} = - \csc^2 x.$

835. $\dfrac{d \sec x}{dx} = \tan x \cdot \sec x.$

836. $\dfrac{d \csc x}{dx} = - \operatorname{ctn} x \cdot \csc x.$

837. $\dfrac{d \sin^{-1} x}{dx} = \dfrac{1}{\sqrt{1 - x^2}}.$

838. $\dfrac{d \cos^{-1} x}{dx} = \dfrac{-1}{\sqrt{1 - x^2}}.$

839. $\dfrac{d \tan^{-1} x}{dx} = \dfrac{1}{1 + x^2}.$

840. $\dfrac{d \operatorname{ctn}^{-1} x}{dx} = - \dfrac{1}{1 + x^2}.$

841. $\dfrac{d \sec^{-1} x}{dx} = \dfrac{1}{x \sqrt{x^2 - 1}}.$

842. $\dfrac{d \csc^{-1} x}{dx} = - \dfrac{1}{x \sqrt{x^2 - 1}}.$

843. $\dfrac{d \sinh x}{dx} = \cosh x.$

844. $\dfrac{d \cosh x}{dx} = \sinh x.$

845. $\dfrac{d \tanh x}{dx} = \operatorname{sech}^2 x.$

846. $\dfrac{d \operatorname{ctnh} x}{dx} = - \operatorname{csch}^2 x.$

847. $\dfrac{d \operatorname{sech} x}{dx} = - \operatorname{sech} x \cdot \tanh x.$

848. $\dfrac{d \operatorname{csch} x}{dx} = - \operatorname{csch} x \cdot \operatorname{ctnh} x.$

849. $\dfrac{d \sinh^{-1} x}{dx} = \dfrac{1}{\sqrt{x^2 + 1}}.$

850. $\dfrac{d \cosh^{-1} x}{dx} = \dfrac{1}{\sqrt{x^2 - 1}}.$

851. $\dfrac{d \tanh^{-1} x}{dx} = \dfrac{1}{1 - x^2}.$

852. $\dfrac{d \operatorname{ctnh}^{-1} x}{dx} = \dfrac{1}{1 - x^2}.$

853. $\dfrac{d \operatorname{sech}^{-1} x}{dx} = \dfrac{-1}{x \sqrt{1 - x^2}}.$

854. $\dfrac{d \operatorname{csch}^{-1} x}{dx} = \dfrac{-1}{x \sqrt{x^2 + 1}}.$

855. $\dfrac{d}{db} \displaystyle\int_a^b f(x)\, dx = f(b).$

856. $\dfrac{d}{da} \displaystyle\int_a^b f(x)\, dx = - f(a).$

857. $\dfrac{d}{dc} \displaystyle\int_a^b f(x,c)\, dx = \int_a^b D_c f(x,c) \cdot dx + f(b,c) \dfrac{db}{dc} - f(a,c) \dfrac{da}{dc}$

858. $\dfrac{d^n (u \cdot v)}{dx^n} = v \cdot \dfrac{d^n u}{dx^n} + n \cdot \dfrac{dv}{dx} \cdot \dfrac{d^{n-1} u}{dx^{n-1}}$

$$+ \dfrac{n(n-1)}{2!} \cdot \dfrac{d^2 v}{dx^2} \cdot \dfrac{d^{n-2} u}{dx^{n-2}} + \cdots + u \dfrac{d^n v}{dx^n}.$$

859. If $f(x, y, z, \cdots)$ is a homogeneous function of the nth order, so that $f(\lambda x, \lambda y, \lambda z, \cdots) \equiv \lambda^n f(x, y, z, \cdots)$,

$$x \cdot D_x f + y \cdot D_y f + z \cdot D_z f + \cdots \equiv n f.$$

860. If $x = \phi(y)$,

$$\frac{dy}{dx} = \frac{1}{\phi'(y)}, \quad \frac{d^2y}{dx^2} = -\frac{\phi''(y)}{[\phi'(y)]^3},$$

$$\frac{d^3y}{dx^3} = \frac{3[\phi''(y)]^2 - \phi'(y) \cdot \phi'''(y)}{[\phi'(y)]^5}.$$

861. If $x = f(t)$ and $y = \phi(t)$,

$$\frac{dy}{dx} = \frac{\phi'(t)}{f'(t)}, \quad \frac{d^2y}{dx^2} = \frac{f'(t) \cdot \phi''(t) - f''(t) \cdot \phi'(t)}{[f'(t)]^3}.$$

862. If $f(x, y) = 0$,

$$\frac{dy}{dx} = -\frac{\partial f}{\partial x} \Big/ \frac{\partial f}{\partial y} \equiv -\frac{D_x f}{D_y f},$$

$$\frac{d^2y}{dx^2} = -\frac{D_x^2 f \cdot (D_y f)^2 - 2 D_x D_y f \cdot D_x f \cdot D_y f + D_y^2 f \cdot (D_x f)^2}{(D_y f)^3}$$

863. If $y = f(u, v)$, $u = \phi(x)$, and $v = \psi(x)$,

$$\frac{df}{dx} = \frac{\partial f}{\partial u} \cdot \frac{du}{dx} + \frac{\partial f}{\partial v} \cdot \frac{dv}{dx} = u' \cdot D_u f + v' \cdot D_v f,$$

$$\frac{d^2f}{dx^2} = \frac{\partial^2 f}{\partial u^2} \cdot \left(\frac{du}{dx}\right)^2 + 2\frac{\partial^2 f}{\partial u \cdot \partial v} \cdot \frac{du}{dx} \frac{dv}{dx} + \frac{\partial^2 f}{\partial^2 v} \cdot \left(\frac{dv}{dx}\right)^2$$

$$+ \frac{\partial f}{\partial u} \cdot \frac{d^2u}{dx^2} + \frac{\partial f}{\partial v} \cdot \frac{d^2v}{dx^2}$$

$$= u'^2 \cdot D_u^2 f + 2 u' \cdot v' \cdot D_u D_v f + v'^2 \cdot D_v^2 f$$

$$+ u'' \cdot D_u f + v'' \cdot D_v f.$$

864. If $f(x, y, z) = 0$, $D_x z = -D_x f / D_z f$,

$$D_x^2 z = -[D_x^2 f \cdot (D_z f)^2$$

$$- 2 D_z f \cdot D_x f \cdot D_x D_y f + D_z^2 f (D_x f)^2] / (D_z f)^3,$$

$$D_x D_y z = -[D_x D_y f \cdot (D_z f)^2 - D_z f D_x f \cdot D_y D_z f$$

$$+ D_z f \cdot D_y f \cdot D_x D_z f + D_x f \cdot D_y f \cdot D_z^2 f] / (D_z f)^3.$$

865. If $V = \phi(u, v)$, $u = f_1(x, y)$, and $v = f_2(x, y)$,

$$D_x V = D_u \phi \cdot D_x u + D_v \phi \cdot D_x v,$$

$$D_x^2 V = D_u^2 \phi \cdot (D_x u)^2 + D_v^2 \phi \cdot (D_x v)^2 + 2 D_u D_v \phi \cdot D_x u \cdot D_x v$$
$$+ D_u \phi D_x^2 u + D_v \phi \cdot D_x^2 v,$$

$$D_y D_x V = D_u^2 \phi \cdot D_x u \cdot D_y u + D_v^2 \phi \cdot D_x v \cdot D_y v$$
$$+ D_u D_v \phi (D_x v \cdot D_y u + D_x u \cdot D_y v)$$
$$+ D_u \phi \cdot D_x D_y u + D_v \phi \cdot D_x D_y v,$$

$$D_x^2 V + D_y^2 V = D_u^2 \phi \cdot [(D_x u)^2 + (D_y u)^2]$$
$$+ D_v^2 \phi \cdot [(D_x v)^2 + (D_y v)^2]$$
$$+ 2 D_u D_v \phi \cdot [D_x u \cdot D_x v + D_y u \cdot D_y v]$$
$$+ D_u \phi \cdot [D_x^2 u + D_y^2 u]$$
$$+ D_v \phi \cdot [D_x^2 v + D_y^2 v].$$

In the special case, $u \equiv r \equiv \sqrt{x^2 + y^2}$, $v \equiv \theta \equiv \tan^{-1}(y/x)$, we have $D_r x = \cos\theta = x / \sqrt{x^2 + y^2}$; $D_r y = \sin\theta = y / \sqrt{x^2 + y^2}$;

$$D_\theta x = -r\sin\theta = -y; \quad D_\theta y = r\cos\theta = x;$$
$$D_x r = x / \sqrt{x^2 + y^2} = \cos\theta; \quad D_y r = y / \sqrt{x^2 + y^2} = \sin\theta;$$
$$D_x \theta = -y / (x^2 + y^2) = -\sin\theta / r;$$
$$D_y \theta = x / (x^2 + y^2) = \cos\theta / r; \quad \text{and}$$
$$D_x^2 V + D_y^2 V = D_r^2 V + \frac{1}{r} \cdot D_r V + \frac{1}{r^2} \cdot D_\theta^2 V.$$

866. If $V = \phi(u, v)$, $u = f_1(r, \theta)$, and $v = f_2(r, \theta)$,

$$D_r^2 V + \frac{1}{r} \cdot D_r V + \frac{1}{r^2} \cdot D_\theta^2 V = D_u^2 V \cdot \left[(D_r u)^2 + \frac{(D_\theta u)^2}{r^2} \right]$$

$$+ D_v^2 V \cdot \left[(D_r v)^2 + \frac{(D_\theta v)^2}{r^2} \right]$$

$$+ 2 D_u D_v V \left[D_r u \cdot D_r v + \frac{D_\theta u \cdot D_\theta v}{r^2} \right] +$$

$$+ D_u V \left[D_r^2 u + \frac{1}{r} \cdot D_r u + \frac{1}{r^2} \cdot D_\theta^2 u \right]$$

$$+ D_v V \left[D_r^2 v + \frac{1}{r} \cdot D_r v + \frac{1}{r^2} \cdot D_\theta^2 v \right].$$

867. If $V = \phi(u, v, w)$, $u = f_1(x, y, z)$, $v = f_2(x, y, z)$, and
$$w = f_3(x, y, z),$$

$$D_x V = D_u V \cdot D_x u + D_v V \cdot D_x v + D_w V \cdot D_x w,$$

$$\begin{aligned}
D_x^2 V = {}& D_u^2 V \cdot (D_x u)^2 + D_v^2 V \cdot (D_x v)^2 + D_w^2 V \cdot (D_x w)^2 \\
& + D_u V \cdot D_x^2 u + D_v V \cdot D_x^2 v + D_w V \cdot D_x^2 w \\
& + 2 (D_u D_v V \cdot D_x u \cdot D_x v + D_u D_w V \cdot D_x u \cdot D_x w \\
& + D_v D_w V \cdot D_x v \cdot D_x w).
\end{aligned}$$

$$\begin{aligned}
D_x^2 V + D_y^2 V + D_z^2 V = {}& D_u^2 V \cdot [(D_x u)^2 + (D_y u)^2 + (D_z u)^2] \\
& + D_v^2 V \cdot [(D_x v)^2 + (D_y v)^2 + (D_z v)^2] \\
& + D_w^2 V [(D_x w)^2 + (D_y w)^2 + (D_z w)^2] \\
& + 2 D_u D_v V \cdot [D_x u \cdot D_x v + D_y u \cdot D_y v + D_z u \cdot D_z v] \\
& + 2 D_v D_w V \cdot [D_x v \cdot D_x w + D_y v \cdot D_y w + D_z v \cdot D_z w] \\
& + 2 D_w D_u V \cdot [D_x w \cdot D_x u + D_y w \cdot D_y u + D_z w \cdot D_z u] \\
& + D_u V \cdot [D_x^2 u + D_y^2 u + D_z^2 u] \\
& + D_v V \cdot [D_x^2 v + D_y^2 v + D_z^2 v] \\
& + D_w V \cdot [D_x^2 w + D_y^2 w + D_z^2 w].
\end{aligned}$$

In particular, if
$$x \equiv r \sin \theta \cos \phi, \ y \equiv r \sin \theta \sin \phi, \ z \equiv r \cos \theta,$$
so that $u \equiv r^2 \equiv x^2 + y^2 + z^2$, $v \equiv \theta \equiv \tan^{-1}(\sqrt{x^2 + y^2}/z)$,
$w \equiv \phi \equiv \tan^{-1}(y/x)$, we have
$$D_r z = \cos \theta = z / \sqrt{x^2 + y^2 + z^2};$$
$$D_r x = \sin \theta \cos \phi = x / \sqrt{x^2 + y^2 + z^2};$$

$$D_r y = \sin \theta \sin \phi = y / \sqrt{x^2 + y^2 + z^2};$$

$$D_\theta z = - r \sin \theta = - \sqrt{x^2 + y^2};$$

$$D_\theta x = r \cos \theta \cos \phi = zx / \sqrt{x^2 + y^2};$$

$$D_\theta y = r \cos \theta \sin \phi = zy / \sqrt{x^2 + y^2};$$

$$D_\phi z = 0;$$

$$D_\phi x = - r \sin \theta \sin \phi = - y;$$

$$D_\phi y = r \sin \theta \cos \phi = x;$$

$$D_z r = z / r = \cos \theta;$$

$$D_z \theta = - \sqrt{x^2 + y^2} / r^2 = - \sin \theta / r;$$

$$D_z \phi = 0;$$

$$D_x r = x / r = \sin \theta \cos \phi;$$

$$D_x \theta = xz / r^2 \sqrt{x^2 + y^2} = \cos \theta \cos \phi / r;$$

$$D_x \phi = - y / (x^2 + y^2) = - \sin \phi / r \sin \theta;$$

$$D_y r = y / r = \sin \theta \sin \phi;$$

$$D_y \theta = zy / r^2 \sqrt{x^2 + y^2} = \cos \theta \sin \phi / r;$$

$$D_y \phi = x / (x^2 + y^2) = \cos \phi / r \sin \theta;$$

$$(D_x r)^2 + (D_y r)^2 + (D_z r)^2 = 1;$$

$$(D_x \theta)^2 + (D_y \theta)^2 + (D_z \theta)^2 = 1 / r^2;$$

$$(D_x \phi)^2 + (D_y \phi)^2 + (D_z \phi)^2 = 1 / r^2 \sin^2 \theta;$$

$$(D_x V)^2 + (D_y V)^2 + (D_z V)^2$$
$$= (D_r V)^2 + \left(\frac{D_\theta V}{r} \right)^2 + \left(\frac{D_\phi V}{r \sin \theta} \right)^2;$$

$$D_x^2 V + D_y^2 V + D_z^2 V$$
$$= \frac{1}{r^2 \sin \theta} \left[D_r(r^2 \cdot D_r V) \cdot \sin \theta + \frac{D_\phi^2 V}{\sin \theta} + D_\theta(\sin \theta \cdot D_\theta V) \right].$$

868. If $x = f_1(u, v),\ y = f_2(u, v),\ z = f_3(u, v)$,

$$D_x z = \frac{D_u f_3 \cdot D_v f_2 - D_v f_3 \cdot D_u f_2}{D_u f_1 \cdot D_v f_2 - D_v f_1 \cdot D_u f_2}$$

$$D_y z = \frac{D_v f_3 \cdot D_u f_1 - D_u f_3 \cdot D_v f_1}{D_u f_1 \cdot D_v f_2 - D_v f_1 \cdot D_u f_2}.$$

869. If $x = f(z, u)$, and $y = \phi(z, u)$,

$$D_x z = D_u \phi / (D_z f \cdot D_u \phi - D_z \phi \cdot D_u f),$$

$$D_y z = D_u f / (D_z \phi \cdot D_u f - D_z f \cdot D_u \phi).$$

870. If $F_1(x, y, z, u, v) = 0$,

$$F_2(x, y, z, u, v) = 0, \text{ and } F_3(x, y, z, u, v) = 0,$$

$$D_x z \cdot \begin{vmatrix} D_z F_1 & D_u F_1 & D_v F_1 \\ D_z F_2 & D_u F_2 & D_v F_2 \\ D_z F_3 & D_u F_3 & D_v F_3 \end{vmatrix} = - \begin{vmatrix} D_x F_1 & D_u F_1 & D_v F_1 \\ D_x F_2 & D_u F_2 & D_v F_2 \\ D_x F_3 & D_u F_3 & D_v F_3 \end{vmatrix}.$$

871. If $F_1(x, y, z) = 0$, and $F_2(x, y, z) = 0$,

$$\frac{dy}{D_z F_1 \cdot D_x F_2 - D_z F_2 \cdot D_x F_1} = \frac{dz}{D_x F_1 \cdot D_y F_2 - D_x F_2 \cdot D_y F_1}$$

$$\frac{dx}{D_y F_1 \cdot D_z F_2 - D_y F_2 \cdot D_z F_1}.$$

If each of the quantities $y_1,\ y_2,\ y_3,\ \cdots y_n$ is a function of the n variables $x_1,\ x_2,\ x_3,\ \cdots x_n$, the determinant,

$$\begin{vmatrix} D_{x_1} y_1 & D_{x_2} y_1 & D_{x_3} y_1 \cdots \\ D_{x_1} y_2 & D_{x_2} y_2 & D_{x_3} y_2 \cdots \\ \cdot & \cdot & \cdot \\ \cdot & \cdot & \cdot \\ D_{x_1} y_n & D_{x_2} y_n & D_{x_3} y_n \cdots D_{x_n} y_n \end{vmatrix}$$

is called the *functional determinant* or the *Jacobian* of the y's with respect to the x's and is denoted by the expression,

$$\frac{\partial (y_1, \ y_2, \ y_3, \ \cdots \ y_n)}{\partial (x_1, \ x_2, \ x_3, \ \cdots \ x_n)}, \text{ or by } J \ (y_1, \ y_2, \ \cdots \ y_n).$$

872. $\dfrac{\partial (y_1, \ y_2, \ y_3, \ \cdots \ y_n)}{\partial (x_1, \ x_2, \ x_3, \ \cdots \ x_n)} \cdot \dfrac{\partial (x_1, \ x_2, \ x_3, \ \cdots \ x_n)}{\partial (y_1, \ y_2, \ y_3, \ \cdots \ y_n)} \equiv 1.$

873. $\dfrac{\partial (y_1, \ y_2, \ y_3, \ \cdots \ y_n)}{\partial (z_1, \ z_2, \ z_3, \ \cdots \ z_n)} \cdot \dfrac{\partial (z_1, \ z_2, \ z_3, \ \cdots \ z_n)}{\partial (x_1, \ x_2, \ x_3, \ \cdots \ x_n)}$

$$\equiv \frac{\partial (y_1, \ y_2, \ y_3, \ \cdots \ y_n)}{\partial (x_1, \ x_2, \ x_3, \ \cdots \ x_n)}.$$

If the y's are not all independent but are connected by an equation of the form $\phi (y_1, y_2, y_3, \cdots y_n) = 0$, the Jacobian of the y's with respect to the x's vanishes identically; and, conversely, if the Jacobian vanishes identically, the y's are connected by one or more relations of the above-mentioned form.

The *directional derivative* of any scalar point function, u, at any point, P, in any fixed direction PQ', is the limit, as PQ approaches zero, of the ratio of $u_Q - u_P$ to PQ, where Q is a point on the straight line PQ' between P and Q'. The *gradient*, h_u, of the function u at P is the directional derivative of u at P taken in the direction in which u increases most rapidly. This direction is normal to the surface of constant u which passes through P.

874. $h_u^2 \equiv (D_x u)^2 + (D_y u)^2 + (D_z u)^2.$

The directional derivative of any scalar point function at any point in any given direction is evidently equal to the product of the gradient and the cosine of the angle between the given direction and that in which the function increases most rapidly.

The *normal derivative*, at any point, P, of a point function u, taken with respect to another point function v, is the limit as PQ approaches zero of the ratio of $u_Q - u_P$ to $v_Q - v_P$, where Q is a point so chosen on the normal at P of the surface of constant v which passes through P, that $v_Q - v_P$ is positive. If (u, v) denotes the angle between the directions in which u and v increase most rapidly, the normal derivatives of u with respect to v, and of v with respect to u may be written

$$h_u \cos (u, v) \div h_v, \text{ and } h_v \cdot \cos (u, v) \div h_u$$

respectively. If $h_u = h_v$, these derivatives are equal.

G. — MISCELLANEOUS FORMULAS.

If s is a plane analytic closed curve, n its normal drawn from within outwards, and dA the element of plane area within s, the usual integral transformation formulas for the functions u and v which, with their derivatives of the first order, are continuous everywhere within s, may be written —

875. $\displaystyle\int u \cdot \cos (x, n) \, ds = \int\int D_x u \cdot dA.$

876. $\displaystyle\int [u \cdot \cos (x, n) + v \cdot \cos (y, n)] \, ds = \int\int (D_x u + D_y v) \, dA.$

877. $\displaystyle\int D_n u \cdot ds = \int\int (D_x^2 u + D_y^2 u) \, dA.$

878. $\displaystyle\int\int (D_x u \cdot D_x v + D_y u \cdot D_y v) \, dA$

$$= \int u \cdot D_n v \cdot ds - \int\int u \, (D_x^2 v + D_y^2 v) \, dA$$

$$= \int v \cdot D_n u \cdot ds - \int\int v \, (D_x^2 u + D_y^2 v) \, dA.$$

879. $\displaystyle\int\int \lambda \, (D_x u \cdot D_x v + D_y u \cdot D_y v) \, dA = \int \lambda \cdot u \cdot D_n v \cdot ds$

$$- \int\int u \, [D_x (\lambda \cdot D_x v) + D_y (\lambda \cdot D_y v)] \, dA.$$

If ξ and η are two analytic functions which define a set of orthogonal curvilinear coördinates, and if (ξ, n) and (η, n) represent the angles between n and the directions in which ξ and η, respectively, increase most rapidly.

880. $\displaystyle\int\int h_\xi \cdot h_\eta \cdot D_\eta \left(\frac{u}{h_\xi}\right) dA = \int u \cdot \cos(\eta, n)\, ds.$

881. $\displaystyle\int\int h_\xi \cdot h_\eta \cdot D_\xi \left(\frac{u}{h_\eta}\right) dA = \int u \cdot \cos(\xi, n)\, ds.$

882. If r is the distance from a fixed point, Q, in the coördinate plane,

$$\int \frac{\cos(r, n)\, ds}{r} = 0,\ \pi,\ \text{or}\ 2\,\pi, \text{ according as } Q \text{ is without,}$$

on, or within s.

If S is an analytic closed surface, n its normal drawn from within outwards, and $d\tau$ the element of volume shut in by S, the usual integral transformation formulas may be written —

883. $\displaystyle\int\int u \cos(x, n)\, dS = \int\int\int D_x u \cdot d\tau.$

884. $\displaystyle\int\int [u \cos(x, n) + v \cos(y, n) + w \cos(z, n)]\, dS$
$$= \int\int\int (D_x u + D_y v + D_z w)\, d\tau.$$

885. $\displaystyle\int\int D_n u \cdot ds = \int\int\int (D_x^2 u + D_y^2 u + D_z^2 u)\, d\tau.$

886. $\displaystyle\int\int\int (D_x u \cdot D_x v + D_y u \cdot D_y v + D_z u \cdot D_z v)\, d\tau$
$$= \int\int u \cdot D_n v \cdot dS - \int\int\int u (D_x^2 v + D_y^2 v + D_z^2 v)\, d\tau$$
$$= \int\int v \cdot D_n u \cdot dS - \int\int\int v (D_x^2 u + D_y^2 u + D_z^2 u)\, d\tau.$$

887. $\displaystyle \iiint \lambda \left(D_x u \cdot D_x v + D_y u \cdot D_y v + D_z u \cdot D_z v \right) d\tau$

$$= \iint \lambda \cdot v \cdot D_n u \cdot dS$$

$$- \iiint v \left[D_x \left(\lambda D_x u \right) + D_y \left(\lambda D_y u \right) + D_z \left(\lambda D_z u \right) \right] d\tau.$$

If ξ, η, ζ are three analytic functions which define a system of orthogonal curvilinear coördinates,

888. $\displaystyle \iiint h_\xi \cdot h_\eta \cdot h_\zeta \cdot D_\xi \left(\frac{u}{h_\eta \cdot h_\zeta} \right) d\tau = \iint u \cdot \cos (\xi, n) \, dS.$

889. $\displaystyle \iiint h_\xi \cdot h_\eta \cdot h_\zeta \cdot D_\eta \left(\frac{u}{h_\xi \cdot h_\zeta} \right) d\tau = \iint u \cdot \cos (\eta, n) \, dS.$

890. $\displaystyle \iiint h_\xi \cdot h_\eta \cdot h_\zeta \cdot D_\zeta \left(\frac{u}{h_\xi \cdot h_\eta} \right) d\tau = \iint u \cdot \cos (\zeta, n) \, dS.$

891. If r is the distance from a fixed point, Q,

$$\int \frac{\cos (r, n)}{r^2} \, dS = 0, \ 2\pi, \ \text{or} \ 4\pi \text{ according as } Q \text{ is without,}$$

on, or within S.

———

Stokes's Theorem. — The line integral, taken around a closed curve, of the tangential component of a vector point function, is equal to the surface integral, taken over a surface bounded by the curve, of the normal component of the curl of the vector, the direction of integration around the curve forming a right-handed screw rotation about the normals.

If X, Y, Z are the components of the vector,

892. $\displaystyle \int (X \, dx + Y \, dy + Z \, dz) = \iint \left[(D_y Z - D_z Y) \cos (x, n) \right.$

$$+ (D_z X - D_x Z) \cos (y, n)$$

$$\left. + (D_x Y - D_y X) \cos (z, n) \right] dS.$$

Equations 893 to 897 give Poisson's Equation in orthogonal Cartesian, in cylindrical, in spherical, and in orthogonal curvilinear coördinates.

893. $\overline{\nabla}^2 V \equiv D_x^2 V + D_y^2 V + D_z^2 V = -4\pi\rho.$

894. $\dfrac{1}{r} \cdot D_r(r \cdot D_r V) + \dfrac{1}{r^2} \cdot D_\theta^2 V + D_z^2 V = -4\pi\rho.$

895. $\sin\theta \cdot D_r(r^2 \cdot D_r V) + \dfrac{D_\phi^2 V}{\sin\theta}$

$$+ D_\theta(\sin\theta \cdot D_\theta V) = -4\pi\rho r^2 \sin\theta.$$

896. $h_\xi^2 \cdot D_\xi^2 V + h_\eta^2 \cdot D_\eta^2 V + h_\zeta^2 \cdot D_\zeta^2 V$

$$+ D_\xi V \cdot \overline{\nabla}^2 \xi + D_\eta V \cdot \overline{\nabla}^2 \eta + D_\zeta V \cdot \overline{\nabla}^2 \zeta = -4\pi\rho.$$

897. $h_\xi \cdot h_\eta \cdot h_\zeta \left\{ D_\xi\left(\dfrac{h_\xi}{h_\eta h_\zeta} \cdot D_\xi V\right) + D_\eta\left(\dfrac{h_\eta}{h_\xi h_\zeta} \cdot D_\eta V\right) \right.$

$$\left. + D_\zeta\left(\dfrac{h_\zeta}{h_\xi h_\eta} \cdot D_\zeta V\right) \right\} = -4\pi\rho.$$

H. — CERTAIN CONSTANTS.

$$\pi = 3.14159\ 26535\ 89793$$
$$\log_{10}\pi = 0.49714\ 98726\ 94134$$
$$\frac{1}{\pi} = 0.31830\ 98861\ 83791$$
$$\pi^2 = 9.86960\ 44010\ 89359$$
$$\sqrt{\pi} = 1.77245\ 38509\ 05516$$
$$\log_{10} 2 = 0.30102\ 99956\ 63981$$
$$e = 2.71828\ 18284\ 59045$$
$$\log_{10} e = 0.43429\ 44819\ 03252$$
$$\log_e 10 = 2.30258\ 50929\ 94046$$
$$\log_e 2 = 0.69314\ 71805\ 59945$$
$$\log_{10}\log_{10} e = 9.63778\ 43113\ 00537$$
$$\log_e \pi = 1.14472\ 98858\ 49400$$

I. — GENERAL FORMULAS OF INTEGRATION.

F and f represent functions of x, and F', f', F'', f'', their first and second derivatives with respect to x.

898. $\displaystyle\int F' \cdot f \cdot dx = F \cdot f - \int F \cdot f' \cdot dx.$

899. $\displaystyle\int (F)^n \cdot F' \cdot dx = (F)^{n+1}/(n+1).$

900. $\displaystyle\int (aF + b)^n \cdot F' \cdot dx = (aF + b)^{n+1}/a \, (n+1).$

901. $\displaystyle\int (F + f)^n \cdot dx = \int F(F+f)^{n-1} dx + \int f(F+f)^{n-1} dx.$

902. $\displaystyle\int F'/(F)^n \cdot dx = -1/(n-1)(F)^{n-1}, \; \int F'/F \cdot dx = \log F.$

903. $\displaystyle\int (F' \cdot f - F \cdot f')/(f)^2 \cdot dx = F/f.$

904. $\displaystyle\int (F' \cdot f - F \cdot f')/Ff \cdot dx = \log (F/f).$

905. $\displaystyle\int \frac{dx}{F \cdot (x^2 - a^2)} = \frac{1}{2a} \int \frac{dx}{F \cdot (x - a)} - \frac{1}{2a} \int \frac{dx}{F \cdot (x + a)}$

906. $\displaystyle\int \frac{dx}{F(F \pm f)} = \pm \int \frac{dx}{F \cdot f} \mp \int \frac{dx}{f(F \pm f)}.$

907. $\displaystyle\int \frac{F' \cdot dx}{\sqrt{aF + b}} = (2\sqrt{aF + b})/a.$

908. $\displaystyle\int \frac{F' \cdot dx}{\sqrt{F^2 + a}} = \log (F + \sqrt{F^2 + a}).$

909. $\displaystyle\int \frac{F \cdot dx}{(F + a)(F + b)} = \frac{a}{a - b} \int \frac{dx}{F + a} - \frac{b}{a - b} \int \frac{dx}{F + b}.$

910. $\displaystyle\int \frac{F \cdot dx}{(F + f)^n} = \int \frac{dx}{(F + f)^{n-1}} - \int \frac{f \, dx}{(F + f)^n}.$

911. $\displaystyle\int \frac{F' \cdot dx}{p^2 + q^2 F^2} = \frac{1}{pq} \cdot \tan^{-1} \frac{qF}{p}, \; \int \frac{F' \cdot dx}{q^2 F^2 - p^2} = \frac{1}{2pq} \log \frac{qF - p}{qF + p}$

912. $\int \dfrac{F^{2n} \cdot dx}{1 - F'^{2n}} = -x + \int \dfrac{dx}{1 - F^{2n}}.$

913. $\int \dfrac{F' \cdot dx}{F^2 + a^2} = \dfrac{1}{a} \tan^{-1} \left(\dfrac{F}{a} \right).$

914. $\int \dfrac{F' \cdot dx}{a^2 F^2 - b^2} = \dfrac{1}{2\,ab} \log \dfrac{aF - b}{aF + b}.$

915. $\int \dfrac{F^{2n} \cdot dx}{F^{2n} - b^2} = \int \dfrac{F^n \cdot dx}{2\,(F^n - b)} + \int \dfrac{F^n \cdot dx}{2\,(F^n + b)}.$

916. $\int \dfrac{F' \cdot dx}{\sqrt{b^2 - F^2}} = \sin^{-1} \left(\dfrac{F}{b} \right).$

917. $\int \dfrac{F' \cdot dx}{aF^2 + bF} = \dfrac{1}{b} \log \dfrac{F}{aF + b}.$

918. $\int \dfrac{F' \cdot dx}{aF^2 - bF} = \dfrac{1}{b} \log \dfrac{aF - b}{F}.$

919. $\int \dfrac{F' \cdot dx}{F \sqrt{F^2 - b^2}} = \dfrac{1}{b} \sec^{-1} \left(\dfrac{F}{b} \right).$

920. $\int \dfrac{(F' \cdot f - F \cdot f')\, dx}{F^2 + f^2} = \tan^{-1} \left(\dfrac{F}{f} \right).$

921. $\int \dfrac{(F' \cdot f - F \cdot f')\, dx}{F^2 - f^2} = \dfrac{1}{2} \log \left(\dfrac{F - f}{F + f} \right).$

J. — INTEGRALS USEFUL IN THE THEORY OF ALTERNATING CURRENTS.

922. $\int \sin(\omega t + \phi)\, dt = -\dfrac{1}{\omega} \cdot \cos(\omega t + \phi).$

923. $\int \cos(\omega t + \phi)\, dt = \dfrac{1}{\omega} \cdot \sin(\omega t + \phi).$

924. $\int \sin^2(\omega t + \phi)\, dt = \dfrac{1}{2}\, t - \dfrac{1}{4\,\omega} \sin 2\,(\omega t + \phi).$

925. $\int \sin{(\omega t + \phi)} \cdot \cos{(\omega t + \phi)}\, dt = \frac{1}{2\,\omega} \cdot \sin^2{(\omega t + \phi)}.$

926. $\int \cos^2{(\omega t + \phi)}\, dt = \frac{1}{2}\,t + \frac{1}{4\,\omega} \sin 2\,(\omega t + \phi).$

927. $\int \sin{(\omega t + \lambda)} \cdot \sin{(\omega t + \mu)}\, dt = \frac{\cos{(\mu - \lambda)}}{2\,\omega}\,(\omega t)$
$$- \frac{\sin{(\omega t + \lambda)} \cdot \cos{(\omega t + \mu)}}{2\,\omega}.$$

928. $\int \sin{(\omega t + \lambda)} \cdot \cos{(\omega t + \mu)}\, dt = \frac{\sin{(\omega t + \lambda)} \cdot \sin{(\omega t + \mu)}}{2\,\omega}$
$$- \frac{\sin{(\mu - \lambda)}}{2\,\omega}\,(\omega t).$$

929. $\int \cos{(\omega t + \lambda)} \cdot \cos{(\omega t + \mu)}\, dt = \frac{\cos{(\mu - \lambda)}}{2\,\omega}\,(\omega t)$
$$+ \frac{\sin{(\omega t + \lambda)} \cdot \cos{(\omega t + \lambda)}}{2\,\omega}.$$

930. $\int \sin{(mt + \lambda)} \cdot \sin{(nt + \mu)}\, dt = \frac{\sin{\left[mt - nt + \lambda - \mu\right]}}{2\,(m - n)}$
$$- \frac{\sin{\left[mt + nt + \lambda + \mu\right]}}{2\,(m + n)}.$$

931. $\int \cos{(mt + \lambda)} \cdot \cos{(nt + \mu)}\, dt = \frac{\sin{\left[mt + nt + \lambda + \mu\right]}}{2\,(m + n)}$
$$+ \frac{\sin{\left[mt - nt + \lambda - \mu\right]}}{2\,(m - n)}.$$

932. $\int \sin{(mt + \lambda)} \cdot \cos{(nt + \mu)}\, dt = - \frac{\cos{\left[mt + nt + \lambda + \mu\right]}}{2\,(m + n)}$
$$- \frac{\cos{\left[mt - nt + \lambda - \mu\right]}}{2\,(m - n)}.$$

933. $\displaystyle\int \cos\,(\omega t + \lambda + mx) \cdot \cos\,(\omega t + \lambda - mx)\,dx$

$$= \cos^2(\omega t + \lambda)\left[\frac{mx + \sin\,mx \cdot \cos\,mx}{2\,m}\right]$$

$$- \sin^2(\omega t + \lambda)\left[\frac{mx - \sin\,mx \cdot \cos\,mx}{2\,m}\right].$$

$$\left\{\begin{array}{l} m \cdot \sin(\omega t + \phi) + n \cdot \cos(\omega t + \phi) = \sqrt{m^2 + n^2} \cdot \sin(\omega t + \phi + \partial) \\ \text{where } \tan\,\partial = n/m. \\ m \cdot \sin(\omega t + \phi) - n \cdot \cos(\omega t + \phi) = \sqrt{m^2 + n^2} \cdot \sin(\omega t + \phi - \partial). \end{array}\right\}$$

934. $\displaystyle\int e^{(-b\,\pm\,ci)\,t}\,dt = \frac{-\,b \mp ci}{b^2 + c^2}\,e^{(-b\,\pm\,ci)\,t}$

$$= \frac{e^{-bt}}{b^2 + c^2}\left[(c \cdot \sin\,ct - b \cdot \cos\,ct) \mp i\,(b \cdot \sin\,ct + c \cdot \cos\,ct)\right]$$

$$= \frac{e^{-bt}}{\sqrt{b^2 + c^2}}\left[\sin\,(ct - \delta) \mp i \cdot \cos\,(ct - \delta)\right],$$
$$\text{where } \tan\,\delta = b/c.$$

935. $\displaystyle\int e^{\alpha t} \cdot \cos\,(\omega t + \phi)\,dt$

$$= \frac{e^{\alpha t}}{\alpha^2 + \omega^2}\left[\omega \sin\,(\omega t + \phi) + \alpha \cdot \cos\,(\omega t + \phi)\right]$$

$$= \frac{e^{\alpha t}}{\sqrt{\alpha^2 + \omega^2}}\cos\left[\omega t + \phi - \tan^{-1}(\omega/\alpha)\right].$$

936. $\displaystyle\int e^{\alpha t} \cdot \sin\,(\omega t + \phi)\,dt$

$$= \frac{e^{\alpha t}}{\alpha^2 + \omega^2}\left[\alpha \cdot \sin\,(\omega t + \phi) - \omega \cdot \cos\,(\omega t + \phi)\right]$$

$$= \frac{e^{\alpha t}}{\sqrt{\alpha^2 + \omega^2}}\sin\left[\omega t + \phi - \tan^{-1}(\omega/\alpha)\right].$$

937. $\displaystyle\int \left[e^{\alpha t} \cdot \sin\,(\omega t + \phi)\right]^2\,dt$

$$= \frac{e^{2\,\alpha t}}{4}\left[\frac{1}{\alpha} - \frac{\omega \cdot \sin\,2\,(\omega t + \phi) + \alpha \cdot \cos\,2\,(\omega t + \phi)}{\alpha^2 + \omega^2}\right]$$

$$= \frac{e^{2\,\alpha t}}{4}\left[\frac{1}{\alpha} - \frac{\cos\left[2\,\omega t + 2\,\phi - \tan^{-1}(\omega/\alpha)\right]}{\sqrt{\alpha^2 + \omega^2}}\right].$$

938. $\int \left[e^{at} \cdot \cos(\omega t + \phi) \right]^2 dt$

$$= \frac{e^{2at}}{4} \left[\frac{1}{\alpha} + \frac{\omega \cdot \sin 2(\omega t + \phi) + \alpha \cdot \cos 2(\omega t + \phi)}{\alpha^2 + \omega^2} \right]$$

$$= \frac{e^{2at}}{4} \left[\frac{1}{\alpha} + \frac{\cos \left[2\,\omega t + 2\,\phi - \tan^{-1}(\omega/\alpha) \right]}{\sqrt{\alpha^2 + \omega^2}} \right].$$

In the case of a direct trigonometric function of $(\omega t + \phi)$, $T = 2\,\pi/\omega$ is called the *period* or the *cycle*. The mean value for any whole number of periods, reckoned from any epoch, of $\sin(\omega t + \phi)$, $\cos(\omega t + \phi)$, or $\sin(\omega t + \phi) \cdot \cos(\omega t + \phi)$, is zero, whereas the mean value for any whole number of half periods, reckoned from any epoch, of either $\sin^2(\omega t + \phi)$ or $\cos^2(\omega t + \phi)$ is one half. The mean value of $\sin(\omega t)$ from $t = 0$ to $t = \frac{1}{2}\,T$, or of $\cos(\omega t)$ from $-\frac{1}{4}\,T$ to $+\frac{1}{4}\,T$, is $2/\pi$ or 0.6366.

The mean value, for any number of whole periods, of either $\sin(\omega t + \lambda) \cdot \sin(\omega t + \mu)$ or $\cos(\omega t + \lambda) \cdot \cos(\omega t + \mu)$ is $\frac{1}{2} \cdot \cos(\lambda - \mu)$, while the mean value of $\sin(\omega t + \lambda) \cdot \cos(\omega t + \mu)$ is $\frac{1}{2} \sin(\lambda - \mu)$.

INTERPOLATION.

If values of an analytic function, $f(x)$, are given in a table for a number of values of the argument x, separated from one another consecutively by the constant small interval, δ, the differences between successive tabular values of the function are called *first tabular differences*, the differences of these first differences, *second tabular differences*, and so on. The tabular differences of the first, second, third, and fourth orders corresponding to $x = a$ are

$$\Delta_1 \equiv f(a + \delta) - f(a),$$
$$\Delta_2 \equiv f(a + 2\delta) - 2 \cdot f(a + \delta) + f(a),$$
$$\Delta_3 \equiv f(a + 3\delta) - 3 \cdot f(a + 2\delta) + 3 \cdot f(a + \delta) - f(a),$$
$$\Delta_4 \equiv f(a + 4\delta) - 4 \cdot f(a + 3\delta) + 6 \cdot f(a + 2\delta) - 4 \cdot f(a + \delta) + f(a),$$

where $f(a)$ is any tabulated value.

The value of the function for $x = (a + h)$, where $h = k\delta$, is

$$f(a + h) = f(a) + k \cdot \Delta_1 + \frac{k(k-1)}{2!} \cdot \Delta_2 + \frac{k(k-1)(k-2)}{3!} \cdot \Delta_3$$
$$+ \frac{k(k-1)(k-2)(k-3)}{4!} \cdot \Delta_4 + \cdots.$$

TABLES.

The Probability Integral.

$$\left(\frac{2}{\sqrt{\pi}} \int_0^x e^{-x^2} dx.\right)$$

x	0	1	2	3	4	5	6	7	8	9
0.00	0.00000	00113	00226	00339	00451	00564	00677	00790	00903	01016
0.01	0.01128	01241	01354	01467	01580	01692	01805	01918	02031	02144
0.02	0.02256	02369	02482	02595	02708	02820	02933	03046	03159	03271
0.03	0.03384	03497	03610	03722	03835	03948	04060	04173	04286	04398
0.04	0.04511	04624	04736	04849	04962	05074	05187	05299	05412	05525
0.05	0.05637	05750	05862	05975	06087	06200	06312	06425	06537	06650
0.06	0.06762	06875	06987	07099	07212	07324	07437	07549	07661	07773
0.07	0.07886	07998	08110	08223	08335	08447	08559	08671	08784	08896
0.08	0.09008	09120	09232	09344	09456	09568	09680	09792	09904	10016
0.09	0.10128	10240	10352	10464	10576	10687	10799	10911	11023	11135
0.10	0.11246	11358	11470	11581	11693	11805	11916	12028	12139	12251
0.11	0.12362	12474	12585	12697	12808	12919	13031	13142	13253	13365
0.12	0.13476	13587	13698	13809	13921	14032	14143	14254	14365	14476
0.13	0.14587	14698	14809	14919	15030	15141	15252	15363	15473	15584
0.14	0.15695	15805	15916	16027	16137	16248	16358	16468	16579	16689
0.15	0.16800	16910	17020	17130	17241	17351	17461	17571	17681	17791
0.16	0.17901	18011	18121	18231	18341	18451	18560	18670	18780	18890
0.17	0.18999	19109	19218	19328	19437	19547	19656	19766	19875	19984
0.18	0.20094	20203	20312	20421	20530	20639	20748	20857	20966	21075
0.19	0.21184	21293	21402	21510	21619	21728	21836	21945	22053	22162
0.20	0.22270	22379	22487	22595	22704	22812	22920	23028	23136	23244
0.21	0.23352	23460	23568	23676	23784	23891	23999	24107	24214	24322
0.22	0.24430	24537	24645	24752	24859	24967	25074	25181	25288	25395
0.23	0.25502	25609	25716	25823	25930	26037	26144	26250	26357	26463
0.24	0.26570	26677	26783	26889	26996	27102	27208	27314	27421	27527
0.25	0.27633	27739	27845	27950	28056	28162	28268	28373	28479	28584
0.26	0.28690	28795	28901	29006	29111	29217	29322	29427	29532	29637
0.27	0.29742	29847	29952	30056	30161	30266	30370	30475	30579	30684
0.28	0.30788	30892	30997	31101	31205	31309	31413	31517	31621	31725
0.29	0.31828	31922	32036	32139	32243	32346	32450	32553	32656	32760
0.30	0.32863	32966	33069	33172	33275	33378	33480	33583	33686	33788
0.31	0.33891	33993	34096	34198	34300	34400	34505	34607	34709	34811
0.32	0.34913	35014	35116	35218	35319	35421	35523	35624	35725	35827
0.33	0.35928	36029	36130	36231	36332	36433	36534	36635	36735	36836
0.34	0.36936	37037	37137	37238	37338	37438	37538	37638	37738	37838
0.35	0.37938	38038	38138	38237	38337	38436	38536	38635	38735	38834
0.36	0.38933	39032	39131	39230	39329	39428	39526	39625	39724	39822
0.37	0.39921	40019	40117	40215	40314	40412	40510	40608	40705	40803
0.38	0.40901	40999	41096	41194	41291	41388	41486	41583	41680	41777
0.39	0.41874	41971	42068	42164	42261	42358	42454	42550	42647	42743
0.40	0.42839	42935	43031	43127	43223	43319	43415	43510	43606	43701
0.41	0.43797	43892	43988	44083	44178	44273	44368	44463	44557	44652
0.42	0.44747	44841	44936	45030	45124	45219	45313	45407	45501	45595
0.43	0.45689	45782	45876	45970	46063	46157	46250	46343	46436	46529
0.44	0.46623	46715	46808	46901	46994	47086	47179	47271	47364	47456
0.45	0.47548	47640	47732	47824	47916	48008	48100	48191	48283	48374
0.46	0.48466	48557	48648	48739	48830	48921	49012	49103	49193	49284
0.47	0.49375	49465	49555	49646	49736	49826	49916	50006	50096	50185
0.48	0.50275	50365	50454	50543	50633	50722	50811	50900	50989	51078
0.49	0.51167	51256	51344	51433	51521	51609	51698	51786	51874	51962

The Probability Integral.

$$\left(\frac{2}{\sqrt{\pi}}\int_0^x e^{-x^2}dx.\right)$$

x	0	1	2	3	4	5	6	7	8	9
0.50	0.52050	52138	52226	52313	52401	52488	52576	52663	52750	52837
0.51	0.52924	53011	53098	53185	53272	53358	53445	53531	53617	53704
0.52	0.53790	53876	53962	54048	54134	54219	54305	54390	54476	54561
0.53	0.54646	54732	54817	54902	54987	55071	55156	55241	55325	55410
0.54	0.55494	55578	55662	55746	55830	55914	55998	56082	56165	56249
0.55	0.56332	56416	56499	56582	56665	56748	56831	56914	56996	57079
0.56	0.57162	57244	57326	57409	57491	57573	57655	57737	57818	57900
0.57	0.57982	58063	58144	58226	58307	58388	58469	58550	58631	58712
0.58	0.58792	58873	58953	59034	59114	59194	59274	59354	59434	59514
0.59	0.59594	59673	59753	59832	59912	59991	60070	60149	60228	60307
0.60	0.60386	60464	60543	60621	60700	60778	60856	60934	61012	61090
0.61	0.61168	61246	61323	61401	61478	61556	61633	61710	61787	61864
0.62	0.61941	62018	62095	62171	62248	62324	62400	62477	62553	62629
0.63	0.62705	62780	62856	62932	63007	63083	63158	63233	63309	63384
0.64	0.63459	63533	63608	63683	63757	63832	63906	63981	64055	64129
0.65	0.64203	64277	64351	64424	64498	64572	64645	64718	64791	64865
0.66	0.64938	65011	65083	65156	65229	65301	65374	65446	65519	65591
0.67	0.65663	65735	65807	65878	65950	66022	66093	66165	66236	66307
0.68	0.66378	66449	66520	66591	66662	66732	66803	66873	66944	67014
0.69	0.67084	67154	67224	67294	67364	67433	67503	67572	67642	67711
0.70	0.67780	67849	67918	67987	68056	68125	68193	68262	68330	68398
0.71	0.68467	68535	68603	68671	68/38	68806	68874	68941	69009	69076
0.72	0.69143	69210	69278	69344	69411	69478	69545	69611	69678	69744
0.73	0.69810	69877	69943	70009	70075	70140	70206	70272	70337	70403
0.74	0.70468	70533	70598	70663	70728	70793	70858	70922	70987	71051
0.75	0.71116	71180	71244	71308	71372	71436	71500	71563	71627	71690
0.76	0.71754	71817	71880	71943	72006	72069	72132	72195	72257	72320
0.77	0.72382	72444	72507	72569	72631	72693	72755	72816	72878	72940
0.78	0.73001	73062	73124	73185	73246	73307	73368	73429	73489	73550
0.79	0.73610	73671	73731	73791	73851	73911	73971	74031	74091	74151
0.80	0.74210	74270	74329	74388	74447	74506	74565	74624	74683	74742
0.81	0.74800	74859	74917	74976	75034	75092	75150	75208	75266	75323
0.82	0.75381	75439	75496	75553	75611	75668	75725	75782	75839	75896
0.83	0.75952	76009	76066	76122	76178	76234	76291	76347	76403	76459
0.84	0.76514	76570	76626	76681	76736	76792	76847	76902	76957	77012
0.85	0.77067	77122	77176	77231	77285	77340	77394	77448	77502	77556
0.86	0.77610	77664	77718	77771	77825	77878	77932	77985	78038	78091
0.87	0.78144	78197	78250	78302	78355	78408	78460	78512	78565	78617
0.88	0.78669	78721	78773	78824	78876	78928	78979	79031	79082	79133
0.89	0.79184	79235	79286	79337	79388	79439	79489	79540	79590	79641
0.90	0.79691	79741	79791	79841	79891	79941	79990	80040	80090	80139
0.91	0.80188	80238	80287	80336	80385	80434	80482	80531	80580	80628
0.92	0.80677	80725	80773	80822	80870	80918	80966	81013	81061	81109
0.93	0.81156	81204	81251	81299	81346	81393	81440	81487	81534	81580
0.94	0.81627	81674	81720	81767	81813	81859	81905	81951	81997	82043
0.95	0.82089	82135	82180	82226	82271	82317	82362	82407	82452	82497
0.96	0.82542	82587	82632	82677	82721	82766	82810	82855	82899	82943
0.97	0.82987	83031	83075	83119	83162	83206	83250	83293	83337	83380
0.98	0.83423	83466	83509	83552	83595	83638	83681	83723	83766	83808
0.99	0.83851	83893	83935	83977	84020	84061	84103	84145	84187	84229

TABLES.

The Probability Integral.

$$\left(\frac{2}{\sqrt{\pi}} \int_0^x e^{-x^2} dx. \right)$$

x	0	1	2	3	4	5	6	7	8	9
1.00	0.84270	84312	84353	84394	84435	84477	84518	84559	84600	84640
1.01	0.84681	84722	84762	84803	84843	84883	84924	84964	85004	85044
1.02	0.85084	85124	85163	85203	85243	85282	85322	85361	85400	85439
1.03	0.85478	85517	85556	85595	85634	85673	85711	85750	85788	85827
1.04	0.85865	85903	85941	85979	86017	86055	86093	86131	86169	86206
1.05	0.86244	86281	86318	86356	86393	86430	86467	86504	86541	86578
1.06	0.86614	86651	86688	86724	86760	86797	86833	86869	86905	86941
1.07	0.86977	87013	87049	87085	87120	87156	87191	87227	87262	87297
1.08	0.87333	87368	87403	87438	87473	87507	87542	87577	87611	87646
1.09	0.87680	87715	87749	87783	87817	87851	87885	87919	87953	87987
1.10	0.88021	88054	88088	88121	88155	88188	88221	88254	88287	88320
1.11	0.88353	88386	88419	88452	88484	88517	88549	88582	88614	88647
1.12	0.88679	88711	88743	88775	88807	88807	88871	88902	88934	88966
1.13	0.88997	89029	89060	89091	89122	89154	89185	89216	89247	89277
1.14	0.89308	89339	89370	89400	89431	89461	89492	89522	89552	89582
1.15	0.89612	89642	89672	89702	89732	89762	89792	89821	89851	89880
1.16	0.89910	89939	89968	89997	90027	90056	90085	90114	90142	90171
1.17	0.90200	90229	90257	90286	90314	90343	90371	90399	90428	90456
1.18	0.90484	90512	90540	90568	90595	90623	90651	90678	90706	90733
1.19	0.90761	90788	90815	90843	90870	90897	90924	90951	90978	91005
1.20	0.91031	91058	91085	91111	91138	91164	91191	91217	91243	91269
1.21	0.91296	91322	91348	91374	91399	91425	91451	91477	91502	91528
1.22	0.91553	91579	91604	91630	91655	91680	91705	91730	91755	91780
1.23	0.91805	91830	91855	91879	91904	91929	91953	91978	92002	92026
1.24	0.92051	92075	92099	92123	92147	92171	92195	92219	92243	92266
1.25	0.92290	92314	92337	92361	92384	92408	92431	92454	92477	92500
1.26	0.92524	92547	92570	92593	92615	92638	92661	92684	92706	92729
1.27	0.92751	92774	92796	92819	92841	92863	92885	92907	92929	92951
1.28	0.92973	92995	93017	93039	93061	93082	93104	93126	93147	93168
1.29	0.93190	93211	93232	93254	93275	93296	93317	93338	93359	93380
1.30	0.93401	93422	93442	93463	93484	93504	93525	93545	93566	93586
1.31	0.93606	93627	93647	93667	93687	93707	93727	93747	93767	93787
1.32	0.93807	93826	93846	93866	93885	93905	93924	93944	93963	93982
1.33	0.94002	94021	94040	94059	94078	94097	94116	94135	94154	94173
1.34	0.94191	94210	94229	94247	94266	94284	94303	94321	94340	94358
1.35	0.94376	94394	94413	94431	94449	94467	94485	94503	94521	94538
1.36	0.94556	94574	94592	94609	94627	94644	94662	94679	94697	94714
1.37	0.94731	94748	94766	94783	94800	94817	94834	94851	94868	94885
1.38	0.94902	94918	94935	94952	94968	94985	95002	95018	95035	95051
1.39	0.95067	95084	95100	95116	95132	95148	95165	95181	95197	95213
1.40	0.95229	95244	95260	95276	95292	95307	95323	95339	95354	95370
1.41	0.95385	95401	95416	95431	95447	95462	95477	95492	95507	95523
1.42	0.95538	95553	95568	95582	95597	95612	95627	95642	95656	95671
1.43	0.95686	95700	95715	95729	95744	95758	95773	95787	95801	95815
1.44	0.95830	95844	95858	95872	95886	95900	95914	95928	95942	95956
1.45	0.95970	95983	95997	96011	96024	96038	96051	96065	96078	96092
1.46	0.96105	96119	96132	96145	96159	96172	96185	96198	96211	96224
1.47	0.96237	96250	96263	96276	96289	96302	96315	96327	96340	96353
1.48	0.96365	96378	96391	96403	96416	96428	96440	96453	96465	96478
1.49	0.96490	96502	96514	96526	96539	96551	96563	96575	96587	96599

The Probability Integral.

$$\left(\frac{2}{\sqrt{\pi}}\int_0^x e^{-x^2}dx.\right)$$

x	0	2	4	6	8	x	0	2	4	6	8
1.50	0.96611	96634	96658	96681	96705	2.00	0.99532	99536	99540	99544	99548
1.51	0.96728	96751	96774	96796	96819	2.01	0.99552	99556	99560	99564	99568
1.52	0.96841	96864	96886	96908	96930	2.02	0.99572	99576	99580	99583	99587
1.53	0.96952	96973	96995	97016	97037	2.03	0.99591	99594	99598	99601	99605
1.54	0.97059	97080	97100	97121	97142	2.04	0.99609	99612	99616	99619	99622
1.55	0.97162	97183	97203	97223	97243	2.05	0.99626	99629	99633	99636	99639
1.56	0.97263	97283	97302	97322	97341	2.06	0.99642	99646	99649	99652	99655
1.57	0.97360	97379	97398	97417	97436	2.07	0.99658	99661	99664	99667	99670
1.58	0.97455	97473	97492	97510	97528	2.08	0.99673	99676	99679	99682	99685
1.59	0.97546	97564	97582	97600	97617	2.09	0.99688	99691	99694	99697	99699
1.60	0.97635	97652	97670	97687	97704	2.10	0.99702	99705	99707	99710	99713
1.61	0.97721	97738	97754	97771	97787	2.11	0.99715	99718	99721	99723	99726
1.62	0.97804	97820	97836	97852	97868	2.12	0.99728	99731	99733	99736	99738
1.63	0.97884	97900	97916	97931	97947	2.13	0.99741	99743	99745	99748	99750
1.64	0.97962	97977	97993	98008	98023	2.14	0.99753	99755	99757	99759	99762
1.65	0.98038	98052	98067	98082	98096	2.15	0.99764	99766	99768	99770	99773
1.66	0.98110	98125	98139	98153	98167	2.16	0.99775	99777	99779	99781	99783
1.67	0.98181	98195	98209	98222	98236	2.17	0.99785	99787	99789	99791	99793
1.68	0.98249	98263	98276	98289	98302	2.18	0.99795	99797	99799	99801	99803
1.69	0.98315	98328	98341	98354	98366	2.19	0.99805	99806	99808	99810	99812
1.70	0.98379	98392	98404	98416	98429	2.20	0.99814	99815	99817	99819	99821
1.71	0.98441	98453	98465	98477	98489	2.21	0.99822	99824	99826	99827	99829
1.72	0.98500	98512	98524	98535	98546	2.22	0.99831	99832	99834	99836	99837
1.73	0.98558	98569	98580	98591	98602	2.23	0.99839	99840	99842	99843	99845
1.74	0.98613	98624	98635	98646	98657	2.24	0.99846	99848	99849	99851	99852
1.75	0.98667	98678	98688	98699	98709	2.25	0.99854	99855	99857	99858	99859
1.76	0.98719	98729	98739	98749	98759	2.26	0.99861	99862	99863	99865	99866
1.77	0.98769	98779	98789	98798	98808	2.27	0.99867	99869	99870	99871	99873
1.78	0.98817	98827	98836	98846	98855	2.28	0.99874	99875	99876	99877	99879
1.79	0.98864	98873	98882	98891	98900	2.29	0.99880	99881	99882	99883	99885
1.80	0.98909	98918	98927	98935	98944	2.30	0.99886	99887	99888	99889	99890
1.81	0.98952	98961	98969	98978	98986	2.31	0.99891	99892	99893	99894	99896
1.82	0.98994	99003	99011	99019	99027	2.32	0.99897	99898	99899	99900	99901
1.83	0.99035	99043	99050	99058	99066	2.33	0.99902	99903	99904	99905	99906
1.84	0.99074	99081	99089	99096	99104	2.34	0.99906	99907	99908	99909	99910
1.85	0.99111	99118	99126	99133	99140	2.35	0.99911	99912	99913	99914	99915
1.86	0.99147	99154	99161	99168	99175	2.36	0.99915	99916	99917	99918	99919
1.87	0.99182	99189	99196	99202	99209	2.37	0.99920	99920	99921	99922	99923
1.88	0.99216	99222	99229	99235	99242	2.38	0.99924	99924	99925	99926	99927
1.89	0.99248	99254	99261	99267	99273	2.39	0.99928	99928	99929	99930	99930
1.90	0.99279	99285	99291	99297	99303	2.40	0.99931	99932	99933	99933	99934
1.91	0.99309	99315	99321	99326	99332	2.41	0.99935	99935	99936	99937	99937
1.92	0.99338	99343	99349	99355	99360	2.42	0.99938	99939	99939	99940	99940
1.93	0.99366	99371	99376	99382	99387	2.43	0.99941	99942	99942	99943	99943
1.94	0.99392	99397	99403	99408	99413	2.44	0.99944	99945	99945	99946	99946
1.95	0.99418	99423	99428	99433	99438	2.45	0.99947	99947	99948	99949	99949
1.96	0.99443	99447	99452	99457	99462	2.46	0.99950	99950	99951	99951	99952
1.97	0.99466	99471	99476	99480	99485	2.47	0.99952	99953	99953	99954	99954
1.98	0.99489	99494	99498	99502	99507	2.48	0.99955	99955	99956	99956	99957
1.99	0.99511	99515	99520	99524	99528	2.49	0.99957	99958	99958	99958	99959
2.00	0.99532	99536	99540	99544	99548	2.50	0.99959	99960	99960	99961	99961

The Probability Integral.

$$\left(\frac{2}{\sqrt{\pi}}\int_0^x e^{-x^2}dx.\right)$$

x	0	1	2	3	4	5	6	7	8	9
2.5	0.99959	99961	99963	99965	99967	99969	99971	99972	99974	99975
2.6	0.99976	99978	99979	99980	99981	99982	99983	99984	99985	99986
2.7	0.99987	99987	99988	99989	99989	99990	99991	99991	99992	99992
2.8	0.99992	99993	99993	99994	99994	99994	99995	99995	99995	99996
2.9	0.99996	99996	99996	99997	99997	99997	99997	99997	99997	99998
3.0	0.99998	99998	99998	99998	99998	99998	99998	99998	99999	99999

The value, I, of the Probability Integral may always be found from the convergent series

$$I = \frac{2}{\sqrt{\pi}}\left(x - \frac{x^3}{3\cdot 1!} + \frac{x^5}{5\cdot 2!} - \frac{x^7}{7\cdot 3!} + \cdots\right),$$

but for large values of x, the semiconvergent series

$$I = 1 - \frac{e^{-x^2}}{x\sqrt{\pi}}\left(1 - \frac{1}{2\,x^2} + \frac{1\cdot 3}{(2x^2)^2} - \frac{1\cdot 3\cdot 5}{(2x^2)^3} + \cdots\right)$$

is convenient.

Values of the Complete Elliptic Integrals, K and E, for Different Values of the Modulus, k.

$$K = \int_0^{\frac{\pi}{2}} \frac{dz}{\sqrt{1 - k^2 \sin^2 z}}; \quad E = \int_0^{\frac{\pi}{2}} \sqrt{1 - k^2 \sin^2 z} \cdot dz.$$

$\sin^{-1} k$	K	E	$\sin^{-1} k$	K	E	$\sin^{-1} k$	K	E
0°	1.5708	1.5708	30°	1.6858	1.4675	60°	2.1565	1.2111
1°	1.5709	1.5707	31°	1.6941	1.4608	61°	2.1842	1.2015
2°	1.5713	1.5703	32°	1.7028	1.4539	62°	2.2132	1.1920
3°	1.5719	1.5697	33°	1.7119	1.4469	63°	2.2435	1.1824
4°	1.5727	1.5689	34°	1.7214	1.4397	64°	2.2754	1.1732
5°	1.5738	1.5678	35°	1.7312	1.4323	65°	2.3088	1.1638
6°	1.5751	1.5665	36°	1.7415	1.4248	66°	2.3439	1.1545
7°	1.5767	1.5649	37°	1.7522	1.4171	67°	2.3809	1.1453
8°	1.5785	1.5632	38°	1.7633	1.4092	68°	2.4198	1.1362
9°	1.5805	1.5611	39°	1.7748	1.4013	69°	2.4610	1.1272
10°	1.5828	1.5589	40°	1.7868	1.3931	70°	2.5046	1.1184
11°	1.5854	1.5564	41°	1.7992	1.3849	71°	2.5507	1.1096
12°	1.5882	1.5537	42°	1.8122	1.3765	72°	2.5998	1.1011
13°	1.5913	1.5507	43°	1.8256	1.3680	73°	2.6521	1.0927
14°	1.5946	1.5476	44°	1.8396	1.3594	74°	2.7081	1.0844
15°	1.5981	1.5442	45°	1.8541	1.3506	75°	2.7681	1.0764
16°	1.6020	1.5405	46°	1.8691	1.3418	76°	2.8327	1.0686
17°	1.6061	1.5367	47°	1.8848	1.3329	77°	2.9026	1.0611
18°	1.6105	1.5326	48°	1.9011	1.3238	78°	2.9786	1.0538
19°	1.6151	1.5283	49°	1.9180	1.3147	79°	3.0617	1.0468
20°	1.6200	1.5238	50°	1.9356	1.3055	80°	3.1534	1.0401
21°	1.6252	1.5191	51°	1.9539	1.2963	81°	3.2553	1.0338
22°	1.6307	1.5141	52°	1.9729	1.2870	82°	3.3699	1.0278
23°	1.6365	1.5090	53°	1.9927	1.2776	83°	3.5004	1.0223
24°	1.6426	1.5037	54°	2.0133	1.2681	84°	3.6519	1.0172
25°	1.6490	1.4981	55°	2.0347	1.2587	85°	3.8317	1.0127
26°	1.6557	1.4924	56°	2.0571	1.2492	86°	4.0528	1.0086
27°	1.6627	1.4864	57°	2.0804	1.2397	87°	4.3387	1.0053
28°	1.6701	1.4803	58°	2.1047	1.2301	88°	4.7427	1.0026
29°	1.6777	1.4740	59°	2.1300	1.2206	89°	5.4349	1.0008

TABLES.

Values of $F(k, \phi)$ for Certain Values of k and ϕ.

$$F(k, \phi) = \int_0^\phi \frac{dz}{\sqrt{1 - k^2 \sin^2 z}}.$$

ϕ	$\alpha = \sin^{-1}k.$								
	$0°$	$10°$	$15°$	$30°$	$45°$	$60°$	$75°$	$80°$	$90°$
1°	0.0174	0.0174	0.0174	0.0174	0.0174	0.0174	0.0174	0.0174	0.0174
2°	0.0349	0.0349	0.0349	0.0349	0.0349	0.0349	0.0349	0.0349	0.0349
3°	0.0524	0.0524	0.0524	0.0524	0.0524	0.0524	0.0524	0.0524	0.0524
4°	0.0698	0.0698	0.0698	0.0698	0.0698	0.0699	0.0699	0.0699	0.0699
5°	0.0873	0.0873	0.0873	0.0873	0.0873	0.0874	0.0874	0.0874	0.0874
10°	0.1745	0.1746	0.1746	0.1748	0.1750	0.1752	0.1754	0.1754	0.1754
15°	0.2618	0.2619	0.2620	0.2625	0.2633	0.2641	0.2646	0.2647	0.2648
20°	0.3491	0.3493	0.3495	0.3508	0.3526	0.3545	0.3559	0.3562	0.3564
25°	0.4363	0.4367	0.4372	0.4397	0.4433	0.4470	0.4498	0.4504	0.4509
30°	0.5236	0.5243	0.5251	0.5294	0.5356	0.5422	0.5474	0.5484	0.5493
35°	0.6109	0.6119	0.6132	0.6200	0.6300	0.6408	0.6495	0.6513	0.6528
40°	0.6981	0.6997	0.7016	0.7116	0.7267	0.7436	0.7574	0.7604	0.7629
45°	0.7854	0.7876	0.7902	0.8044	0.8260	0.8512	0.8727	0.8774	0.8814
50°	0.8727	0.8756	0.8792	0.8982	0.9283	0.9646	0.9971	1.0044	1.0107
55°	0.9599	0.9637	0.9683	0.9933	1.0337	1.0848	1.1331	1.1444	1.1542
60°	1.0472	1.0519	1.0577	1.0896	1.1424	1.2125	1.2837	1.3014	1.3170
65°	1.1345	1.1402	1.1474	1.1869	1.2545	1.3489	1.4532	1.4810	1.5064
70°	1.2217	1.2286	1.2373	1.2853	1.3697	1.4944	1.6468	1.6918	1.7354
75°	1.3090	1.3171	1.3273	1.3846	1.4879	1.6492	1.8714	1.9468	2.0276
80°	1.3963	1.4056	1.4175	1.4846	1.6085	1.8125	2.1339	2.2653	2.4362
85°	1.4835	1.4942	1.5078	1.5850	1.7308	1.9826	2.4366	2.6694	3.1313
86°	1.5010	1.5120	1.5259	1.6052	1.7554	2.0172	2.5013	2.7612	3.3547
87°	1.5184	1.5297	1.5439	1.6253	1.7801	2.0519	2.5670	2.8561	3.6425
88°	1.5359	1.5474	1.5620	1.6454	1.8047	2.0867	2.6336	2.9537	4.0481
89°	1.5533	1.5651	1.5801	1.6656	1.8294	2.1216	2.7007	3.0530	4.7414
90°	1.5708	1.5828	1.5981	1.6858	1.8541	2.1565	2.7681	3.1534	Inf.

Values of $E(k, \phi)$ for Certain Values of k and ϕ.

$$E(k, \phi) = \int_0^\phi \sqrt{1 - k^2 \sin^2 z} \cdot dz.$$

ϕ	$\alpha = \sin^{-1} k.$								
	0°	10°	15°	30°	45°	60°	75°	80°	90°
1°	0.0174	0.0174	0.0174	0.0174	0.0174	0.0174	0.0174	0.0174	0.0174
2°	0.0349	0.0349	0.0349	0.0349	0.0349	0.0349	0.0349	0.0349	0.0349
3°	0.0524	0.0524	0.0524	0.0524	0.0524	0.0523	0.0523	0.0523	0.0523
4°	0.0698	0.0698	0.0698	0.0698	0.0698	0.0698	0.0698	0.0698	0.0698
5°	0.0873	0.0873	0.0873	0.0872	0.0872	0.0872	0.0872	0.0872	0.0872
10°	0.1745	0.1745	0.1745	0.1743	0.1741	0.1739	0.1737	0.1737	0.1736
15°	0.2618	0.2617	0.2616	0.2611	0.2603	0.2596	0.2590	0.2589	0.2588
20°	0.3491	0.3489	0.3486	0.3473	0.3456	0.3438	0.3425	0.3422	0.3420
25°	0.4363	0.4359	0.4354	0.4330	0.4296	0.4261	0.4236	0.4230	0.4226
30°	0.5236	0.5229	0.5221	0.5179	0.5120	0.5061	0.5016	0.5007	0.5000
35°	0.6109	0.6098	0.6085	0.6019	0.5928	0.5833	0.5762	0.5748	0.5736
40°	0.6981	0.6966	0.6947	0.6851	0.6715	0.6575	0.6468	0.6446	0.6428
45°	0.7854	0.7832	0.7806	0.7672	0.7482	0.7282	0.7129	0.7097	0.7071
50°	0.8727	0.8698	0.8663	0.8483	0.8226	0.7954	0.7741	0.7697	0.7660
55°	0.9599	0.9562	0.9517	0.9284	0.8949	0.8588	0.8302	0.8242	0.8192
60°	1.0472	1.0426	1.0368	1.0076	0.9650	0.9184	0.8808	0.8728	0.8660
65°	1.1345	1.1288	1.1218	1.0858	1.0329	0.9743	0.9258	0.9152	0.9063
70°	1.2217	1.2149	1.2065	1.1632	1.0990	1.0266	0.9652	0.9514	0.9397
75°	1.3090	1.3010	1.2911	1.2399	1.1635	1.0759	0.9992	0.9814	0.9659
80°	1.3963	1.3870	1.3755	1.3161	1.2266	1.1225	1.0282	1.0054	0.9848
85°	1.4835	1.4729	1.4598	1.3919	1.2889	1.1673	1.0534	1.0244	0.9962
86°	1.5010	1.4901	1.4767	1.4070	1.3012	1.1761	1.0581	1.0277	0.9976
87°	1.5184	1.5073	1.4936	1.4221	1.3136	1.1848	1.0628	1.0309	0.9986
88°	1.5359	1.5245	1.5104	1.4372	1.3260	1.1936	1.0674	1.0340	0.9994
89°	1.5533	1.5417	1.5273	1.4524	1.3383	1.2023	1.0719	1.0371	0.9998
90°	1.5708	1.5589	1.5442	1.4675	1.3506	1.2111	1.0764	1.0401	1.0000

Hyperbolic Sines [$\sinh x = \tfrac{1}{2}(e^x - e^{-x})$].

x	0	1	2	3	4	5	6	7	8	9	Avg. diff.
0.0	.0000	.0100	.0200	.0300	.0400	.0500	.0600	.0701	.0801	.0901	100
1	.1002	.1102	.1203	.1304	.1405	.1506	.1607	.1708	.1810	.1911	101
2	.2013	.2115	.2218	.2320	.2423	.2526	.2629	.2733	.2837	.2941	103
3	.3045	.3150	.3255	.3360	.3466	.3572	.3678	.3785	.3892	.4000	106
4	.4108	.4216	.4325	.4434	.4543	.4653	.4764	.4875	.4986	.5098	110
0.5	.5211	.5324	.5438	.5552	.5666	.5782	.5897	.6014	.6131	.6248	116
6	.6367	.6485	.6605	.6725	.6846	.6967	.7090	.7213	.7336	.7461	122
7	.7586	.7712	.7838	.7966	.8094	.8223	.8353	.8484	.8615	.8748	130
8	.8881	.9015	.9150	.9286	.9423	.9561	.9700	.9840	.9981	1.012	138
9	1.027	1.041	1.055	1.070	1.085	1.099	1.114	1.129	1.145	1.160	15
1.0	1.175	1.191	1.206	1.222	1.238	1.254	1.270	1.286	1.303	1.319	16
1	1.336	1.352	1.369	1.386	1.403	1.421	1.438	1.456	1.474	1.491	17
2	1.509	1.528	1.546	1.564	1.583	1.602	1.621	1.640	1.659	1.679	19
3	1.698	1.718	1.738	1.758	1.779	1.799	1.820	1.841	1.862	1.883	21
4	1.904	1.926	1.948	1.970	1.992	2.014	2.037	2.060	2.083	2.106	22
1.5	2.129	2.153	2.177	2.201	2.225	2.250	2.274	2.299	2.324	2.350	25
6	2.376	2.401	2.428	2.454	2.481	2.507	2.535	2.562	2.590	2.617	27
7	2.646	2.674	2.703	2.732	2.761	2.790	2.820	2.850	2.881	2.911	30
8	2.942	2.973	3.005	3.037	3.069	3.101	3.134	3.167	3.200	3.234	33
9	3.268	3.303	3.337	3.372	3.408	3.443	3.479	3.516	3.552	3.589	36
2.0	3.627	3.665	3.703	3.741	3.780	3.820	3.859	3.899	3.940	3.981	39
1	4.022	4.064	4.106	4.148	4.191	4.234	4.278	4.322	4.367	4.412	44
2	4.457	4.503	4.549	4.596	4.643	4.691	4.739	4.788	4.837	4.887	48
3	4.937	4.988	5.039	5.090	5.142	5.195	5.248	5.302	5.356	5.411	53
4	5.466	5.522	5.578	5.635	5.693	5.751	5.810	5.869	5.929	5.989	58
2.5	6.050	6.112	6.174	6.237	6.300	6.365	6.429	6.495	6.561	6.627	64
6	6.695	6.763	6.831	6.901	6.971	7.042	7.113	7.185	7.258	7.332	71
7	7.406	7.481	7.557	7.634	7.711	7.789	7.868	7.948	8.028	8.110	79
8	8.192	8.275	8.359	8.443	8.529	8.615	8.702	8.790	8.879	8.969	87
9	9.060	9.151	9.244	9.337	9.431	9.527	9.623	9.720	9.819	9.918	96
3.0	10.02	10.12	10.22	10.32	10.43	10.53	10.64	10.75	10.86	10.97	11
1	11.08	11.19	11.30	11.42	11.53	11.65	11.76	11.88	12.00	12.12	12
2	12.25	12.37	12.49	12.62	12.75	12.88	13.01	13.14	13.27	13.40	13
3	13.54	13.67	13.81	13.95	14.09	14.23	14.38	14.52	14.67	14.82	14
4	14.97	15.12	15.27	15.42	15.58	15.73	15.89	16.05	16.21	16.38	16
3.5	16.54	16.71	16.88	17.05	17.22	17.39	17.57	17.74	17.92	18.10	17
6	18.29	18.47	18.66	18.84	19.03	19.22	19.42	19.61	19.81	20.01	19
7	20.21	20.41	20.62	20.83	21.04	21.25	21.46	21.68	21.90	22.12	21
8	22.34	22.56	22.79	23.02	23.25	23.49	23.72	23.96	24.20	24.45	24
9	24.69	24.94	25.19	25.44	25.70	25.96	26.22	26.48	26.75	27.02	26
4.0	27.29	27.56	27.84	28.12	28.40	28.69	28.98	29.27	29.56	29.86	29
1	30.16	30.47	30.77	31.08	31.39	31.71	32.03	32.35	32.68	33.00	32
2	33.34	33.67	34.01	34.35	34.70	35.05	35.40	35.75	36.11	36.48	35
3	36.84	37.21	37.59	37.97	38.35	38.73	39.12	39.52	39.91	40.31	39
4	40.72	41.13	41.54	41.96	42.38	42.81	43.24	43.67	44.11	44.56	43
4.5	45.00	45.46	45.91	46.37	46.84	47.31	47.79	48.27	48.75	49.24	47
6	49.74	50.24	50.74	51.25	51.77	52.29	52.81	53.34	53.88	54.42	52
7	54.97	55.52	56.08	56.64	57.21	57.79	58.37	58.96	59.55	60.15	58
8	60.75	61.36	61.98	62.60	63.23	63.87	64.51	65.16	65.81	66.47	64
9	67.14	67.82	68.50	69.19	69.88	70.58	71.29	72.01	72.73	73.46	71
5.0	74.20										

If $x > 5$, $\sinh x = \tfrac{1}{2}(e^x)$ and $\log_{10} \sinh x = (0.4343)x + 0.6990 - 1$, correct to four significant figures.

Hyperbolic Cosines $[\cosh x = \tfrac{1}{2}(e^x + e^{-x})]$.

x	0	1	2	3	4	5	6	7	8	9	Avg. diff.
0.0	1.000	1.000	1.000	1.000	1.001	1.001	1.002	1.002	1.003	1.004	1
1	1.005	1.006	1.007	1.008	1.010	1.011	1.013	1.014	1.016	1.018	2
2	1.020	1.022	1.024	1.027	1.029	1.031	1.034	1.037	1.039	1.042	3
3	1.045	1.048	1.052	1.055	1.058	1.062	1.066	1.069	1.073	1.077	4
4	1.081	1.085	1.090	1.094	1.098	1.103	1.108	1.112	1.117	1.122	5
0.5	1.128	1.133	1.138	1.144	1.149	1.155	1.161	1.167	1.173	1.179	6
6	1.185	1.192	1.198	1.205	1.212	1.219	1.226	1.233	1.240	1.248	7
7	1.255	1.263	1.271	1.278	1.287	1.295	1.303	1.311	1.320	1.329	8
8	1.337	1.346	1.355	1.365	1.374	1.384	1.393	1.403	1.413	1.423	10
9	1.433	1.443	1.454	1.465	1.475	1.486	1.497	1.509	1.520	1.531	11
1.0	1.543	1.555	1.567	1.579	1.591	1.604	1.616	1.629	1.642	1.655	13
1	1.669	1.682	1.696	1.709	1.723	1.737	1.752	1.766	1.781	1.796	14
2	1.811	1.826	1.841	1.857	1.872	1.888	1.905	1.921	1.937	1.954	16
3	1.971	1.988	2.005	2.023	2.040	2.058	2.076	2.095	2.113	2.132	18
4	2.151	2.170	2.189	2.209	2.229	2.249	2.269	2.290	2.310	2.331	20
1.5	2.352	2.374	2.395	2.417	2.439	2.462	2.484	2.507	2.530	2.554	23
6	2.577	2.601	2.625	2.650	2.675	2.700	2.725	2.750	2.776	2.802	25
7	2.828	2.855	2.882	2.909	2.936	2.964	2.992	3.021	3.049	3.078	28
8	3.107	3.137	3.167	3.197	3.228	3.259	3.290	3.321	3.353	3.385	31
9	3.418	3.451	3.484	3.517	3.551	3.585	3.620	3.655	3.690	3.726	34
2.0	3.762	3.799	3.835	3.873	3.910	3.948	3.987	4.026	4.065	4.104	38
1	4.144	4.185	4.226	4.267	4.309	4.351	4.393	4.436	4.480	4.524	42
2	4.568	4.613	4.658	4.704	4.750	4.797	4.844	4.891	4.939	4.988	47
3	5.037	5.087	5.137	5.188	5.239	5.290	5.343	5.395	5.449	5.503	52
4	5.557	5.612	5.667	5.723	5.780	5.837	5.895	5.954	6.013	6.072	58
2.5	6.132	6.193	6.255	6.317	6.379	6.443	6.507	6.571	6.636	6.702	64
6	6.769	6.836	6.904	6.973	7.042	7.112	7.183	7.255	7.327	7.400	70
7	7.473	7.548	7.623	7.699	7.776	7.853	7.932	8.011	8.091	8.171	78
8	8.253	8.335	8.418	8.502	8.587	8.673	8.759	8.847	8.935	9.024	86
9	9.115	9.206	9.298	9.391	9.484	9.579	9.675	9.772	9.869	9.968	95
3.0	10.07	10.17	10.27	10.37	10.48	10.58	10.69	10.79	10.90	11.01	11
1	11.12	11.23	11.35	11.46	11.57	11.69	11.81	11.92	12.04	12.16	12
2	12.29	12.41	12.53	12.66	12.79	12.91	13.04	13.17	13.31	13.44	13
3	13.57	13.71	13.85	13.99	14.13	14.27	14.41	14.56	14.70	14.85	14
4	15.00	15.15	15.30	15.45	15.61	15.77	15.92	16.08	16.25	16.41	16
3.5	16.57	16.74	16.91	17.08	17.25	17.42	17.60	17.77	17.95	18.13	17
6	18.31	18.50	18.68	18.87	19.06	19.25	19.44	19.64	19.84	20.03	19
7	20.24	20.44	20.64	20.85	21.06	21.27	21.49	21.70	21.92	22.14	21
8	22.36	22.59	22.81	23.04	23.27	23.51	23.74	23.98	24.22	24.47	23
9	24.71	24.96	25.21	25.46	25.72	25.98	26.24	26.50	26.77	27.04	26
4.0	27.31	27.58	27.86	28.14	28.42	28.71	29.00	29.29	29.58	29.88	29
1	30.18	30.48	30.79	31.10	31.41	31.72	32.04	32.37	32.69	33.02	32
2	33.35	33.69	34.02	34.37	34.71	35.06	35.41	35.77	36.13	36.49	35
3	36.86	37.23	37.60	37.98	38.36	38.75	39.13	39.53	39.93	40.33	39
4	40.73	41.14	41.55	41.97	42.39	42.82	43.25	43.68	44.12	44.57	43
4.5	45.01	45.47	45.92	46.38	46.85	47.32	47.80	48.28	48.76	49.25	47
6	49.75	50.25	50.75	51.26	51.78	52.30	52.82	53.35	53.89	54.43	52
7	54.98	55.53	56.09	56.65	57.22	57.80	58.38	58.96	59.56	60.15	58
8	60.76	61.37	61.99	62.61	63.24	63.87	64.52	65.16	65.82	66.48	64
9	67.15	67.82	68.50	69.19	69.89	70.59	71.30	72.02	72.74	73.47	71
5.0	74.21										

If $x > 5$, $\cosh x = \tfrac{1}{2}(e^x)$ and $\log_{10} \cosh x = (0.4343)x + 0.6990 - 1$, correct to four significant figures.

Hyperbolic Tangents [$\tanh x = (e^x - e^{-x})/(e^x + e^{-x}) = \sinh x/\cosh x$].

x	0	1	2	3	4	5	6	7	8	9	Avg. diff.
0.0	.0000	.0100	.0200	.0300	.0400	.0500	.0599	.0699	.0798	.0898	100
1	.0997	.1096	.1194	.1293	.1391	.1489	.1587	.1684	.1781	.1878	98
2	.1974	.2070	.2165	.2260	.2355	.2449	.2543	.2636	.2729	.2821	94
3	.2913	.3004	.3095	.3185	.3275	.3364	.3452	.3540	.3627	.3714	89
4	.3800	.3885	.3969	.4053	.4136	.4219	.4301	.4382	.4462	.4542	82
0.5	.4621	.4700	.4777	.4854	.4930	.5005	.5080	.5154	.5227	.5299	75
6	.5370	.5441	.5511	.5581	.5649	.5717	.5784	.5850	.5915	.5980	67
7	.6044	.6107	.6169	.6231	.6291	.6352	.6411	.6469	.6527	.6584	60
8	.6640	.6696	.6751	.6805	.6858	.6911	.6963	.7014	.7064	.7114	52
9	.7163	.7211	.7259	.7306	.7352	.7398	.7443	.7487	.7531	.7574	45
1.0	.7616	.7658	.7699	.7739	.7779	.7818	.7857	.7895	.7932	.7969	39
1	.8005	.8041	.8076	.8110	.8144	.8178	.8210	.8243	.8275	.8306	33
2	.8337	.8367	.8397	.8426	.8455	.8483	.8511	.8538	.8565	.8591	28
3	.8617	.8643	.8668	.8693	.8717	.8741	.8764	.8787	.8810	.8832	24
4	.8854	.8875	.8896	.8917	.8937	.8957	.8977	.8996	.9015	.9033	20
1.5	.9052	.9069	.9087	.9104	.9121	.9138	.9154	.9170	.9186	.9202	17
6	.9217	.9232	.9246	.9261	.9275	.9289	.9302	.9316	.9329	.9342	14
7	.9354	.9367	.9379	.9391	.9402	.9414	.9425	.9436	.9447	.9458	11
8	.9468	.9478	.9488	.9498	.9508	.9518	.9527	.9536	.9545	.9554	9
9	.9562	.9571	.9579	.9587	.9595	.9603	.9611	.9619	.9626	.9633	8
2.0	.9640	.9647	.9654	.9661	.9668	.9674	.9680	.9687	.9693	.9699	6
1	.9705	.9710	.9716	.9722	.9727	.9732	.9738	.9743	.9748	.9753	5
2	.9757	.9762	.9767	.9771	.9776	.9780	.9785	.9789	.9793	.9797	4
3	.9801	.9805	.9809	.9812	.9816	.9820	.9823	.9827	.9830	.9834	4
4	.9837	.9840	.9843	.9846	.9849	.9852	.9855	.9858	.9861	.9863	3
2.5	.9866	.9869	.9871	.9874	.9876	.9879	.9881	.9884	.9886	.9888	2
6	.9890	.9892	.9895	.9897	.9899	.9901	.9903	.9905	.9906	.9908	2
7	.9910	.9912	.9914	.9915	.9917	.9919	.9920	.9922	.9923	.9925	2
8	.9926	.9928	.9929	.9931	.9932	.9933	.9935	.9936	.9937	.9938	1
2.9	.9940	.9941	.9942	.9943	.9944	.9945	.9946	.9947	.9949	.9950	1
3.	.9951	.9959	.9967	.9973	.9978	.9982	.9985	.9988	.9990	.9992	4
4.	.9993	.9995	.9996	.9996	.9997	.9998	.9998	.9988	.9990	.9992	1
5.	.9999	If $x > 5$, $\tanh x = 1.0000$ to four decimal places.									

Multiples of 0.4343   ($0.43429448 = \log_{10} e$).

x	0	1	2	3	4	5	6	7	8	9
0.	0.0000	0.0434	0.0869	0.1303	0.1737	0.2171	0.2606	0.3040	0.3474	0.3909
1.	0.4343	0.4777	0.5212	0.5646	0.6080	0.6514	0.6949	0.7383	0.7817	0.8252
2.	0.8686	0.9120	0.9554	0.9989	1.0423	1.0857	1.1292	1.1726	1.2160	1.2595
3.	1.3029	1.3463	1.3897	1.4332	1.4766	1.5200	1.5635	1.6069	1.6503	1.6937
4.	1.7372	1.7806	1.8240	1.8675	1.9109	1.9543	1.9978	2.0412	2.0846	2.1280
5.	2.1715	2.2149	2.2583	2.3018	2.3452	2.3886	2.4320	2.4755	2.5189	2.5623
6.	2.6058	2.6492	2.6926	2.7361	2.7795	2.8229	2.8663	2.9098	2.9532	2.9966
7.	3.0401	3.0835	3.1269	3.1703	3.2138	3.2572	3.3006	3.3441	3.3875	3.4309
8.	3.4744	3.5178	3.5612	3.6046	3.6481	3.6915	3.7349	3.7784	3.8218	3.8652
9.	3.9087	3.9521	3.9955	4.0389	4.0824	4.1258	4.1692	4.2127	4.2561	4.2995

Multiples of 2.3026   ($2.3025851 = 1/0.4343$).

x	0	1	2	3	4	5	6	7	8	9
0.	0.0000	0.2303	0.4605	0.6908	0.9210	1.1513	1.3816	1.6118	1.8421	2.0723
1.	2.3026	2.5328	2.7631	2.9934	3.2236	3.4539	3.6842	3.9144	4.1447	4.3749
2.	4.6052	4.8354	5.0657	5.2959	5.5262	5.7565	5.9867	6.2170	6.4472	6.6775
3.	6.9078	7.1380	7.3683	7.5985	7.8288	8.0590	8.2893	8.5196	8.7498	8.9801
4.	9.2103	9.4406	9.6709	9.9011	10.131	10.362	10.592	10.822	11.052	11.283
5.	11.513	11.743	11.973	12.204	12.434	12.664	12.894	13.125	13.355	13.585
6.	13.816	14.046	14.276	14.506	14.737	14.967	15.197	15.427	15.658	15.888
7.	16.118	16.348	16.579	16.809	17.039	17.269	17.500	17.730	17.960	18.190
8.	18.421	18.651	18.881	19.111	19.342	19.572	19.802	20.032	20.263	20.493
9.	20.723	20.954	21.184	21.414	21.644	21.875	22.105	22.335	22.565	22.796

Exponentials [e^n and e^{-n}].

n	e^n	Diff	n	e^n	Diff	n	e^n	n	e^{-n}	Diff	n	e^{-n}	n	e^{-n}
0.00	1.000	10	0.50	1.649	16	1.0	2.718*	0.00	1.000	−10	0.50	.607	1.0	.368*
.01	1.010	10	.51	1.665	17	.1	3.004	.01	0.990	−10	.51	.600	.1	.333
.02	1.020	10	.52	1.682	17	.2	3.320	.02	.980	−10	.52	.595	.2	.301
.03	1.030	11	.53	1.699	17	.3	3.669	.03	.970	−9	.53	.589	.3	.273
.04	1.041	10	.54	1.716	17	.4	4.055	.04	.961	−10	.54	.583	.4	.247
0.05	1.051	11	0.55	1.733	18	1.5	4.482	0.05	.951	−9	0.55	.577	1.5	.223
.06	1.062	11	.56	1.751	17	.6	4.953	.06	.942	−10	.56	.571	.6	.202
.07	1.073	10	.57	1.768	18	.7	5.474	.07	.932	−9	.57	.566	.7	.183
.08	1.083	11	.58	1.786	18	.8	6.050	.08	.923	−9	.58	.560	.8	.165
.09	1.094	11	.59	1.804	18	.9	6.686	.09	.914	−9	.59	.554	.9	.150
0.10	1.105	11	0.60	1.822	18	2.0	7.389	0.10	.905	−9	0.60	.549	2.0	.135
.11	1.116	11	.61	1.840	19	.1	8.166	.11	.896	−9	.61	.543	.1	.122
.12	1.127	12	.62	1.859	19	.2	9.025	.12	.887	−9	.62	.538	.2	.111
.13	1.139	11	.63	1.878	18	.3	9.974	.13	.878	−9	.63	.533	.3	.100
.14	1.150	12	.64	1.896	20	.4	11.02	.14	.869	−8	.64	.527	.4	.0907
0.15	1.162	12	0.65	1.916	19	2.5	12.18	0.15	.861	−9	0.65	.522	2.5	.0821
.16	1.174	11	.66	1.935	19	.6	13.46	.16	.852	−8	.66	.517	.6	.0743
.17	1.185	12	.67	1.954	20	.7	14.88	.17	.844	−9	.67	.512	.7	.0672
.18	1.197	12	.68	1.974	20	.8	16.44	.18	.835	−8	.68	.507	.8	.0608
.19	1.209	12	.69	1.994	20	.9	18.17	.19	.827	−8	.69	.502	.9	.0550
0.20	1.221	13	0.70	2.014	20	3.0	20.09	0.20	.819	−8	0.70	.497	3.0	.0498
.21	1.234	12	.71	2.034	20	.1	22.20	.21	.811	−8	.71	.492	.1	.0450
.22	1.246	13	.72	2.054	21	.2	24.53	.22	.803	−8	.72	.487	.2	.0408
.23	1.259	12	.73	2.075	21	.3	27.11	.23	.795	−8	.73	.482	.3	.0369
.24	1.271	13	.74	2.096	21	.4	29.96	.24	.787	−8	.74	.477	.4	.0334
0.25	1.284	13	0.75	2.117	21	3.5	33.12	0.25	.779	−8	0.75	.472	3.5	.0302
.26	1.297	13	.76	2.138	22	.6	36.60	.26	.771	−8	.76	.468	.6	.0273
.27	1.310	13	.77	2.160	21	.7	40.45	.27	.763	−7	.77	.463	.7	.0247
.28	1.323	13	.78	2.181	22	.8	44.70	.28	.756	−8	.78	.458	.8	.0224
.29	1.336	14	.79	2.203	23	.9	49.40	.29	.748	−7	.79	.454	.9	.0202
0.30	1.350	13	0.80	2.226	22	4.0	54.60	0.30	.741	−8	0.80	.449	4.0	.0183
.31	1.363	14	.81	2.248	22	.1	60.34	.31	.733	−7	.81	.445	.1	.0166
.32	1.377	14	.82	2.270	23	.2	66.69	.32	.726	−7	.82	.440	.2	.0150
.33	1.391	14	.83	2.293	23	.3	73.70	.33	.719	−7	.83	.436	.3	.0136
.34	1.405	14	.84	2.316	24	.4	81.45	.34	.712	−7	.84	.432	.4	.0123
0.35	1.419	14	0.85	2.340	23	4.5	90.02	0.35	.705	−7	0.85	.427	4.5	.0111
.36	1.433	15	.86	2.363	24	5.0	148.4	.36	.698	−7	.86	.423	5.0	.00674
.37	1.448	14	.87	2.387	24	6.0	403.4	37	.691	−7	.87	.419	6.0	.00248
.38	1.462	15	.88	2.411	24	7.0	1097.	.38	.684	−7	.88	.415	7.0	.000912
.39	1.477	15	.89	2.435	25			.39	.677	−7	.89	.411		
0.40	1.492	15	0.90	2.460	24	8.0	2981.	0.40	.670	−6	0.90	.407	8.0	.000335
.41	1.507	15	.91	2.484	25	9.0	8103.	.41	.664	−7	.91	.403	9.0	.000123
.42	1.522	15	.92	2.509	26	10.0	22026.	.42	.657	−6	.92	.399	10.0	.000045
.43	1.537	16	.93	2.535	25	π/2	4.810	.43	.651	−7	.93	.395	π/2	.208
.44	1.553	15	.94	2.560	26	2π/2	23.14	.44	.644	−6	.94	.391	2π/2	.0432
0.45	1.568	16	0.95	2.586	26	3π/2	111.3	0.45	.638	−7	0.95	.387	3π/2	.00898
.46	1.584	16	.96	2.612	26	4π/2	535.5	.46	.631	−6	.96	.383	4π/2	.00187
.47	1.600	16	.97	2.638	26	5π/2	2576.	.47	.625	−6	.97	.379	5π/2	.000388
.48	1.616	16	.98	2.664	27	6π/2	12392.	.48	.619	−6	.98	.375	6π/2	.000081
.49	1.632	17	.99	2.691	27	7π/2	59610.	.49	.613	−6	.99	.372	7π/2	.000017
0.50	1.649		1.00	2.718		8π/2	286751.	0.50	0.607		1.00	.368	8π/2	.000003

* NOTE 1. — Do not interpolate in this column. $e = 2.71828$ $1/e = 0.367879$

$\log_{10} e = 0.4343$ $1/(0.4343) = 2.3026$ $\log_{10}(0.4343) = 1.6378$ $\log_{10}(e^n) = n(0.4343)$

NOTE 2. — This page and the three that precede it are taken from E. V. Huntington's Handbook of Mathematics for Engineers, published by the McGraw-Hill Book Company, Inc.

The Common Logarithms of e^x and e^{-x}.

x	$\log_{10} e^x$	$\log_{10} e^{-x}$
0.00001	0.0000043429	$\bar{1}.9999956571$
0.00002	0.0000086859	$\bar{1}.9999913141$
0.00003	0.0000130288	$\bar{1}.9999869712$
0.00004	0.0000173718	$\bar{1}.9999826282$
0.00005	0.0000217147	$\bar{1}.9999782853$
0.00006	0.0000260577	$\bar{1}.9999739423$
0.00007	0.0000304006	$\bar{1}.9999695994$
0.00008	0.0000347436	$\bar{1}.9999652564$
0.00009	0.0000390865	$\bar{1}.9999609135$
0.00010	0.0000434294	$\bar{1}.9999565706$
0.00020	0.0000863589	$\bar{1}.9999131411$
0.00030	0.0001302883	$\bar{1}.9998697117$
0.00040	0.0001737178	$\bar{1}.9998262822$
0.00050	0.0002171472	$\bar{1}.9997828528$
0.00060	0.0002605767	$\bar{1}.9997394233$
0.00070	0.0003040061	$\bar{1}.9996959939$
0.00080	0.0003474356	$\bar{1}.9996525644$
0.00090	0.0003908650	$\bar{1}.9996091350$
0.00100	0.0004342945	$\bar{1}.9995657055$
0.00200	0.0008685890	$\bar{1}.9991314110$
0.00300	0.0013028834	$\bar{1}.9986971166$
0.00400	0.0017371779	$\bar{1}.9982628221$
0.00500	0.0021714724	$\bar{1}.9978285276$
0.00600	0.0026057669	$\bar{1}.9973942331$
0.00700	0.0030400614	$\bar{1}.9969599386$
0.00800	0.0034743559	$\bar{1}.9965256441$
0.00900	0.0039086503	$\bar{1}.9960913497$
0.01000	0.0043429448	$\bar{1}.9956570552$
0.02000	0.0086858896	$\bar{1}.9913141104$
0.03000	0.0130288345	$\bar{1}.9869711655$
0.04000	0.0173717793	$\bar{1}.9826282207$
0.05000	0.0217147241	$\bar{1}.9782852759$
0.06000	0.0260576689	$\bar{1}.9739423311$
0.07000	0.0304006137	$\bar{1}.9695993863$

TABLES.

x	$\log_{10} e^x$	$\log_{10} e^{-x}$
0.08000	0.0347435586	$\bar{1}$.9652564414
0.09000	0.0390865034	$\bar{1}$.9609134966
0.10000	0.0434294482	$\bar{1}$.9565705518
0.20000	0.0868588964	$\bar{1}$.9131411036
0.30000	0.1302883446	$\bar{1}$.8697116554
0.40000	0.1737177928	$\bar{1}$.8262822072
0.50000	0.2171472410	$\bar{1}$.7828527590
0.60000	0.2605766891	$\bar{1}$.7394233109
0.70000	0.3040061373	$\bar{1}$.6959938627
0.80000	0.3474355855	$\bar{1}$.6525644145
0.90000	0.3908650337	$\bar{1}$.6091349663
1.00000	0.4342944819	$\bar{1}$.5657055181
2.00000	0.8685889638	$\bar{1}$.1314110362
3.00000	1.3028834457	$\bar{2}$.6971165543
4.00000	1.7371779276	$\bar{2}$.2628220724
5.00000	2.1714724095	$\bar{3}$.8285275905
6.00000	2.6057668914	$\bar{3}$.3942331086
7.00000	3.0400613733	$\bar{4}$.9599386267
8.00000	3.4743558552	$\bar{4}$.5256441448
9.00000	3.9086503371	$\bar{4}$.0913496629
10.00000	4.3429448190	$\bar{5}$.6570551810
20.00000	8.6858896381	$\bar{9}$.3141103619
30.00000	13.0288344571	$\overline{14}$.9711655429
40.00000	17.3717792761	$\overline{18}$.6282207239
50.00000	21.7147240952	$\overline{22}$.2852759048
60.00000	26.0576689142	$\overline{27}$.9423310858
70.00000	30.4006137332	$\overline{31}$.5993862668
80.00000	34.7435585523	$\overline{35}$.2564414477
90.00000	39.0865033713	$\overline{40}$.9134966287
100.00000	43.4294481903	$\overline{44}$.5705518097
200.00000	86.8588963807	$\overline{87}$.1411036193
300.00000	130.2883445710	$\overline{131}$.7116554290
400.00000	173.7177927613	$\overline{174}$.2822072387
500.00000	217.1472409516	$\overline{218}$.8527590484

Note: $\log e^{x+y} = \log e^x + \log e^y$. Thus, $\log e^{113.1478} = 49.139465180$.

Five-Place Natural Logarithms.

No.	0	1	2	3	4	5	6	7	8	9	D.
1.00	0.0 0000	0100	0200	0300	0399	0499	0598	0698	0797	0896	100—99
1.01	0.0 0995	1094	1193	1292	1390	1489	1587	1686	1784	1882	99—98
1.02	0.0 1980	2078	2176	2274	2372	2469	2567	2664	2762	2859	98—97
1.03	0.0 2956	3053	3150	3247	3343	3440	3537	3633	3730	3826	97—96
1.04	0.0 3922	4018	4114	4210	4306	4402	4497	4593	4688	4784	96—95
1.05	0.0 4879	4974	5069	5164	5259	5354	5449	5543	5638	5733	95—94
1.06	0.0 5827	5921	6015	6110	6204	6297	6391	6485	6579	6672	94
1.07	0.0 6766	6859	6953	7046	7139	7232	7325	7418	7511	7603	93
1.08	0.0 7696	7789	7881	7973	8066	8158	8250	8342	8434	8526	93—92
1.09	0.0 8618	8709	8801	8893	8984	9075	9167	9258	9349	9430	92—91
1.10	0.0 9531	9622	9713	9803	9894	9985	*0075	0165	0256	0346	91—90
1.11	0.1 0436	0526	0616	0706	0796	0885	0975	1065	1154	1244	90—89
1.12	0.1 1333	1422	1511	1600	1689	1778	1867	1956	2045	2133	89
1.13	0.1 2222	2310	2399	2487	2575	2663	2751	2839	2927	3015	88
1.14	0.1 3103	3191	3278	3366	3453	3540	3628	3715	3802	3889	88—87
1.15	0.1 3976	4063	4150	4237	4323	4410	4497	4583	4669	4756	87—86
1.16	0.1 4842	4928	5014	5100	5186	5272	5358	5444	5529	5615	86
1.17	0.1 5700	5786	5871	5956	6042	6127	6212	6297	6382	6467	85
1.18	0.1 6551	6636	6721	6805	6890	6974	7059	7143	7227	7311	85—84
1.19	0.1 7395	7479	7563	7647	7731	7815	7898	7982	8065	8149	84—83
1.20	0.1 8232	8315	8399	8482	8565	8648	8731	8814	8897	8979	83
1.21	0.1 9062	9145	9227	9310	9392	9474	9557	9639	9721	9803	83—82
1.22	0.1 9885	9967	*0049	0131	0212	0294	0376	0457	0539	0620	82—81
1.23	0.2 0701	0783	0864	0945	1026	1107	1188	1269	1350	1430	81
1.24	0.2 1511	1592	1672	1753	1833	1914	1994	2074	2154	2234	81—80
1.25	0.2 2314	2394	2474	2554	2634	2714	2793	2873	2952	3032	80—79
1.26	0.2 3111	3191	3270	3349	3428	3507	3586	3665	3744	3823	79
1.27	0.2 3902	3980	4059	4138	4216	4295	4373	4451	4530	4608	79—78
1.28	0.2 4686	4764	4842	4920	4998	5076	5154	5231	5309	5387	78
1.29	0.2 5464	5542	5619	5697	5774	5851	5928	6005	6082	6159	77
1.30	0.2 6236	6313	6390	6467	6544	6620	6697	6773	6850	6926	77—76
1.31	0.2 7003	7079	7155	7231	7308	7384	7460	7536	7612	7687	76
1.32	0.2 7763	7839	7915	7990	8066	8141	8217	8292	8367	8443	76—75
1.33	0.2 8518	8593	8668	8743	8818	8893	8968	9043	9118	9192	75
1.34	0.2 9267	9342	9416	9491	9565	9639	9714	9788	9862	9936	75—74
1.35	0.3 0010	0085	0158	0232	0306	0380	0454	0528	0601	0675	74
1.36	0.3 0748	0822	0895	0969	1042	1115	1189	1262	1335	1408	74—73
1.37	0.3 1481	1554	1627	1700	1773	1845	1918	1991	2063	2136	73—72
1.38	0.3 2208	2281	2353	2426	2498	2570	2642	2714	2786	2858	72
1.39	0.3 2930	3002	3074	3146	3218	3289	3361	3433	3504	3576	72—71
1.40	0.3 3647	3719	3790	3861	3933	4004	4075	4146	4217	4288	71
1.41	0.3 4359	4430	4501	4572	4642	4713	4784	4854	4925	4995	71—70
1.42	0.3 5066	5136	5206	5277	5347	5417	5487	5557	5627	5697	70
1.43	0.3 5767	5837	5907	5977	6047	6116	6186	6256	6325	6395	70—69
1.44	0.3 6464	6534	6603	6672	6742	6811	6880	6949	7018	7087	69
1.45	0.3 7156	7225	7294	7363	7432	7501	7569	7638	7707	7775	69
1.46	0.3 7844	7912	7981	8049	8117	8186	8254	8322	8390	8458	68
1.47	0.3 8526	8594	8662	8730	8798	8866	8934	9001	9069	9137	68
1.48	0.3 9204	9272	9339	9407	9474	9541	9609	9676	9743	9810	68—67
1.49	0.3 9878	9945	*0012	0079	0146	0213	0279	0346	0413	0480	67
1.50	0.4 0547	0613	0680	0746	0813	0879	0946	1012	1078	1145	67—66
	0	1	2	3	4	5	6	7	8	9	

Five-Place Natural Logarithms.

No.	0	1	2	3	4	5	6	7	8	9	D.
1.50	0.4 0547	0613	0680	0746	0813	0879	0946	1012	1078	1145	67–66
1.51	0.4 1211	1277	1343	1409	1476	1542	1608	1673	1739	1805	66
1.52	0.4 1871	1937	2003	2068	2134	2199	2265	2331	2396	2461	66–65
1.53	0.4 2527	2592	2657	2723	2788	2853	2918	2983	3048	3113	65
1.54	0.4 3178	3243	3308	3373	3438	3502	3567	3632	3696	3761	65–64
1.55	0.4 3825	3890	3954	4019	4083	4148	4212	4276	4340	4404	64
1.56	0.4 4469	4533	4597	4661	4725	4789	4852	4916	4980	5044	64
1.57	0.4 5108	5171	5235	5298	5362	5426	5489	5552	5616	5679	64–63
1.58	0.4 5742	5806	5869	5932	5995	6058	6122	6185	6248	6310	63
1.59	0.4 6373	6436	6499	6562	6625	6687	6750	6813	6875	6938	63
1.60	0.4 7000	7063	7125	7188	7250	7312	7375	7437	7499	7561	62
1.61	0.4 7623	7686	7748	7810	7872	7933	7995	8057	8119	8181	62
1.62	0.4 8243	8304	8366	8428	8489	8551	8612	8674	8735	8797	62–61
1.63	0.4 8858	8919	8981	9042	9103	9164	9225	9287	9348	9409	61
1.64	0.4 9470	9531	9592	9652	9713	9774	9835	9896	9956	*0017	61
1.65	0.5 0078	0138	0199	0259	0320	0380	0441	0501	0561	0622	61–60
1.66	0.5 0682	0742	0802	0862	0922	0983	1043	1103	1163	1222	60
1.67	0.5 1282	1342	1402	1462	1522	1581	1641	1701	1760	1820	60
1.68	0.5 1879	1939	1998	2058	2117	2177	2236	2295	2354	2414	60–59
1.69	0.5 2473	2532	2591	2650	2709	2768	2827	2886	2945	3004	59
1.70	0.5 3063	3122	3180	3239	3298	3357	3415	3474	3532	3591	59–58
1.71	0.5 3649	3708	3766	3825	3883	3941	4000	4058	4116	4174	58
1.72	0.5 4232	4291	4349	4407	4465	4523	4581	4639	4696	4754	58
1.73	0.5 4812	4870	4928	4985	5043	5101	5158	5216	5274	5331	58–57
1.74	0.5 5389	5446	5503	5561	5618	5675	5733	5790	5847	5904	57
1.75	0.5 5962	6019	6076	6133	6190	6247	6304	6361	6418	6475	57
1.76	0.5 6531	6588	6645	6702	6758	6815	6872	6928	6985	7041	57
1.77	0.5 7098	7154	7211	7267	7324	7380	7436	7493	7549	7605	56
1.78	0.5 7661	7718	7774	7830	7886	7942	7998	8054	8110	8166	56
1.79	0.5 8222	8277	8333	8389	8445	8501	8556	8612	8667	8723	56
1.80	0.5 8779	8834	8890	8945	9001	9056	9111	9167	9222	9277	56–55
1.81	0.5 9333	9388	9443	9498	9553	9609	9664	9719	9774	9829	55
1.82	0.5 9884	9939	9993	*0048	0103	0158	0213	0268	0322	0377	55
1.83	•0.6 0432	0486	0541	0595	0650	0704	0759	0813	0868	0922	55–54
1.84	0.6 0977	1031	1085	1139	1194	1248	1302	1356	1410	1464	54
1.85	0.6 1519	1573	1627	1681	1735	1788	1842	1896	1950	2004	54
1.86	0.6 2058	2111	2165	2219	2272	2326	2380	2433	2487	2540	54–53
1.87	0.6 2594	2647	2701	2754	2808	2861	2914	2967	3021	3074	53
1.88	0.6 3127	3180	3234	3287	3340	3393	3446	3499	3552	3605	53
1.89	0.6 3658	3711	3763	3816	3869	3922	3975	4027	4080	4133	53
1.90	0.6 4185	4238	4291	4343	4396	4448	4501	4553	4606	4658	53–52
1.91	0.6 4710	4763	4815	4867	4920	4972	5024	5076	5128	5180	52
1.92	0.6 5233	5285	5337	5389	5441	5493	5545	5596	5648	5700	52
1.93	0.6 5752	5804	5856	5907	5959	6011	6062	6114	6166	6217	52
1.94	0.6 6269	6320	6372	6423	6475	6526	6578	6629	6680	6732	52–51
1.95	0.6 6783	6834	6885	6937	6988	7039	7090	7141	7192	7243	51
1.96	0.6 7294	7345	7396	7447	7498	7549	7600	7651	7702	7753	51
1.97	0.6 7803	7854	7905	7956	8006	8057	8107	8158	8209	8259	51
1.98	0.6 8310	8360	8411	8461	8512	8562	8612	8663	8713	8763	50
1.99	0.6 8813	8864	8914	8964	9014	9064	9115	9165	9215	9265	50
2.00	0.6 9315	9365	9415	9465	9515	9564	9614	9664	9714	9764	50
	0	1	2	3	4	5	6	7	8	9	

Five-Place Natural Logarithms.

No.	0	1	2	3	4	5	6	7	8	9	D.
2.00	0.6 9315	9365	9415	9465	9515	9564	9614	9664	9714	9764	50
2.01	0.6 9813	9863	9913	9963	*0012	0062	0112	0161	0211	0260	50
2.02	0.7 0310	0359	0409	0458	0508	0557	0606	0656	0705	0754	49
2.03	0.7 0804	0853	0902	0951	1000	1050	1099	1148	1197	1246	49
2.04	0.7 1295	1344	1393	1442	1491	1540	1589	1638	1686	1735	49
2.05	0.7 1784	1833	1881	1930	1979	2028	2076	2125	2173	2222	49
2.06	0.7 2271	2319	2368	2416	2465	2513	2561	2610	2658	2707	49–48
2.07	0.7 2755	2803	2851	2900	2948	2996	3044	3092	3141	3189	48
2.08	0.7 3237	3285	3333	3381	3429	3477	3525	3573	3621	3669	48
2.09	0.7 3716	3764	3812	3860	3908	3955	4003	4051	4098	4146	48
2.10	0.7 4194	4241	4289	4336	4384	4432	4479	4527	4574	4621	48–47
2.11	0.7 4669	4716	4764	4811	4858	4905	4953	5000	5047	5094	47
2.12	0.7 5142	5189	5236	5283	5330	5377	5424	5471	5518	5565	47
2.13	0.7 5612	5659	5706	5753	5800	5847	5893	5940	5987	6034	47
2.14	0.7 6081	6127	6174	6221	6267	6314	6361	6407	6454	6500	47
2.15	0.7 6547	6593	6640	6686	6733	6779	6825	6872	6918	6965	47–46
2.16	0.7 7011	7057	7103	7150	7196	7242	7288	7334	7381	7427	46
2.17	0.7 7473	7519	7565	7611	7657	7703	7749	7795	7841	7887	46
2.18	0.7 7932	7978	8024	8070	8116	8162	8207	8253	8299	8344	46
2.19	0.7 8390	8436	8481	8527	8573	8618	8664	8709	8755	8800	46–45
2.20	0.7 8846	8891	8937	8982	9027	9073	9118	9163	9209	9254	45
2.21	0.7 9299	9344	9390	9435	9480	9525	9570	9615	9661	9706	45
2.22	0.7 9751	9796	9841	9886	9931	9976	*0021	0066	0110	0155	45
2.23	0.8 0200	0245	0290	0335	0379	0424	0469	0514	0558	0603	45
2.24	0.8 0648	0692	0737	0781	0826	0871	0915	0960	1004	1049	45–44
2.25	0.8 1093	1137	1182	1226	1271	1315	1359	1404	1448	1492	44
2.26	0.8 1536	1581	1625	1669	1713	1757	1802	1846	1890	1934	44
2.27	0.8 1978	2022	2066	2110	2154	2198	2242	2286	2330	2374	44
2.28	0.8 2418	2461	2505	2549	2593	2637	2680	2724	2768	2812	44
2.29	0.8 2855	2899	2942	2986	3030	3073	3117	3160	3204	3247	44–43
2.30	0.8 3291	3334	3378	3421	3465	3508	3551	3595	3638	3681	43
2.31	0.8 3725	3768	3811	3855	3898	3941	3984	4027	4070	4114	43
2.32	0.8 4157	4200	4243	4286	4329	4372	4415	4458	4501	4544	43
2.33	0.8 4587	4630	4673	4715	4758	4801	4844	4887	4930	4972	43
2.34	0.8 5015	5058	5101	5143	5186	5229	5271	5314	5356	5399	43
2.35	0.8 5442	5484	5527	5569	5612	5654	5697	5739	5781	5824	43–42
2.36	0.8 5866	5909	5951	*5993	6036	6078	6120	6162	6205	6247	42
2.37	0.8 6289	6331	6373	6415	6458	6500	6542	6584	6626	6668	42
2.38	0.8 6710	6752	6794	6836	6878	6920	6962	7004	7046	7087	42
2.39	0.8 7129	7171	7213	7255	7297	7338	7380	7422	7464	7505	42
2.40	0.8 7547	7589	7630	7672	7713	7755	7797	7838	7880	7921	42
2.41	0.8 7963	8004	8046	8087	8129	8170	8211	8253	8294	8335	41
2.42	0.8 8377	8418	8459	8501	8542	8583	8624	8666	8707	8748	41
2.43	0.8 8789	8830	8871	8913	8954	8995	9036	9077	9118	9159	41
2.44	0.8 9200	9241	9282	9323	9364	9405	9445	9486	9527	9568	41
2.45	0.8 9609	9650	9690	9731	9772	9813	9853	9894	9935	9975	41
2.46	0.9 0016	0057	0097	0138	0179	0219	0260	0300	0341	0381	41–40
2.47	0.9 0422	0462	0503	0543	0584	0624	0664	0705	0745	0786	40
2.48	0.9 0826	0866	0906	0947	0987	1027	1067	1108	1148	1188	40
2.49	0.9 1228	1268	1309	1349	1389	1429	1469	1509	1549	1589	40
2.50	0.9 1629	1669	1709	1749	1789	1829	1869	1909	1949	1988	40
	0	**1**	**2**	**3**	**4**	**5**	**6**	**7**	**8**	**9**	

Five-Place Natural Logarithms.

No.	0	1	2	3	4	5	6	7	8	9	D.
2.50	0.9 1629	1669	1709	1749	1789	1829	1869	1909	1949	1988	40
2.51	0.9 2028	2068	2108	2148	2188	2227	2267	2307	2346	2386	40
2.52	0.9 2426	2466	2505	2545	2584	2624	2664	2703	2743	2782	40
2.53	0.9 2822	2861	2901	2940	2980	3019	3059	3098	3138	3177	40–39
2.54	0.9 3216	3256	3295	3334	3374	3413	3452	3492	3531	3570	39
2.55	0.9 3609	3649	3688	3727	3766	3805	3844	3883	3923	3962	39
2.56	0.9 4001	4040	4079	4118	4157	4196	4235	4274	4313	4352	39
2.57	0.9 4391	4429	4468	4507	4546	4585	4624	4663	4701	4740	39
2.58	0.9 4779	4818	4856	4895	4934	4973	5011	5050	5089	5127	39
2.59	0.9 5166	5204	5243	5282	5320	5359	5397	5436	5474	5513	39–38
2.60	0.9 5551	5590	5628	5666	5705	5743	5782	5820	5858	5897	38
2.61	0.9 5935	5973	6012	6050	6088	6126	6165	6203	6241	6279	38
2.62	0.9 6317	6356	6394	6432	6470	6508	6546	6584	6622	6660	38
2.63	0.9 6698	6736	6774	6812	6850	6888	6926	6964	7002	7040	38
2.64	0.9 7078	7116	7154	7191	7229	7267	7305	7343	7380	7418	38
2.65	0.9 7456	7494	7531	7569	7607	7644	7682	7720	7757	7795	38
2.66	0.9 7833	7870	7908	7945	7983	8020	8058	8095	8133	8170	38–37
2.67	0.9 8208	8245	8283	8320	8358	8395	8432	8470	8507	8544	37
2.68	0.9 8582	8619	8656	8694	8731	8768	8805	8843	8880	8917	37
2.69	0.9 8954	8991	9028	9066	9103	9140	9177	9214	9251	9288	37
2.70	0.9 9325	9362	9399	9436	9473	9510	9547	9584	9621	9658	37
2.71	0.9 9695	9732	9769	9806	9842	9879	9916	9953	9990	*0026	37
2.72	1.0 0063	0100	0137	0173	0210	0247	0284	0320	0357	0394	37
2.73	1.0 0430	0467	0503	0540	0577	0613	0650	0686	0723	0759	37
2.74	1.0 0796	0832	0869	0905	0942	0978	1015	1051	1087	1124	36
2.75	1.0 1160	1196	1233	1269	1305	1342	1378	1414	1451	1487	36
2.76	1.0 1523	1559	1596	1632	1668	1704	1740	1776	1813	1849	36
2.77	1.0 1885	1921	1957	1993	2029	2065	2101	2137	2173	2209	36
2.78	1.0 2245	2281	2317	2353	2389	2425	2461	2497	2532	2568	36
2.79	1.0 2604	2640	2676	2712	2747	2783	2819	2855	2890	2926	36
2.80	1.0 2962	2998	3033	3069	3105	3140	3176	3212	3247	3283	36
2.81	1.0 3318	3354	3390	3425	3461	3496	3532	3567	3603	3638	36–35
2.82	1.0 3674	3709	3745	3780	3815	3851	3886	3922	3957	3992	35
2.83	1.0 4028	4063	4098	4134	4169	4204	4239	4275	4310	4345	35
2.84	1.0 4380	4416	4451	4486	4521	4556	4591	4627	4662	4697	35
2.85	1.0 4732	4767	4802	4837	4872	4907	4942	4977	5012	5047	35
2.86	1.0 5082	5117	5152	5187	5222	5257	5292	5327	5361	5396	35
2.87	1.0 5431	5466	5501	5536	5570	5605	5640	5675	5710	5744	35
2.88	1.0 5779	5814	5848	5883	5918	5952	5987	6022	6056	6091	35
2.89	1.0 6126	6160	6195	6229	6264	6299	6333	6368	6402	6437	35–34
2.90	1.0 6471	6506	6540	6574	6609	6643	6678	6712	6747	6781	34
2.91	1.0 6815	6850	6884	6918	6953	6987	7021	7056	7090	7124	34
2.92	1.0 7158	7193	7227	7261	7295	7329	7364	7398	7432	7466	34
2.93	1.0 7500	7534	7568	7603	7637	7671	7705	7739	7773	7807	34
2.94	1.0 7841	7875	7909	7943	7977	8011	8045	8079	8113	8147	34
2.95	1.0 8181	8214	8248	8282	8316	8350	8384	8418	8451	8485	34
2.96	1.0 8519	8553	8586	8620	8654	8688	8721	8755	8789	8823	34
2.97	1.0 8856	8890	8924	8957	8991	9024	9058	9092	9125	9159	34
2.98	1.0 9192	9226	9259	9293	9326	9360	9393	9427	9460	9494	34–33
2.99	1.0 9527	9561	9594	9628	9661	9694	9728	9761	9795	9828	33
3.00	1.0 9861	9895	9928	9961	9994	*0028	0061	0094	0128	0161	33
	0	1	2	3	4	5	6	7	8	9	

Five-Place Natural Logarithms.

No.	0	1	2	3	4	5	6	7	8	9	D.
3.00	1.0 9861	9895	9928	9961	9994	*0028	0061	0094	0128	0161	33
3.01	1.1 0194	0227	0260	0294	0327	0360	0393	0426	0459	0493	33
3.02	1.1 0526	0559	0592	0625	0658	0691	0724	0757	0790	0823	33
3.03	1.1 0856	0889	0922	0955	0988	1021	1054	1087	1120	1153	33
3.04	1.1 1186	1219	1252	1284	1317	1350	1383	1416	1449	1481	33
3.05	1.1 1514	1547	1580	1612	1645	1678	1711	1743	1776	1809	33
3.06	1.1 1841	1874	1907	1939	1972	2005	2037	2070	2103	2135	33
3.07	1.1 2168	2200	2233	2265	2298	2330	2363	2396	2428	2460	33–32
3.08	1.1 2493	2525	2558	2590	2623	2655	2688	2720	2752	2785	32
3.09	1.1 2817	2849	2882	2914	2946	2979	3011	3043	3076	3108	32
3.10	1.1 3140	3172	3205	3237	3269	3301	3334	3366	3398	3430	32
3.11	1.1 3462	3494	3527	3559	3591	3623	3655	3687	3719	3751	32
3.12	1.1 3783	3815	3847	3879	3911	3943	3975	4007	4039	4071	32
3.13	1.1 4103	4135	4167	4199	4231	4263	4295	4327	4359	4390	32
3.14	1.1 4422	4454	4486	4518	4550	4581	4613	4645	4677	4708	32
3.15	1.1 4740	4772	4804	4835	4867	4899	4931	4962	4994	5026	32
3.16	1.1 5057	5089	5120	5152	5184	5215	5247	5278	5310	5342	32
3.17	1.1 5373	5405	5436	5468	5499	5531	5562	5594	5625	5657	32–31
3.18	1.1 5688	5720	5751	5782	5814	5845	5877	5908	5939	5971	31
3.19	1.1 6002	6033	6065	6096	6127	6159	6190	6221	6253	6284	31
3.20	1.1 6315	6346	6378	6409	6440	6471	6502	6534	6565	6596	31
3.21	1.1 6627	6658	6689	6721	6752	6783	6814	6845	6876	6907	31
3.22	1.1 6938	6969	7000	7031	7062	7093	7124	7155	7186	7217	31
3.23	1.1 7248	7279	7310	7341	7372	7403	7434	7465	7496	7526	31
3.24	1.1 7557	7588	7619	7650	7681	7712	7742	7773	7804	7835	31
3.25	1.1 7865	7896	7927	7958	7989	8019	8050	8081	8111	8142	31
3.26	1.1 8173	8203	8234	8265	8295	8326	8357	8387	8418	8448	31
3.27	1.1 8479	8510	8540	8571	8601	8632	8662	8693	8723	8754	31–30
3.28	1.1 8784	8815	8845	8876	8906	8937	8967	8998	9028	9058	30
3.29	1.1 9089	9119	9150	9180	9210	9241	9271	9301	9332	9362	30
3.30	1.1 9392	9423	9453	9483	9513	9544	9574	9604	9634	9665	30
3.31	1.1 9695	9725	9755	9785	9816	9846	9876	9906	9936	9966	30
3.32	1.1 9996	*0027	0057	0087	0117	0147	0177	0207	0237	0267	30
3.33	1.2 0297	0327	0357	0387	0417	0447	0477	0507	0537	0567	30
3.34	1.2 0597	0627	0657	0687	0717	0747	0777	0806	0836	0866	30
3.35	1.2 0896	0926	0956	0986	1015	1045	1075	1105	1135	1164	30
3.36	1.2 1194	1224	1254	1283	1313	1343	1373	1402	1432	1462	30
3.37	1.2 1491	1521	1551	1580	1610	1640	1669	1699	1728	1758	30
3.38	1.2 1788	1817	1847	1876	1906	1935	1965	1994	2024	2053	30
3.39	1.2 2083	2112	2142	2171	2201	2230	2260	2289	2319	2348	29
3.40	1.2 2378	2407	2436	2466	2495	2524	2554	2583	2613	2642	29
3.41	1.2 2671	2701	2730	2759	2788	2818	2847	2876	2906	2935	29
3.42	1.2 2964	2993	3023	3052	3081	3110	3139	3169	3198	3227	29
3.43	1.2 3256	3285	3314	3343	3373	3402	3431	3460	3489	3518	29
3.44	1.2 3547	3576	3605	3634	3663	3692	3721	3750	3779	3808	29
3.45	1.2 3837	3866	3895	3924	3953	3982	4011	4040	4069	4098	29
3.46	1.2 4127	4156	4185	4214	4242	4271	4300	4329	4358	4387	29
3.47	1.2 4415	4444	4473	4502	4531	4559	4588	4617	4646	4674	29
3.48	1.2 4703	4732	4761	4789	4818	4847	4875	4904	4933	4962	29
3.49	1.2 4990	5019	5047	5076	5105	5133	5162	5191	5219	5248	29
3.50	1.2 5276	5305	5333	5362	5391	5419	5448	5476	5505	5533	29–28
	0	1	2	3	4	5	6	7	8	9	

Five-Place Natural Logarithms.

No.	0	1	2	3	4	5	6	7	8	9	D.
3.50	1.2 5276	5305	5333	5362	5391	5419	5448	5476	5505	5533	29-28
3.51	1.2 5562	5590	5619	5647	5675	5704	5732	5761	5789	5818	28
3.52	1.2 5846	5875	5903	5931	5960	5988	6016	6045	6073	6101	28
3.53	1.2 6130	6158	6186	6215	6243	6271	6300	6328	6356	6384	28
3.54	1.2 6413	6441	6469	6497	6526	6554	6582	6610	6638	6667	28
3.55	1.2 6695	6723	6751	6779	6807	6836	6864	6892	6920	6948	28
3.56	1.2 6976	7004	7032	7060	7088	7116	7144	7172	7201	7229	28
3.57	1.2 7257	7285	7313	7341	7369	7397	7424	7452	7480	7508	28
3.58	1.2 7536	7564	7592	7620	7648	7676	7704	7732	7759	7787	28
3.59	1.2 7815	7843	7871	7899	7927	7954	7982	8010	8038	8066	28
3.60	1.2 8093	8121	8149	8177	8204	8232	8260	8288	8315	8343	28
3.61	1.2 8371	8398	8426	8454	8482	8509	8537	8564	8592	8620	28
3.62	1.2 8647	8675	8703	8730	8758	8785	8813	8841	8868	8896	28
3.63	1.2 8923	8951	8978	9006	9033	9061	9088	9116	9143	9171	28-27
3.64	1.2 9198	9226	9253	9281	9308	9336	9363	9390	9418	9445	27
3.65	1.2 9473	9500	9527	9555	9582	9610	9637	9664	9692	9719	27
3.66	1.2 9746	9774	9801	9828	9856	9883	9910	9937	9965	9992	27
3.67	1.3 0019	0046	0074	0101	0128	0155	0183	0210	0237	0264	27
3.68	1.3 0291	0318	0346	0373	0400	0427	0454	0481	0508	0536	27
3.69	1.3 0563	0590	0617	0644	0671	0698	0725	0752	0779	0806	27
3.70	1.3 0833	0860	0887	0914	0941	0968	0995	1022	1049	1076	27
3.71	1.3 1103	1130	1157	1184	1211	1238	1265	1292	1319	1345	27
3.72	1.3 1372	1399	1426	1453	1480	1507	1534	1560	1587	1614	27
3.73	1.3 1641	1668	1694	1721	1748	1775	1802	1828	1855	1882	27
3.74	1.3 1909	1935	1962	1989	2015	2042	2069	2096	2122	2149	27
3.75	1.3 2176	2202	2229	2256	2282	2309	2335	2362	2389	2415	27
3.76	1.3 2442	2468	2495	2522	2548	2575	2601	2628	2654	2681	27
3.77	1.3 2708	2734	2761	2787	2814	2840	2867	2893	2919	2946	27-26
3.78	1.3 2972	2999	3025	3052	3078	3105	3131	3157	3184	3210	26
3.79	1.3 3237	3263	3289	3316	3342	3368	3395	3421	3447	3474	26
3.80	1.3 3500	3526	3553	3579	3605	3632	3658	3684	3710	3737	26
3.81	1.3 3763	3789	3815	3842	3868	3894	3920	3946	3973	3999	26
3.82	1.3 4025	4051	4077	4104	4130	4156	4182	4208	4234	4260	26
3.83	1.3 4286	4313	4339	4365	4391	4417	4443	4469	4495	4521	26
3.84	1.3 4547	4573	4599	4625	4651	4677	4703	4729	4755	4781	26
3.85	1.3 4807	4833	4859	4885	4911	4937	4963	4989	5015	5041	26
3.86	1.3 5067	5093	5119	5144	5170	5196	5222	5248	5274	5300	26
3.87	1.3 5325	5351	5377	5403	5429	5455	5480	5506	5532	5558	26
3.88	1.3 5584	5609	5635	5661	5687	5712	5738	5764	5789	5815	26
3.89	1.3 5841	5867	5892	5918	5944	5969	5995	6021	6046	6072	26
3.90	1.3 6098	6123	6149	6175	6200	6226	6251	6277	6303	6328	26
3.91	1.3 6354	6379	6405	6430	6456	6481	6507	6533	6558	6584	26
3.92	1.3 6609	6635	6660	6686	6711	6737	6762	6788	6813	6838	26-25
3.93	1.3 6864	6889	6915	6940	6966	6991	7016	7042	7067	7093	25
3.94	1.3 7118	7143	7169	7194	7220	7245	7270	7296	7321	7346	25
3.95	1.3 7372	7397	7422	7447	7473	7498	7523	7549	7574	7599	25
3.96	1.3 7624	7650	7675	7700	7725	7751	7776	7801	7826	7851	25
3.97	1.3 7877	7902	7927	7952	7977	8002	8028	8053	8078	8103	25
3.98	1.3 8128	8143	8178	8204	8229	8254	8279	8304	8329	8354	25
3.99	1.3 8379	8404	8429	8454	8479	8504	8529	8554	8579	8604	25
4.00	1.3 8629	8654	8679	8704	8729	8754	8779	8804	8829	8854	25
	0	1	2	3	4	5	6	7	8	9	

Five-Place Natural Logarithms.

No.	0	1	2	3	4	5	6	7	8	9	D.
4.00	1.3 8629	8654	8679	8704	8729	8754	8779	8804	8829	8854	25
4.01	1.3 8879	8904	8929	8954	8979	9004	9029	9054	9078	9103	25
4.02	1.3 9128	9153	9178	9203	9228	9252	9277	9302	9327	9352	25
4.03	1.3 9377	9401	9426	9451	9476	9501	9525	9550	9575	9600	25
4.04	1.3 9624	9649	9674	9699	9723	9748	9773	9798	9822	9847	25
4.05	1.3 9872	9896	9921	9946	9970	9995	*0020	0044	0069	0094	25
4.06	1.4 0118	0143	0168	0192	0217	0241	0266	0291	0315	0340	25
4.07	1.4 0364	0389	0413	0438	0463	0487	0512	0536	0561	0585	25
4.08	1.4 0610	0634	0659	0683	0708	0732	0757	0781	0806	0830	25-24
4.09	1.4 0854	0879	0903	0928	0952	0977	1001	1025	1050	1074	24
4.10	1.4 1099	1123	1147	1172	1196	1221	1245	1269	1294	1318	24
4.11	1.4 1342	1367	1391	1415	1440	1464	1488	1512	1537	1561	24
4.12	1.4 1585	1610	1634	1658	1682	1707	1731	1755	1779	1804	24
4.13	1.4 1828	1852	1876	1900	1925	1949	1973	1997	2021	2045	24
4.14	1.4 2070	2094	2118	2142	2166	2190	2214	2239	2263	2287	24
4.15	1.4 2311	2335	2359	2383	2407	2431	2455	2479	2503	2527	24
4.16	1.4 2552	2576	2600	2624	2648	2672	2696	2720	2744	2768	24
4.17	1.4 2792	2816	2840	2864	2887	2911	2935	2959	2983	3007	24
4.18	1.4 3031	3055	3079	3103	3127	3151	3175	3198	3222	3246	24
4.19	1.4 3270	3294	3318	3342	3365	3389	3413	3437	3461	3485	24
4.20	1.4 3508	3532	3556	3580	3604	3627	3651	3675	3699	3723	24
4.21	1.4 3746	3770	3794	3817	3841	3865	3889	3912	3936	3960	24
4.22	1.4 3984	4007	4031	4055	4078	4102	4126	4149	4173	4197	24
4.23	1.4 4220	4244	4267	4291	4315	4338	4362	4386	4409	4433	24
4.24	1.4 4456	4480	4503	4527	4551	4574	4598	4621	4645	4668	24
4.25	1.4 4692	4715	4739	4762	4786	4809	4833	4856	4880	4903	24-23
4.26	1.4 4927	4950	4974	4997	5021	5044	5068	5091	5115	5138	23
4.27	1.4 5161	5185	5208	5232	5255	5278	5302	5325	5349	5372	23
4.28	1.4 5395	5419	5442	5465	5489	5512	5535	5559	5582	5605	23
4.29	1.4 5629	5652	5675	5699	5722	5745	5768	5792	5815	5838	23
4.30	1.4 5862	5885	5908	5931	5954	5978	6001	6024	6047	6071	23
4.31	1.4 6094	6117	6140	6163	6187	6210	6233	6256	6279	6302	23
4.32	1.4 6326	6349	6372	6395	6418	6441	6464	6487	6511	6534	23
4.33	1.4 6557	6580	6603	6626	6649	6672	6695	6718	6741	6764	23
4.34	1.4 6787	6810	6834	6857	6880	6903	6926	6949	6972	6995	23
4.35	1.4 7018	7041	7064	7087	7109	7132	7155	7178	7201	7224	23
4.36	1.4 7247	7270	7293	7316	7339	7362	7385	7408	7431	7453	23
4.37	1.4 7476	7499	7522	7545	7568	7591	7614	7636	7659	7682	23
4.38	1.4 7705	7728	7751	7773	7796	7819	7842	7865	7887	7910	23
4.39	1.4 7933	7956	7978	8001	8024	8047	8070	8092	8115	8138	23
4.40	1.4 8160	8183	8206	8229	8251	8274	8297	8319	8342	8365	23
4.41	1.4 8387	8410	8433	8455	8478	8501	8523	8546	8569	8591	23
4.42	1.4 8614	8637	8659	8682	8704	8727	8750	8772	8795	8817	23
4.43	1.4 8840	8863	8885	8908	8930	8953	8975	8998	9020	9043	23
4.44	1.4 9065	9088	9110	9133	9155	9178	9200	9223	9245	9268	23
4.45	1.4 9290	9313	9335	9358	9380	9403	9425	9448	9470	9492	23-22
4.46	1.4 9515	9537	9560	9582	9605	9627	9649	9672	9694	9716	22
4.47	1.4 9739	9761	9784	9806	9828	9851	9873	9895	9918	9940	22
4.48	1.4 9962	9985	*0007	0029	0052	0074	0096	0118	0141	0163	22
4.49	1.5 0185	0208	0230	0252	0274	0297	0319	0341	0363	0386	22
4.50	1.5 0408	0430	0452	0474	0497	0519	0541	0563	0585	0608	22
	0	1	2	3	4	5	6	7	8	9	

Five-Place Natural Logarithms.

No.	0	1	2	3	4	5	6	7	8	9	D.
4.50	1.5 0408	0430	0452	0474	0497	0519	0541	0563	0585	0608	22
4.51	1.5 0630	0652	0674	0696	0718	0741	0763	0785	0807	0829	22
4.52	1.5 0851	0873	0895	0918	0940	0962	0984	1006	1028	1050	22
4.53	1.5 1072	1094	1116	1138	1160	1183	1205	1227	1249	1271	22
4.54	1.5 1293	1315	1337	1359	1381	1403	1425	1447	1469	1491	22
4.55	1.5 1513	1535	1557	1579	1601	1623	1645	1666	1688	1710	22
4.56	1.5 1732	1754	1776	1798	1820	1842	1864	1886	1908	1929	22
4.57	1.5 1951	1973	1995	2017	2039	2061	2083	2104	2126	2148	22
4.58	1.5 2170	2192	2214	2235	2257	2279	2301	2323	2344	2366	22
4.59	1.5 2388	2410	2432	2453	2475	2497	2519	2540	2562	2584	22
4.60	1.5 2606	2627	2649	2671	2693	2714	2736	2758	2779	2801	22
4.61	1.5 2823	2844	2866	2888	2910	2931	2953	2975	2996	3018	22
4.62	1.5 3039	3061	3083	3104	3126	3148	3169	3191	3212	3234	22
4.63	1.5 3256	3277	3299	3320	3342	3364	3385	3407	3428	3450	22
4.64	1.5 3471	3493	3515	3536	3558	3579	3601	3622	3644	3665	22
4.65	1.5 3687	3708	3730	3751	3773	3794	3816	3837	3859	3880	22–21
4.66	1.5 3902	3923	3944	3966	3987	4009	4030	4052	4073	4094	21
4.67	1.5 4116	4137	4159	4180	4202	4223	4244	4266	4287	4308	21
4.68	1.5 4330	4351	4373	4394	4415	4437	4458	4479	4501	4522	21
4.69	1.5 4543	4565	4586	4607	4629	4650	4671	4692	4714	4735	21
4.70	1.5 4756	4778	4799	4820	4841	4863	4884	4905	4926	4948	21
4.71	1.5 4969	4990	5011	5032	5054	5075	5096	5117	5138	5160	21
4.72	1.5 5181	5202	5223	5244	5266	5287	5308	5329	5350	5371	21
4.73	1.5 5393	5414	5435	5456	5477	5498	5519	5540	5562	5583	21
4.74	1.5 5604	5625	5646	5667	5688	5709	5730	5751	5772	5793	21
4.75	1.5 5814	5836	5857	5878	5899	5920	5941	5962	5983	6004	21
4.76	1.5 6025	6046	6067	6088	6109	6130	6151	6172	6193	6214	21
4.77	1.5 6235	6256	6277	6298	6318	6339	6360	6381	6402	6423	21
4.78	1.5 6444	6465	6486	6507	6528	6549	6569	6590	6611	6632	21
4.79	1.5 6653	6674	6695	6716	6737	6757	6778	6799	6820	6841	21
4.80	1.5 6862	6882	6903	6924	6945	6966	6987	7007	7028	7049	21
4.81	1.5 7070	7090	7111	7132	7153	7174	7194	7215	7236	7257	21
4.82	1.5 7277	7298	7319	7340	7360	7381	7402	7423	7443	7464	21
4.83	1.5 7485	7505	7526	7547	7567	7588	7609	7629	7650	7671	21
4.84	1.5 7691	7712	7733	7753	7774	7795	7815	7836	7857	7877	21
4.85	1.5 7898	7918	7939	7960	7980	8001	8022	8042	8063	8083	21
4.86	1.5 8104	8124	8145	8166	8186	8207	8227	8248	8268	8289	21
4.87	1.5 8309	8330	8350	8371	8391	8412	8433	8453	8474	8494	21–20
4.88	1.5 8515	8535	8555	8576	8596	8617	8637	8658	8678	8699	20
4.89	1.5 8719	8740	8760	8781	8801	8821	8842	8862	8883	8903	20
4.90	1.5 8924	8944	8964	8985	9005	9026	9046	9066	9087	9107	20
4.91	1.5 9127	9148	9168	9188	9209	9229	9250	9270	9290	9311	20
4.92	1.5 9331	9351	9371	9392	9412	9432	9453	9473	9493	9514	20
4.93	1.5 9534	9554	9574	9595	9615	9635	9656	9676	9696	9716	20
4.94	1.5 9737	9757	9777	9797	9817	9838	9858	9878	9898	9919	20
4.95	1.5 9939	9959	9979	9999	*0020	0040	0060	0080	0100	0120	20
4.96	1.6 0141	0161	0181	0201	0221	0241	0261	0282	0302	0322	20
4.97	1.6 0342	0362	0382	0402	0422	0443	0463	0483	0503	0523	20
4.98	1.6 0543	0563	0583	0603	0623	0643	0663	0683	0704	0724	20
4.99	1.6 0744	0764	0784	0804	0824	0844	0864	0884	0904	0924	20
5.00	1.6 0944	0964	0984	1004	1024	1044	1064	1084	1104	1124	20
	0	1	2	3	4	5	6	7	8	9	

Five-Place Natural Logarithms.

No.	0	1	2	3	4	5	6	7	8	9	D.
5.0	1.6 0944	1144	1343	1542	1741	1939	2137	2334	2531	2728	200–196
5.1	1.6 2924	3120	3315	3511	3705	3900	4094	4287	4481	4673	196–192
5.2	1.6 4866	5058	5250	5441	5632	5823	6013	6203	6393	6582	192–189
5.3	1.6 6771	6959	7147	7335	7523	7710	7896	8083	8269	8455	189–185
5.4	1.6 8640	8825	9010	9194	9378	9562	9745	9928	*0111	0293	185–182
5.5	1.7 0475	0656	0838	1019	1199	1380	1560	1740	1919	2098	182–179
5.6	1.7 2277	2455	2633	2811	2988	3166	3342	3519	3695	3871	178–1⁻3
5.7	1.7 4047	4222	4397	4572	4746	4920	5094	5267	5440	5613	175–173
5.8	1.7 5786	5958	6130	6302	6473	6644	6815	6985	7156	7326	172–170
5.9	1.7 7495	7665	7834	8002	8171	8339	8507	8675	8842	9009	169–167
6.0	1.7 9176	9342	9509	9675	9840	*0006	0171	0336	0500	0665	167–164
6.1	1.8 0829	0993	1156	1319	1482	1645	1808	1970	2132	2294	164–161
6.2	1.8 2455	2616	2777	2938	3098	3258	3418	3578	3737	3896	161–159
6.3	1.8 4055	4214	4372	4530	4688	4845	5003	5160	5317	5473	159–156
6.4	1.8 5630	5786	5942	6097	6253	6408	6563	6718	6872	7026	156–154
6.5	1.8 7180	7334	7487	7641	7794	7947	8099	8251	8403	8555	154–152
6.6	1.8 8707	8858	9010	9160	9311	9462	9612	9762	9912	*0061	151–149
6.7	1.9 0211	0360	0509	0658	0806	0954	1102	1250	1398	1545	149–147
6.8	1.9 1692	1839	1986	2132	2279	2425	2571	2716	2862	3007	147–145
6.9	1.9 3152	3297	3442	3586	3730	3874	4018	4162	4305	4448	145–143
7.0	1.9 4591	4734	4876	5019	5161	5303	5445	5586	5727	5869	143–141
7.1	1.9 6009	6150	6291	6431	6571	6711	6851	6991	7130	7269	141–139
7.2	1.9 7408	7547	7685	7824	7962	8100	8238	8376	8513	8650	139–137
7.3	1.9 8787	8924	9061	9198	9334	9470	9606	9742	9877	*0013	137–135
7.4	2.0 0148	0283	0418	0553	0687	0821	0956	1089	1223	1357	135–133
7.5	2.0 1490	1624	1757	1890	2022	2155	2287	2419	2551	2683	133–132
7.6	2.0 2815	2946	3078	3209	3340	3471	3601	3732	3862	3992	131–130
7.7	2.0 4122	4252	4381	4511	4640	4769	4898	5027	5156	5284	130–128
7.8	2.0 5412	5540	5668	5796	5924	6051	6179	6306	6433	6560	128–127
7.9	2.0 6686	6813	6939	7065	7191	7317	7443	7568	7694	7819	127–125
8.0	2.0 7944	8069	8194	8318	8443	8567	8691	8815	8939	9063	125–124
8.1	2.0 9186	9310	9433	9556	9679	9802	9924	*0047	0169	0291	123–122
8.2	2.1 0413	0535	0657	0779	0900	1021	1142	1263	1384	1505	122–121
8.3	2.1 1626	1746	1866	1986	2106	2226	2346	2465	2585	2704	120–119
8.4	2.1 2823	2942	3061	3180	3298	3417	3535	3653	3771'	3889	119–118
8.5	2.1 4007	4124	4242	4359	4476	4593	4710	4827	4943	5060	118–116
8.6	2.1 5176	5292	5409	5524	5640	5756	5871	5987	6102	6217	116–115
8.7	2.1 6332	6447	6562	6677	6791	6905	7020	7134	7248	7361	115–114
8.8	2.1 7475	7589	7702	7816	7929	8042	8155	8267	8380	8493	114–112
8.9	2.1 8605	8717	8830	8942	9054	9165	9277	9389	9500	9611	112–111
9.0	2.1 9722	9834	9944	*0055	0166	0276	0387	0497	0607	0717	111–110
9.1	2.2 0827	0937	1047	1157	1266	1375	1485	1594	1703	1812	110–109
9.2	2.2 1920	2029	2138	2246	2354	2462	2570	2678	2786	2894	109–108
9.3	2.2 3001	3109	3216	3324	3431	3538	3645	3751	3858	3965	107–106
9.4	2.2 4071	4177	4284	4390	4496	4601	4707	4813	4918	5024	106–105
9.5	2.2 5129	5234	5339	5444	5549	5654	5759	5863	5968	6072	105–104
9.6	2.2 6176	6280	6384	6488	6592	6696	6799	6903	7006	7109	104–103
9.7	2.2 7213	7316	7419	7521	7624	7727	7829	7932	8034	8136	103–102
9.8	2.2 8238	8340	8442	8544	8646	8747	8849	8950	9051	9152	102–101
9.9	2.2 9253	9354	9455	9556	9657	9757	9858	9958	*0058	0158	101–100
10.0	2.3 0259	0358	0458	0558	0658	0757	0857	0956	1055	1154	100–99
	0	1	2	3	4	5	6	7	8	9	

The Natural Logarithms (each increased by 10.) of Numbers between 0.00 and 0.99.

No.	0	1	2	3	4	5	6	7	8	9
0.0		5.395	6.088	6.493	6.781	7.004	7.187	7.341	7.474	7.592
0.1	7.697	7.793	7.880	7.960	8.034	8.103	8.167	8.228	8.285	8.339
0.2	8.391	8.439	8.486	8.530	8.573	8.614	8.653	8.691	8.727	8.762
0.3	8.796	8.829	8.861	8.891	8.921	8.950	8.978	9.006	9.032	9.058
0.4	9.084	9.108	9.132	9.156	9.179	9.201	9.223	9.245	9.266	9.287
0.5	9.307	9.327	9.346	9.365	9.384	9.402	9.420	9.438	9.455	9.472
0.6	9.489	9.506	9.522	9.538	9.554	.9.569	9.584	9.600	9.614	9.629
0.7	9.643	9.658	9.671	9.685	9.699	9.712	9.726	9.739	9.752	9.764
0.8	9.777	9.789	9.802	9.814	9.826	9.837	9.849	9.861	9.872	9.883
0.9	9.895	9.906	9.917	9.927	9.938	9.949	9.959	9.970	9.980	9.990

Note : $\log_e x = \log_{10} x \cdot \log_e 10 = (2.30259) \log_{10} x$.

The Natural Logarithms of Whole Numbers from 10 to 209.

No.	0	1	2	3	4	5	6	7	8	9
1	2.3026	3979	4849	5649	6391	7080	7726	8332	8904	9444
2	2.9957	*0445	0910	1355	1781	2189	2581	2958	3322	3673
3	3.4012	4340	4657	4965	5264	5553	5835	6109	6376	6636
4	3.6889	7136	7377	7612	7842	8067	8286	8501	8712	8918
5	3.9120	9318	9512	9703	9890	*0073	0254	0431	0604	0775
6	4.0943	1109	1271	1431	1589	1744	1897	2047	2195	2341
7	4.2485	2627	2767	2905	3041	3175	3307	3438	3567	3694
8	4.3820	3944	4067	4188	4308	4427	4543	4659	4773	4886
9	4.4998	5109	5218	5326	5433	5539	5643	5747	5850	5951
10	4.6052	6151	6250	6347	6444	6540	6634	6728	6821	6913
11	4.7005	7095	7185	7274	7362	7449	7536	7622	7707	7791
12	4.7875	7958	8040	8122	8203	8283	8363	8442	8520	8598
13	4.8675	8752	8828	8903	8978	9053	9127	9200	9273	9345
14	4.9416	9488	9558	9628	9698	9767	9836	9904	9972	*0039
15	5.0106	0173	0239	0304	0370	0434	0499	0562	0626	0689
16	5.0752	0814	0876	0938	0999	1059	1120	1180	1240	1299
17	5.1358	1417	1475	1533	1591	1648	1705	1762	1818	1874
18	5.1930	1985	2040	2095	2149	2204	2257	2311	2364	2417
19	5.2470	2523	2575	2627	2679	2730	2781	2832	2883	2933
20	5.2983	3033	3083	3132	3181	3230	3279	3327	3375	3423

Note : $\log_e 10 = 2.30258509.$ $\log_e 100 = 4.60517019.$

TABLES.

The Common Logarithms of $\Gamma(n)$ for Values of n between 1 and 2.

$$\Gamma(n) = \int_0^\infty x^{n-1} \cdot e^{-x} dx = \int_0^1 \left[\log \frac{1}{x} \right]^{n-1} dx.$$

n	$\log_{10} \Gamma(n)$	n	$\log_{10} \Gamma(n)$	n	$\log_{10} \Gamma(n)$	n	$\log_{10} \Gamma(n)$	n	$\log_{10} \Gamma(n)$
1.01	$\bar{1}.9975$	1.21	$\bar{1}.9617$	1.41	$\bar{1}.9478$	1.61	$\bar{1}.9517$	1.81	$\bar{1}.9704$
1.02	$\bar{1}.9951$	1.22	$\bar{1}.9605$	1.42	$\bar{1}.9476$	1.62	$\bar{1}.9523$	1.82	$\bar{1}.9717$
1.03	$\bar{1}.9928$	1.23	$\bar{1}.9594$	1.43	$\bar{1}.9475$	1.63	$\bar{1}.9529$	1.83	$\bar{1}.9730$
1.04	$\bar{1}.9905$	1.24	$\bar{1}.9583$	1.44	$\bar{1}.9473$	1.64	$\bar{1}.9536$	1.84	$\bar{1}.9743$
1.05	$\bar{1}.9883$	1.25	$\bar{1}.9573$	1.45	$\bar{1}.9473$	1.65	$\bar{1}.9543$	1.85	$\bar{1}.9757$
1.06	$\bar{1}.9862$	1.26	$\bar{1}.9564$	1.46	$\bar{1}.9472$	1.66	$\bar{1}.9550$	1.86	$\bar{1}.9771$
1.07	$\bar{1}.9841$	1.27	$\bar{1}.9554$	1.47	$\bar{1}.9473$	1.67	$\bar{1}.9558$	1.87	$\bar{1}.9786$
1.08	$\bar{1}.9821$	1.28	$\bar{1}.9546$	1.48	$\bar{1}.9473$	1.68	$\bar{1}.9566$	1.88	$\bar{1}.9800$
1.09	$\bar{1}.9802$	1.29	$\bar{1}.9538$	1.49	$\bar{1}.9474$	1.69	$\bar{1}.9575$	1.89	$\bar{1}.9815$
1.10	$\bar{1}.9783$	1.30	$\bar{1}.9530$	1.50	$\bar{1}.9475$	1.70	$\bar{1}.9584$	1.90	$\bar{1}.9831$
1.11	$\bar{1}.9765$	1.31	$\bar{1}.9523$	1.51	$\bar{1}.9477$	1.71	$\bar{1}.9593$	1.91	$\bar{1}.9846$
1.12	$\bar{1}.9748$	1.32	$\bar{1}.9516$	1.52	$\bar{1}.9479$	1.72	$\bar{1}.9603$	1.92	$\bar{1}.9862$
1.13	$\bar{1}.9731$	1.33	$\bar{1}.9510$	1.53	$\bar{1}.9482$	1.73	$\bar{1}.9613$	1.93	$\bar{1}.9878$
1.14	$\bar{1}.9715$	1.34	$\bar{1}.9505$	1.54	$\bar{1}.9485$	1.74	$\bar{1}.9623$	1.94	$\bar{1}.9895$
1.15	$\bar{1}.9699$	1.35	$\bar{1}.9500$	1.55	$\bar{1}.9488$	1.75	$\bar{1}.9633$	1.95	$\bar{1}.9912$
1.16	$\bar{1}.9684$	1.36	$\bar{1}.9495$	1.56	$\bar{1}.9492$	1.76	$\bar{1}.9644$	1.96	$\bar{1}.9929$
1.17	$\bar{1}.9669$	1.37	$\bar{1}.9491$	1.57	$\bar{1}.9496$	1.77	$\bar{1}.9656$	1.97	$\bar{1}.9946$
1.18	$\bar{1}.9655$	1.38	$\bar{1}.9487$	1.58	$\bar{1}.9501$	1.78	$\bar{1}.9667$	1.98	$\bar{1}.9964$
1.19	$\bar{1}.9642$	1.39	$\bar{1}.9483$	1.59	$\bar{1}.9506$	1.79	$\bar{1}.9679$	1.99	$\bar{1}.9982$
1.20	$\bar{1}.9629$	1.40	$\bar{1}.9481$	1.60	$\bar{1}.9511$	1.80	$\bar{1}.9691$	2.00	0.0000

$$\Gamma(z+1) = z \cdot \Gamma(z), \quad z > 1.$$

NATURAL TRIGONOMETRIC FUNCTIONS.

Angle.	Sin.	Csc.	Tan.	Ctn.	Sec.	Cos.	
0°	0.000	∞	0.000	∞	1.000	1.000	90°
1	0.017	57.30	0.017	57.29	1.000	1.000	89
2	0.035	28.65	0.035	28.64	1.001	0.999	88
3	0.052	19.11	0.052	19.08	1.001	0.999	87
4	0.070	14.34	0.070	14.30	1.002	0.998	86
5°	0.087	11.47	0.087	11.43	1.004	0.996	85°
6	0.105	9.567	0.105	9.514	1.006	0.995	84
7	0.122	8.206	0.123	8.144	1.008	0.993	83
8	0.139	7.185	0.141	7.115	1.010	0.990	82
9	0.156	6.392	0.158	6.314	1.012	0.988	81
10°	0.174	5.759	0.176	5.671	1.015	0.985	80°
11	0.191	5.241	0.194	5.145	1.019	0.982	79
12	0.208	4.810	0.213	4.705	1.022	0.978	78
13	0.225	4.445	0.231	4.331	1.026	0.974	77
14	0.242	4.134	0.249	4.011	1.031	0.970	76
15°	0.259	3.864	0.268	3.732	1.035	0.966	75°
16	0.276	3.628	0.287	3.487	1.040	0.961	74
17	0.292	3.420	0.306	3.271	1.046	0.956	73
18	0.309	3.236	0.325	3.078	1.051	0.951	72
19	0.326	3.072	0.344	2.904	1.058	0.946	71
20°	0.342	2.924	0.364	2.747	1.064	0.940	70°
21	0.358	2.790	0.384	2.605	1.071	0.934	69
22	0.375	2.669	0.404	2.475	1.079	0.927	68
23	0.391	2.559	0.424	2.356	1.086	0.921	67
24	0.407	2.459	0.445	2.246	1.095	0.914	66
25°	0.423	2.366	0.466	2.145	1.103	0.906	65°
26	0.438	2.281	0.488	2.050	1.113	0.899	64
27	0.454	2.203	0.510	1.963	1.122	0.891	63
28	0.469	2.130	0.532	1.881	1.133	0.883	62
29	0.485	2.063	0.554	1.804	1.143	0.875	61
30°	0.500	2.000	0.577	1.732	1.155	0.866	60°
31	0.515	1.942	0.601	1.664	1.167	0.857	59
32	0.530	1.887	0.625	1.600	1.179	0.848	58
33	0.545	1.836	0.649	1.540	1.192	0.839	57
34	0.559	1.788	0.675	1.483	1.206	0.829	56
35°	0.574	1.743	0.700	1.428	1.221	0.819	55°
36	0.588	1.701	0.727	1.376	1.236	0.809	54
37	0.602	1.662	0.754	1.327	1.252	0.799	53
38	0.616	1.624	0.781	1.280	1.269	0.788	52
39	0.629	1.589	0.810	1.235	1.287	0.777	51
40°	0.643	1.556	0.839	1.192	1.305	0.766	50°
41	0.656	1.524	0.869	1.150	1.325	0.755	49
42	0.669	1.494	0.900	1.111	1.346	0.743	48
43	0.682	1.466	0.933	1.072	1.367	0.731	47
44	0.695	1.440	0.966	1.036	1.390	0.719	46
45°	0.707	1.414	1.000	1.000	1.414	0.707	45°
	Cos.	Sec.	Ctn.	Tan.	Csc.	Sin.	Angle.

Logarithms.

N	0	1	2	3	4	5	6	7	8	9	P. P. 1. 2. 3. 4. 5
10	0000	0043	0086	0128	0170	0212	0253	0294	0334	0374	4. 8.12.17.21
11	0414	0453	0492	0531	0569	0607	0645	0682	0719	0755	4. 8.11.15.19
12	0792	0828	0864	0899	0934	0969	1004	1038	1072	1106	3. 7.10.14.17
13	1139	1173	1206	1239	1271	1303	1335	1367	1399	1430	3. 6.10.13.16
14	1461	1492	1523	1553	1584	1614	1644	1673	1703	1732	3. 6. 9.12.15
15	1761	1790	1818	1847	1875	1903	1931	1959	1987	2014	3. 6. 8.11.14
16	2041	2068	2095	2122	2148	2175	2201	2227	2253	2279	3. 5. 8.11.13
17	2304	2330	2355	2380	2405	2430	2455	2480	2504	2529	2. 5. 7.10.12
18	2553	2577	2601	2625	2648	2672	2695	2718	2742	2765	2. 5. 7. 9.12
19	2788	2810	2833	2856	2878	2900	2923	2945	2967	2989	2. 4. 7. 9.11
20	3010	3032	3054	3075	3096	3118	3139	3160	3181	3201	2. 4. 6. 8.11
21	3222	3243	3263	3284	3304	3324	3345	3365	3385	3404	2. 4. 6. 8.10
22	3424	3444	3464	3483	3502	3522	3541	3560	3579	3598	2. 4. 6. 8.10
23	3617	3636	3655	3674	3692	3711	3729	3747	3766	3784	2. 4. 5. 7. 9
24	3802	3820	3838	3856	3874	3892	3909	3927	3945	3962	2. 4. 5. 7. 9
25	3979	3997	4014	4031	4048	4065	4082	4099	4116	4133	2. 3. 5. 7. 9
26	4150	4166	4183	4200	4216	4232	4249	4265	4281	4298	2. 3. 5. 7. 8
27	4314	4330	4346	4362	4378	4393	4409	4425	4440	4456	2. 3. 5. 6. 8
28	4472	4487	4502	4518	4533	4548	4564	4579	4594	4609	2. 3. 5. 6. 8
29	4624	4639	4654	4669	4683	4698	4713	4728	4742	4757	1. 3. 4. 6. 7
30	4771	4786	4800	4814	4829	4843	4857	4871	4886	4900	1. 3. 4. 6. 7
31	4914	4928	4942	4955	4969	4983	4997	5011	5024	5038	1. 3. 4. 6. 7
32	5051	5065	5079	5092	5105	5119	5132	5145	5159	5172	1. 3. 4. 5. 7
33	5185	5198	5211	5224	5237	5250	5263	5276	5289	5302	1. 3. 4. 5. 6
34	5315	5328	5340	5353	5366	5378	5391	5403	5416	5428	1. 3. 4. 5. 6
35	5441	5453	5465	5478	5490	5502	5514	5527	5539	5551	1. 2. 4. 5. 6
36	5563	5575	5587	5599	5611	5623	5635	5647	5658	5670	1. 2. 4. 5. 6
37	5682	5694	5705	5717	5729	5740	5752	5763	5775	5786	1. 2. 3. 5. 6
38	5798	5809	5821	5832	5843	5855	5866	5877	5888	5899	1. 2. 3. 5. 6
39	5911	5922	5933	5944	5955	5966	5977	5988	5999	6010	1. 2. 3. 4. 6
40	6021	6031	6042	6053	6064	6075	6085	6096	6107	6117	1. 2. 3. 4. 5
41	6128	6138	6149	6160	6170	6180	6191	6201	6212	6222	1. 2. 3. 4. 5
42	6232	6243	6253	6263	6274	6284	6294	6304	6314	6325	1. 2. 3. 4. 5
43	6335	6345	6355	6365	6375	6385	6395	6405	6415	6425	1. 2. 3. 4. 5
44	6435	6444	6454	6464	6474	6484	6493	6503	6513	6522	1. 2. 3. 4. 5
45	6532	6542	6551	6561	6571	6580	6590	6599	6609	6618	1. 2. 3. 4. 5
46	6623	6637	6646	6656	6665	6675	6684	6693	6702	6712	1. 2. 3. 4. 5
47	6721	6730	6739	6749	6758	6767	6776	6785	6794	6803	1. 2. 3. 4. 5
48	6812	6821	6830	6839	6848	6857	6866	6875	6884	6893	1. 2. 3. 4. 4
49	6902	6911	6920	6928	6937	6946	6955	6964	6972	6981	1. 2. 3. 4. 4
50	6990	6998	7007	7016	7024	7033	7042	7050	7059	7067	1. 2. 3. 3. 4
51	7076	7084	7093	7101	7110	7118	7126	7135	7143	7152	1. 2. 3. 3. 4
52	7160	7168	7177	7185	7193	7202	7210	7218	7226	7235	1. 2. 2. 3. 4
53	7243	7251	7259	7267	7275	7284	7292	7300	7308	7316	1. 2. 2. 3. 4
54	7324	7332	7340	7348	7356	7364	7372	7380	7388	7396	1. 2. 2. 3. 4

NOTE.— This page and the three that follow it are taken from the Mathematical Tables of Prof. J. M. Peirce, published by Messrs. Ginn & Co.

Logarithms.

N	0	1	2	3	4	5	6	7	8	9	P. P. 1. 2. 3. 4. 5
55	7404	7412	7419	7427	7435	7443	7451	7459	7466	7474	1. 2. 2. 3. 4
56	7482	7490	7497	7505	7513	7520	7528	7536	7543	7551	1. 2. 2. 3. 4
57	7559	7566	7574	7582	7589	7597	7604	7612	7619	7627	1. 2. 2. 3. 4
58	7634	7642	7649	7657	7664	7672	7679	7686	7694	7701	1. 1. 2. 3. 4
59	7709	7716	7723	7731	7738	7745	7752	7760	7767	7774	1. 1. 2. 3. 4
60	7782	7789	7796	7803	7810	7818	7825	7832	7839	7846	1. 1. 2. 3. 4
61	7853	7860	7868	7875	7882	7889	7896	7903	7910	7917	1. 1. 2. 3. 4
62	7924	7931	7938	7945	7952	7959	7966	7973	7980	7987	1. 1. 2. 3. 3
63	7993	8000	8007	8014	8021	8028	8035	8041	8048	8055	1. 1. 2. 3. 3
64	8062	8069	8075	8082	8089	8096	8102	8109	8116	8122	1. 1. 2. 3. 3
65	8129	8136	8142	8149	8156	8162	8169	8176	8182	8189	1. 1. 2. 3. 3
66	8195	8202	8209	8215	8222	8228	8235	8241	8248	8254	1. 1. 2. 3. 3
67	8261	8267	8274	8280	8287	8293	8299	8306	8312	8319	1. 1. 2. 3. 3
68	8325	8331	8338	8344	8351	8357	8363	8370	8376	8382	1. 1. 2. 3. 3
69	8388	8395	8401	8407	8414	8420	8426	8432	8439	8445	1. 1. 2. 3. 3
70	8451	8457	8463	8470	8476	8482	8488	8494	8500	8506	1. 1. 2. 2. 3
71	8513	8519	8525	8531	8537	8543	8549	8555	8561	8567	1. 1. 2. 2. 3
72	8573	8579	8585	8591	8597	8603	8609	8615	8621	8627	1. 1. 2. 2. 3
73	8633	8639	8645	8651	8657	8663	8669	8675	8681	8686	1. 1. 2. 2. 3
74	8692	8698	8704	8710	8716	8722	8727	8733	8739	8745	1. 1. 2. 2. 3
75	8751	8756	8762	8768	8774	8779	8785	8791	8797	8802	1. 1. 2. 2. 3
76	8808	8814	8820	8825	8831	8837	8842	8848	8854	8859	1. 1. 2. 2. 3
77	8865	8871	8876	8882	8887	8893	8899	8904	8910	8915	1. 1. 2. 2. 3
78	8921	8927	8932	8938	8943	8949	8954	8960	8965	8971	1. 1. 2. 2. 3
79	8976	8982	8987	8993	8998	9004	9009	9015	9020	9025	1. 1. 2. 2. 3
80	9031	9036	9042	9047	9053	9058	9063	9069	9074	9079	1. 1. 2. 2. 3
81	9085	9090	9096	9101	9106	9112	9117	9122	9128	9133	1. 1. 2. 2. 3
82	9138	9143	9149	9154	9159	9165	9170	9175	9180	9186	1. 1. 2. 2. 3
83	9191	9196	9201	9206	9212	9217	9222	9227	9232	9238	1. 1. 2. 2. 3
84	9243	9248	9253	9258	9263	9269	9274	9279	9284	9289	1. 1. 2. 2. 3
85	9294	9299	9304	9309	9315	9320	9325	9330	9335	9340	1. 1. 2. 2. 3
86	9345	9350	9355	9360	9365	9370	9375	9380	9385	9390	1. 1. 2. 2. 3
87	9395	9400	9405	9410	9415	9420	9425	9430	9435	9440	0. 1. 1. 2. 2
88	9445	9450	9455	9460	9465	9469	9474	9479	9484	9489	0. 1. 1. 2. 2
89	9494	9499	9504	9509	9513	9518	9523	9528	9533	9538	0. 1. 1. 2. 2
90	9542	9547	9552	9557	9562	9566	9571	9576	9581	9586	0. 1. 1. 2. 2
91	9590	9595	9600	9605	9609	9614	9619	9624	9628	9633	0. 1. 1. 2. 2
92	9638	9643	9647	9652	9657	9661	9666	9671	9675	9680	0. 1. 1. 2. 2
93	9685	9689	9694	9699	9703	9708	9713	9717	9722	9727	0. 1. 1. 2. 2
94	9731	9736	9741	9745	9750	9754	9759	9763	9768	9773	0. 1. 1. 2. 2
95	9777	9782	9786	9791	9795	9800	9805	9809	9814	9818	0. 1. 1. 2. 2
96	9823	9827	9832	9836	9841	9845	9850	9854	9859	9863	0. 1. 1. 2. 2
97	9868	9872	9877	9881	9886	9890	9894	9899	9903	9908	0. 1. 1. 2. 2
98	9912	9917	9921	9926	9930	9934	9939	9943	9948	9952	0. 1. 1. 2. 2
99	9956	9961	9965	9969	9974	9978	9983	9987	9991	9996	0. 1. 1. 2. 2

$\log \pi = 0.49715 -.$ $\log e = 0.43429 +.$

Logarithms.

N	0	1	2	3	4	5	6	7	8	9	10
100	0000	0004	0009	0013	0017	0022	0026	0030	0035	0039	0043
101	0043	0048	0052	0056	0060	0065	0069	0073	0077	0082	0086
102	0086	0090	0095	0099	0103	0107	0111	0116	0120	0124	0128
103	0128	0133	0137	0141	0145	0149	0154	0158	0162	0166	0170
104	0170	0175	0179	0183	0187	0191	0195	0199	0204	0208	0212
105	0212	0216	0220	0224	0228	0233	0237	0241	0245	0249	0253
106	0253	0257	0261	0265	0269	0273	0278	0282	0286	0290	0294
107	0294	0298	0302	0306	0310	0314	0318	0322	0326	0330	0334
108	0334	0338	0342	0346	0350	0354	0358	0362	0366	0370	0374
109	0374	0378	0382	0386	0390	0394	0398	0402	0406	0410	0414
110	0414	0418	0422	0426	0430	0434	0438	0441	0445	0449	0453
111	0453	0457	0461	0465	0469	0473	0477	0481	0484	0488	0492
112	0492	0496	0500	0504	0508	0512	0515	0519	0523	0527	0531
113	0531	0535	0538	0542	0546	0550	0554	0558	0561	0565	0569
114	0569	0573	0577	0580	0584	0588	0592	0596	0599	0603	0607
115	0607	0611	0615	0618	0622	0626	0630	0633	0637	0641	0645
116	0645	0648	0652	0656	0660	0663	0667	0671	0674	0678	0682
117	0682	0686	0689	0693	0697	0700	0704	0708	0711	0715	0719
118	0719	0722	0726	0730	0734	0737	0741	0745	0748	0752	0755
119	0755	0759	0763	0766	0770	0774	0777	0781	0785	0788	0792
120	0792	0795	0799	0803	0806	0810	0813	0817	0821	0824	0828
121	0828	0831	0835	0839	0842	0846	0849	0853	0856	0860	0864
122	0864	0867	0871	0874	0878	0881	0885	0888	0892	0896	0899
123	0899	0903	0906	0910	0913	0917	0920	0924	0927	0931	0934
124	0934	0938	0941	0945	0948	0952	0955	0959	0962	0966	0969
125	0969	0973	0976	0980	0983	0986	0990	0993	0997	1000	1004
126	1004	1007	1011	1014	1017	1021	1024	1028	1031	1035	1038
127	1038	1041	1045	1048	1052	1055	1059	1062	1065	1069	1072
128	1072	1075	1079	1082	1086	1089	1092	1096	1099	1103	1106
129	1106	1109	1113	1116	1119	1123	1126	1129	1133	1136	1139
130	1139	1143	1146	1149	1153	1156	1159	1163	1166	1169	1173
131	1173	1176	1179	1183	1186	1189	1193	1196	1199	1202	1206
132	1206	1209	1212	1216	1219	1222	1225	1229	1232	1235	1239
133	1239	1242	1245	1248	1252	1255	1258	1261	1265	1268	1271
134	1271	1274	1278	1281	1284	1287	1290	1294	1297	1300	1303
135	1303	1307	1310	1313	1316	1319	1323	1326	1329	1332	1335
136	1335	1339	1342	1345	1348	1351	1355	1358	1361	1364	1367
137	1367	1370	1374	1377	1380	1383	1386	1389	1392	1396	1399
138	1399	1402	1405	1408	1411	1414	1418	1421	1424	1427	1430
139	1430	1433	1436	1440	1443	1446	1449	1452	1455	1458	1461
140	1461	1464	1467	1471	1474	1477	1480	1483	1486	1489	1492
141	1492	1495	1498	1501	1504	1508	1511	1514	1517	1520	1523
142	1523	1526	1529	1532	1535	1538	1541	1544	1547	1550	1553
143	1553	1556	1559	1562	1565	1569	1572	1575	1578	1581	1584
144	1584	1587	1590	1593	1596	1599	1602	1605	1608	1611	1614
145	1614	1617	1620	1623	1626	1629	1632	1635	1638	1641	1644
146	1644	1647	1649	1652	1655	1658	1661	1664	1367	1670	1673
147	1673	1676	1679	1682	1685	1688	1691	1694	1697	1700	1703
148	1703	1706	1708	1711	1714	1717	1720	1723	1726	1729	1732
149	1732	1735	1738	1741	1744	1746	1749	1752	1755	1758	1761

Logarithms.

N	0	1	2	3	4	5	6	7	8	9	10
150	1761	1764	1767	1770	1772	1775	1778	1781	1784	1787	1790
151	1790	1793	1796	1798	1801	1804	1807	1810	1813	1816	1818
152	1818	1821	1824	1827	1830	1833	1836	1838	1841	1844	1847
153	1847	1850	1853	1855	1858	1861	1864	1867	1870	1872	1875
154	1875	1878	1881	1884	1886	1889	1892	1895	1898	1901	1903
155	1903	1906	1909	1912	1915	1917	1920	1923	1926	1928	1931
156	1931	1934	1937	1940	1942	1945	1948	1951	1953	1956	1959
157	1959	1962	1965	1967	1970	1973	1976	1978	1981	1984	1987
158	1987	1989	1992	1995	1998	2000	2003	2006	2009	2011	2014
159	2014	2017	2019	2022	2025	2028	2030	2033	2036	2038	2041
160	2041	2044	2047	2049	2052	2055	2057	2060	2063	2066	2068
161	2068	2071	2074	2076	2079	2082	2084	2087	2090	2092	2095
162	2095	2098	2101	2103	2106	2109	2111	2114	2117	2119	2122
163	2122	2125	2127	2130	2133	2135	2138	2140	2143	2146	2148
164	2148	2151	2154	2156	2159	2162	2164	2167	2170	2172	2175
165	2175	2177	2180	2183	2185	2188	2191	2193	2196	2198	2201
166	2201	2204	2206	2209	2212	2214	2217	2219	2222	2225	2227
167	2227	2230	2232	2235	2238	2240	2243	2245	2248	2251	2253
168	2253	2256	2258	2261	2263	2266	2269	2271	2274	2276	2279
169	2279	2281	2284	2287	2289	2292	2294	2297	2299	2302	2304
170	2304	2307	2310	2312	2315	2317	2320	2322	2325	2327	2330
171	2330	2333	2335	2338	2340	2343	2345	2348	2350	2353	2355
172	2355	2358	2360	2363	2365	2368	2370	2373	2375	2378	2380
173	2380	2383	2385	2388	2390	2393	2395	2398	2400	2403	2405
174	2405	2408	2410	2413	2415	2418	2420	2423	2425	2428	2430
175	2430	2433	2435	2438	2440	2443	2445	2448	2450	2453	2455
176	2455	2458	2460	2463	2465	2467	2470	2472	2475	2477	2480
177	2480	2482	2485	2487	2490	2492	2494	2497	2499	2502	2504
178	2504	2507	2509	2512	2514	2516	2519	2521	2524	2526	2529
179	2529	2531	2533	2536	2538	2541	2543	2545	2548	2550	2553
180	2553	2555	2558	2560	2562	2565	2567	2570	2572	2574	2577
181	2577	2579	2582	2584	2586	2589	2591	2594	2596	2598	2601
182	2601	2603	2605	2608	2610	2613	2615	2617	2620	2622	2625
183	2625	2627	2629	2632	2634	2636	2639	2641	2643	2646	2648
184	2648	2651	2653	2655	2658	2660	2662	2665	2667	2669	2672
185	2672	2674	2676	2679	2681	2683	2686	2688	2690	2693	2695
186	2695	2697	2700	2702	2704	2707	2709	2711	2714	2716	2718
187	2718	2721	2723	2725	2728	2730	2732	2735	2737	2739	2742
188	2742	2744	2746	2749	2751	2753	2755	2758	2760	2762	2765
189	2765	2767	2769	2772	2774	2776	2778	2781	2783	2785	2788
190	2788	2790	2792	2794	2797	2799	2801	2804	2806	2808	2810
191	2810	2813	2815	2817	2819	2822	2824	2826	2828	2831	2833
192	2833	2835	2838	2840	2842	2844	2847	2849	2851	2853	2856
193	2856	2858	2860	2862	2865	2867	2869	2871	2874	2876	2878
194	2878	2880	2882	2885	2887	2889	2891	2894	2896	2898	2900
195	2900	2903	2905	2907	2909	2911	2914	2916	2918	2920	2923
196	2923	2925	2927	2929	2931	2934	2936	2938	2940	2942	2945
197	2945	2947	2949	2951	2953	2956	2958	2960	2962	2964	2967
198	2967	2969	2971	2973	2975	2978	2980	2982	2984	2986	2989
199	2989	2991	2993	2995	2997	2999	3002	3004	3006	3008	3010

Trigonometric Functions.

RADIANS.	DEGREES.	SINES.		COSINES.		TANGENTS.		COTANGENTS.			
		Nat.	Log.	Nat.	Log.	Nat.	Log.	Nat.	Log.		
0.0000	0° 00′	.0000	∞	1.0000	0.0000	.0000	∞	∞	∞	90° 00′	1.5708
0.0029	10	.0029	7.4637	1.0000	.0000	.0029	7.4637	343.77	2.5363	50	1.5679
0.0058	20	.0058	.7648	1.0000	.0000	.0058	.7648	171.89	.2352	40	1.5650
0.0087	30	.0087	.9408	1.0000	.0000	.0087	.9409	114.59	.0591	30	1.5621
0.0116	40	.0116	8.0658	.9999	.0000	.0116	8.0658	85.940	1.9342	20	1.5592
0.0145	50	.0145	.1627	.9999	.0000	.0145	.1627	68.750	.8373	10	1.5563
0.0175	1° 00′	.0175	8.2419	.9998	9.9999	.0175	8.2419	57.290	1.7581	89° 00′	1.5533
0.0204	10	.0204	.3088	.9998	.9999	.0204	.3089	49.104	.6911	50	1.5504
0.0233	20	.0233	.3668	.9997	.9999	.0233	.3669	42.964	.6331	40	1.5475
0.0262	30	.0262	.4179	.9997	.9999	.0262	.4181	38.188	.5819	30	1.5446
0.0291	40	.0291	.4637	.9996	.9998	.0291	.4638	34.368	.5362	20	1.5417
0.0320	50	.0320	.5050	.9995	.9998	.0320	.5053	31.242	.4947	10	1.5388
0.0349	2° 00′	.0349	8.5428	.9994	9.9997	.0349	8.5431	28.636	1.4569	88° 00′	1.5359
0.0378	10	.0378	.5776	.9993	.9997	.0378	.5779	26.432	.4221	50	1.5330
0.0407	20	.0407	.6097	.9992	.9996	.0407	.6101	24.542	.3899	40	1.5301
0.0436	30	.0436	.6397	.9990	.9996	.0437	.6401	22.904	.3599	30	1.5272
0.0465	40	.0465	.6677	.9989	.9995	.0466	.6682	21.470	.3318	20	1.5243
0.0495	50	.0494	.6940	.9988	.9995	.0495	.6945	20.206	.3055	10	1.5213
0.0524	3° 00′	.0523	8.7188	.9986	9.9994	.0524	8.7194	19.081	1.2806	87° 00′	1.5184
0.0553	10	.0552	.7423	.9985	.9993	.0553	.7429	18.075	.2571	50	1.5155
0.0582	20	.0581	.7645	.9983	.9993	.0582	.7652	17.169	.2348	40	1.5126
0.0611	30	.0610	.7857	.9981	.9992	.0612	.7865	16.350	.2135	30	1.5097
0.0640	40	.0640	.8059	.9980	.9991	.0641	.8067	15.605	.1933	20	1.5068
0.0669	50	.0669	.8251	.9978	.9990	.0670	.8261	14.924	.1739	10	1.5039
0.0698	4° 00′	.0698	8.8436	.9976	9.9989	.0699	8.8446	14.301	1.1554	86° 00′	1.5010
0.0727	10	.0727	.8613	.9974	.9989	.0729	.8624	13.727	.1376	50	1.4981
0.0756	20	.0756	.8783	.9971	.9988	.0758	.8795	13.197	.1205	40	1.4952
0.0785	30	.0785	.8946	.9969	.9987	.0787	.8960	12.706	.1040	30	1.4923
0.0814	40	.0814	.9104	.9967	.9986	.0816	.9118	12.251	.0882	20	1.4893
0.0844	50	.0843	.9256	.9964	.9985	.0846	.9272	11.826	.0728	10	1.4864
0.0873	5° 00′	.0872	8.9403	.9962	9.9983	.0875	8.9420	11.430	1.0580	85° 00′	1.4835
0.0902	10	.0901	.9545	.9959	.9982	.0904	.9563	11.059	.0437	50	1.4806
0.0931	20	.0929	.9682	.9957	.9981	.0934	.9701	10.712	.0299	40	1.4777
0.0960	30	.0958	.9816	.9954	.9980	.0963	.9836	10.385	.0164	30	1.4748
0.0989	40	.0987	.9945	.9951	.9979	.0992	.9966	10.078	.0034	20	1.4719
0.1018	50	.1016	9.0070	.9948	.9977	.1022	9.0093	9.7882	0.9907	10	1.4690
0.1047	6° 00′	.1045	9.0192	.9945	9.9976	.1051	9.0216	9.5144	0.9784	84° 00′	1.4661
0.1076	10	.1074	.0311	.9942	.9975	.1080	.0336	9.2553	.9664	50	1.4632
0.1105	20	.1103	.0426	.9939	.9973	.1110	.0453	9.0098	.9547	40	1.4603
0.1134	30	.1132	.0539	.9936	.9972	.1139	.0567	8.7769	.9433	30	1.4574
0.1164	40	.1161	.0648	.9932	.9971	.1169	.0678	8.5555	.9322	20	1.4544
0.1193	50	.1190	.0755	.9929	.9969	.1198	.0786	8.3450	.9214	10	1.4515
0.1222	7° 00′	.1219	9.0859	.9925	9.9968	.1228	9.0891	8.1443	0.9109	83° 00′	1.4486
0.1251	10	.1248	.0961	.9922	.9966	.1257	.0995	7.9530	.9005	50	1.4457
0.1280	20	.1276	.1060	.9918	.9964	.1287	.1096	7.7704	.8904	40	1.4428
0.1309	30	.1305	.1157	.9914	.9963	.1317	.1194	7.5958	.8806	30	1.4399
0.1338	40	.1334	.1252	.9911	.9961	.1346	.1291	7.4287	.8709	20	1.4370
0.1367	50	.1363	.1345	.9907	.9959	.1376	.1385	7.2687	.8615	10	1.4341
0.1396	8° 00′	.1392	9.1436	.9903	9.9958	.1405	9.1478	7.1154	0.8522	82° 00′	1.4312
0.1425	10	.1421	.1525	.9899	.9956	.1435	.1569	6.9682	.8431	50	1.4283
0.1454	20	.1449	.1612	.9894	.9954	.1465	.1658	6.8269	.8342	40	1.4254
0.1484	30	.1478	.1697	.9890	.9952	.1495	.1745	6.6912	.8255	30	1.4224
0.1513	40	.1507	.1781	.9886	.9950	.1524	.1831	6.5606	.8169	20	1.4195
0.1542	50	.1536	.1863	.9881	.9948	.1554	.1915	6.4348	.8085	10	1.4166
0.1571	9° 00′	.1564	9.1943	.9877	9.9946	.1584	9.1997	6.3138	0.8003	81° 00′	1.4137
		Nat.	Log.	Nat.	Log.	Nat.	Log.	Nat.	Log.		
		COSINES.		SINES.		COTANGENTS.		TANGENTS.		DEGREES.	RADIANS.

Trigonometric Functions.

RADIANS.	DEGREES.	SINES. Nat.	Log.	COSINES. Nat.	Log.	TANGENTS. Nat.	Log.	COTANGENTS. Nat.	Log.		
0.1571	9° 00′	.1564	9.1943	.9877	9.9946	.1584	9.1997	6.3138	0.8003	81° 00′	1.4137
0.1600	10	.1593	.2022	.9872	.9944	.1614	.2078	6.1970	.7922	50	1.4108
0.1629	20	.1622	.2100	.9868	.9942	.1644	.2158	6.0844	.7842	40	1.4079
0.1658	30	.1650	.2176	.9863	.9940	.1673	.2236	5.9758	.7764	30	1.4050
0.1687	40	.1679	.2251	.9858	.9938	.1703	.2313	5.8708	.7687	20	1.4021
0.1716	50	.1708	.2324	.9853	.9936	.1733	.2389	5.7694	.7611	10	1.3992
0.1745	10° 00′	.1736	9.2397	.9848	9.9934	.1763	9.2463	5.6713	0.7537	80° 00′	1.3963
0.1774	10	.1765	.2468	.9843	.9931	.1793	.2536	5.5764	.7464	50	1.3934
0.1804	20	.1794	.2538	.9838	.9929	.1823	.2609	5.4845	.7391	40	1.3904
0.1833	30	.1822	.2606	.9833	.9927	.1853	.2680	5.3955	.7320	30	1.3875
0.1862	40	.1851	.2674	.9827	.9924	.1883	.2750	5.3093	.7250	20	1.3846
0.1891	50	.1880	.2740	.9822	.9922	.1914	.2819	5.2257	.7181	10	1.3817
0.1920	11° 00′	.1908	9.2806	.9816	9.9919	.1944	9.2887	5.1446	0.7113	79° 00′	1.3788
0.1949	10	.1937	.2870	.9811	.9917	.1974	.2953	5.0658	.7047	50	1.3759
0.1978	20	.1965	.2934	.9805	.9914	.2004	.3020	4.9894	.6980	40	1.3730
0.2007	30	.1994	.2997	.9799	.9912	.2035	.3085	4.9152	.6915	30	1.3701
0.2036	40	.2022	.3058	.9793	.9909	.2065	.3149	4.8430	.6851	20	1.3672
0.2065	5C	.2051	.3119	.9787	.9907	.2095	.3212	4.7729	.6788	10	1.3643
0.2094	12° 00′	.2079	9.3179	.9781	9.9904	.2126	9.3275	4.7046	0.6725	78° 00′	1.3614
0.2123	10	.2108	.3238	.9775	.9901	.2156	.3336	4.6382	.6664	50	1.3584
0.2153	20	.2136	.3296	.9769	.9899	.2186	.3397	4.5736	.6603	40	1.3555
0.2182	30	.2164	.3353	.9763	.9896	.2217	.3458	4.5107	.6542	30	1.3526
0.2211	40	.2193	.3410	.9757	.9893	.2247	.3517	4.4494	.6483	20	1.3497
0.2240	50	.2221	.3466	.9750	.9890	.2278	.3576	4.3897	.6424	10	1.3468
0.2269	13° 00′	.2250	9.3521	.9744	9.9887	.2309	9.3634	4.3315	0.6366	77° 00′	1.3439
0.2298	10	.2278	.3575	.9737	.9884	.2339	.3691	4.2747	.6309	50	1.3410
0.2327	20	.2306	.3629	.9730	.9881	.2370	.3748	4.2193	.6252	40	1.3381
0.2356	30	.2334	.3682	.9724	.9878	.2401	.3804	4.1653	.6196	30	1.3352
0.2385	40	.2363	.3734	.9717	.9875	.2432	.3859	4.1126	.6141	20	1.3323
0.2414	50	.2391	.3786	.9710	.9872	.2462	.3914	4.0611	.6086	10	1.3294
0.2443	14° 00′	.2419	9.3837	.9703	9.9869	.2493	9.3968	4.0108	0.6032	76° 00′	1.3265
0.2473	10	.2447	.3887	.9696	.9866	.2524	.4021	3.9617	.5979	50	1.3235
0.2502	20	.2476	.3937	.9689	.9863	.2555	.4074	3.9136	.5926	40	1.3206
0.2531	30	.2504	.3986	.9681	.9859	.2586	.4127	3.8667	.5873	30	1.3177
0.2560	40	.2532	.4035	.9674	.9856	.2617	.4178	3.8208	.5822	20	1.3148
0.2589	50	.2560	.4083	.9667	.9853	.2648	.4230	3.7760	.5770	10	1.3119
0.2618	15° 00′	.2588	9.4130	.9659	9.9849	.2679	9.4281	3.7321	0.5719	75° 00′	1.3090
0.2647	10	.2616	.4177	.9652	.9846	.2711	.4331	3.6891	.5669	50	1.3061
0.2676	20	.2644	.4223	.9644	.9843	.2742	.4381	3.6470	.5619	40	1.3032
0.2705	30	.2672	.4269	.9636	.9839	.2773	.4430	3.6059	.5570	30	1.3003
0.2734	40	.2700	.4314	.9628	.9836	.2805	.4479	3.5656	.5521	20	1.2974
0.2763	50	.2728	.4359	.9621	.9832	.2836	.4527	3.5261	.5473	10	1.2945
0.2793	16° 00′	.2756	9.4403	.9613	9.9828	.2867	9.4575	3.4874	0.5425	74° 00′	1.2915
0.2822	10	.2784	.4447	.9605	.9825	.2899	.4622	3.4495	.5378	50	1.2886
0.2851	20	.2812	.4491	.9596	.9821	.2931	.4669	3.4124	.5331	40	1.2857
0.2880	30	.2840	.4533	.9588	.9817	.2962	.4716	3.3759	.5284	30	1.2828
0.2909	40	.2868	.4576	.9580	.9814	.2994	.4762	3.3402	.5238	20	1.2799
0.2938	50	.2896	.4618	.9572	.9810	.3026	.4808	3.3052	.5192	10	1.2770
0.2967	17° 00′	.2924	9.4659	.9563	9.9806	.3057	9.4853	3.2709	0.5147	73° 00	1.2741
0.2996	10	.2952	.4700	.9555	.9802	.3089	.4898	3.2371	.5102	50	1.2712
0.3025	20	.2979	.4741	.9546	.9798	.3121	.4943	3.2041	.5057	40	1.2683
0.3054	30	.3007	.4781	.9537	.9794	.3153	.4987	3.1716	.5013	30	1.2654
0.3083	40	.3035	.4821	.9528	.9790	.3185	.5031	3.1397	.4969	20	1.2625
0.3113	50	.3062	.4861	.9520	.9786	.3217	.5075	3.1084	.4925	10	1.2595
0.3142	18° 00′	.3090	9.4900	.9511	9.9782	.3249	9.5118	3.0777	0.4882	72° 00′	1.2566
		Nat.	Log.	Nat.	Log.	Nat.	Log.	Nat.	Log.		
		COSINES.		SINES.		COTANGENTS.		TANGENTS.		DEGREES.	RADIANS.

TABLES.

Trigonometric Functions.

RADIANS.	DEGREES.	SINES.		COSINES.		TANGENTS.		COTANGENTS.			
		Nat.	Log.	Nat.	Log.	Nat.	Log.	Nat.	Log.		
0.3142	18° 00′	.3090	9.4900	.9511	9.9782	.3249	9.5118	3 0777	0.4882	72° 00′	1.2566
0.3171	10	.3118	.4939	.9502	.9778	.3281	.5161	3.0475	.4839	50	1.2537
0.3200	20	.3145	.4977	.9492	.9774	.3314	.5203	3.0178	.4797	40	1.2508
0.3229	30	.3173	.5015	.9483	.9770	.3346	.5245	2 9887	.4755	30	1.2479
0.3258	40	.3201	.5052	.9474	.9765	.3378	.5287	2.9600	.4713	20	1.2450
0.3287	50	.3228	.5090	.9465	.9761	.3411	.5329	2.9319	.4671	10	1.2421
0.3316	19° 00′	.3256	9.5126	.9455	9.9757	.3443	9.5370	2.9042	0.4630	71° 00′	1.2392
0.3345	10	.3283	.5163	.9446	.9752	.3476	.5411	2.8770	.4589	50	1.2363
0.3374	20	.3311	.5199	.9436	.9748	.3508	.5451	2.8502	.4549	40	1.2334
0.3403	30	.3338	.5235	.9426	.9743	.3541	.5491	2.8239	.4509	30	1.2305
0.3432	40	.3365	.5270	.9417	.9739	.3574	.5531	2.7980	.4469	20	1.2275
0.3462	50	.3393	.5306	.9407	.9734	.3607	.5571	2.7725	.4429	10	1.2246
0.3491	20° 00′	.3420	9.5341	.9397	9.9730	.3640	9.5611	2.7475	0.4389	70° 00′	1.2217
0.3520	10	.3448	.5375	.9387	.9725	.3673	.5650	2.7228	.4350	50	1.2188
0.3549	20	.3475	.5409	.9377	.9721	.3706	.5689	2.6985	.4311	40	1.2159
0.3578	30	.3502	.5443	.9367	.9716	.3739	.5727	2.6746	.4273	30	1.2130
0.3607	40	.3529	.5477	.9356	.9711	.3772	.5766	2.6511	.4234	20	1.2101
0.3636	50	.3557	.5510	.9346	.9706	.3805	.5804	2.6279	.4196	10	1.2072
0.3665	21° 00′	.3584	9.5543	.9336	9.9702	.3839	9.5842	2 6051	0.4158	69° 00′	1.2043
0.3694	10	.3611	.5576	.9325	.9697	.3872	.5879	2.5826	.4121	50	1.2014
0.3723	20	.3638	.5609	.9315	.9692	.3906	.5917	2.5605	.4083	40	1.1985
0.3752	30	.3665	.5641	.9304	.9687	.3939	.5954	2.5386	.4046	30	1.1956
0.3782	40	.3692	.5673	.9293	.9682	.3973	.5991	2.5172	.4009	20	1.1926
0.3811	50	.3719	.5704	.9283	.9677	.4006	.6028	2.4960	.3972	10	1.1897
0.3840	22° 00′	.3746	9.5736	.9272	9.9672	.4040	9.6064	2.4751	0.3936	68° 00′	1.1868
0.3869	10	.3773	.5767	.9261	.9667	.4074	.6100	2.4545	.3900	50	1.1839
0.3898	20	.3800	.5798	.9250	.9661	.4108	.6136	2.4342	.3864	40	1.1810
0.3927	30	.3827	.5828	.9239	.9656	.4142	.6172	2.4142	.3828	30	1.1781
0.3956	40	.3854	.5859	.9228	.9651	.4176	.6208	2.3945	.3792	20	1.1752
0.3985	50	.3881	.5889	.9216	.9646	.4210	.6243	2.3750	.3757	10	1.1723
0.4014	23° 00′	.3907	9.5919	.9205	9.9640	.4245	9.6279	2.3559	0.3721	67° 00′	1.1694
0.4043	10	.3934	.5948	.9194	.9635	.4279	.6314	2.3369	.3686	50	1.1665
0.4072	20	.3961	.5978	.9182	.9629	.4314	.6348	2.3183	.3652	40	1.1636
0.4102	30	.3987	.6007	.9171	.9624	.4348	.6383	2.2998	.3617	30	1.1606
0.4131	40	.4014	.6036	.9159	.9618	.4383	.6417	2.2817	.3583	20	1.1577
0.4160	50	.4041	.6065	.9147	.9613	.4417	.6452	2.2637	.3548	10	1.1548
0.4189	24° 00′	.4067	9.6093	.9135	9.9607	.4452	9.6486	2.2460	0.3514	66° 00′	1.1519
0.4218	10	.4094	.6121	.9124	.9602	.4487	.6520	2.2286	.3480	50	1.1490
0.4247	20	.4120	.6149	.9112	.9596	.4522	.6553	2.2113	.3447	40	1.1461
0.4276	30	.4147	.6177	.9100	.9590	.4557	.6587	2.1943	.3413	30	1.1432
0.4305	40	.4173	.6205	.9088	.9584	.4592	.6620	2.1775	.3380	20	1.1403
0.4334	50	.4200	.6232	.9075	.9579	.4628	.6654	2.1609	.3346	10	1.1374
0.4363	25° 00′	.4226	9.6259	.9063	9.9573	.4663	9.6687	2.1445	0.3313	65° 00′	1.1345
0.4392	10	.4253	.6286	.9051	.9567	.4699	.6720	2.1283	.3280	50	1.1316
0.4422	20	.4279	.6313	.9038	.9561	.4734	.6752	2.1123	.3248	40	1.1286
0.4451	30	.4305	.6340	.9026	.9555	.4770	.6785	2.0965	.3215	30	1.1257
0.4480	40	.4331	.6366	.9013	.9549	.4806	.6817	2.0809	.3183	20	1.1228
0.4509	50	.4358	.6392	.9001	.9543	.4841	.6850	2.0655	.3150	10	1.1199
0.4538	26° 00′	.4384	9.6418	.8988	9.9537	.4877	9.6882	2.0503	0.3118	64° 00′	1.1170
0.4567	10	.4410	.6444	.8975	.9530	.4913	.6914	2 0353	.3086	50	1.1141
0.4596	20	.4436	.6470	.8962	.9524	.4950	.6946	2.0204	.3054	40	1.1112
0.4625	30	.4462	.6495	.8949	.9518	.4986	.6977	2.0057	.3023	30	1.1083
0.4654	40	.4488	.6521	.8936	.9512	.5022	.7009	1.9912	.2991	20	1.1054
0.4683	50	.4514	.6546	.8923	.9505	.5059	.7040	1.9768	.2960	10	1.1025
0.4712	27° 00′	.4540	9.6570	.8910	9.9499	.5095	9.7072	1.9626	0.2928	63° 00′	1.0996
		Nat.	Log.	Nat.	Log.	Nat.	Log.	Nat.	Log.		
		COSINES.		SINES.		COTANGENTS.		TANGENTS.		DEGREES.	RADIANS.

Trigonometric Functions.

RADIANS.	DEGREES.	SINES. Nat.	Log.	COSINES. Nat.	Log.	TANGENTS. Nat.	Log.	COTANGENTS. Nat.	Log.		
0.4712	27° 00′	.4540	9.6570	.8910	9.9499	.5095	9.7072	1.9626	0.2928	63° 00′	1.0996
0.4741	10	.4566	.6595	.8897	.9492	.5132	.7103	1.9486	.2897	50	1.0966
0.4771	20	.4592	.6620	.8884	.9486	.5169	.7134	1.9347	.2866	40	1.0937
0.4800	30	.4617	.6644	.8870	.9479	.5206	.7165	1.9210	.2835	30	1.0908
0.4829	40	.4643	.6668	.8857	.9473	.5243	.7196	1.9074	.2804	20	1.0879
0.4858	50	.4669	.6692	.8843	.9466	.5280	.7226	1.8940	.2774	10	1.0850
0.4887	28° 00′	.4695	9.6716	.8829	9.9459	.5317	9.7257	1.8807	0.2743	62° 00′	1.0821
0.4916	10	.4720	.6740	.8816	.9453	.5354	.7287	1.8676	.2713	50	1.0792
0.4945	20	.4746	.6763	.8802	.9446	.5392	.7317	1.8546	.2683	40	1.0763
0.4974	30	.4772	.6787	.8788	.9439	.5430	.7348	1.8418	.2652	30	1.0734
0.5003	40	.4797	.6810	.8774	.9432	.5467	.7378	1.8291	.2622	20	1.0705
0.5032	50	.4823	.6833	.8760	.9425	.5505	.7408	1.8165	.2592	10	1.0676
0.5061	29° 00′	.4848	9.6856	.8746	9.9418	.5543	9.7438	1.8040	0.2562	61° 00′	1.0647
0.5091	10	.4874	.6878	.8732	.9411	.5581	.7467	1.7917	.2533	50	1.0617
0.5120	20	.4899	.6901	.8718	.9404	.5619	.7497	1.7796	.2503	40	1.0588
0.5149	30	.4924	.6923	.8704	.9397	.5658	.7526	1.7675	.2474	30	1.0559
0.5178	40	.4950	.6946	.8689	.9390	.5696	.7556	1.7556	.2444	20	1.0530
0.5207	50	.4975	.6968	.8675	.9383	.5735	.7585	1.7437	.2415	10	1.0501
0.5236	30° 00′	.5000	9.6990	.8660	9.9375	.5774	9.7614	1.7321	0.2386	60° 00′	1.0472
0.5265	10	.5025	.7012	.8646	.9368	.5812	.7644	1.7205	.2356	50	1.0443
0.5294	20	.5050	.7033	.8631	.9361	.5851	.7673	1.7090	.2327	40	1.0414
0.5323	30	.5075	.7055	.8616	.9353	.5890	.7701	1.6977	.2299	30	1.0385
0.5352	40	.5100	.7076	.8601	.9346	.5930	.7730	1.6864	.2270	20	1.0356
0.5381	50	.5125	.7097	.8587	.9338	.5969	.7759	1.6753	.2241	10	1.0327
0.5411	31° 00′	.5150	9.7118	.8572	9.9331	.6009	9.7788	1.6643	0.2212	59° 00′	1.0297
0.5440	10	.5175	.7139	.8557	.9323	.6048	.7816	1.6534	.2184	50	1.0268
0.5469	20	.5200	.7160	.8542	.9315	.6088	.7845	1.6426	.2155	40	1.0239
0.5498	30	.5225	.7181	.8526	.9308	.6128	.7873	1.6319	.2127	30	1.0210
0.5527	40	.5250	.7201	.8511	.9300	.6168	.7902	1.6212	.2098	20	1.0181
0.5556	50	.5275	.7222	.8496	.9292	.6208	.7930	1.6107	.2070	10	1.0152
0.5585	32° 00′	.5299	9.7242	.8480	9.9284	.6249	9.7958	1.6003	0.2042	58° 00′	1.0123
0.5614	10	.5324	.7262	.8465	.9276	.6289	.7986	1.5900	.2014	50	1.0094
0.5643	20	.5348	.7282	.8450	.9268	.6330	.8014	1.5798	.1986	40	1.0065
0.5672	30	.5373	.7302	.8434	.9260	.6371	.8042	1.5697	.1958	30	1.0036
0.5701	40	.5398	.7322	.8418	.9252	.6412	.8070	1.5597	.1930	20	1.0007
0.5730	50	.5422	.7342	.8403	.9244	.6453	.8097	1.5497	.1903	10	0.9977
0.5760	33° 00′	.5446	9.7361	.8387	9.9236	.6494	9.8125	1.5399	0.1875	57° 00′	0.9948
0.5789	10	.5471	.7380	.8371	.9228	.6536	.8153	1.5301	.1847	50	0.9919
0.5818	20	.5495	.7400	.8355	.9219	.6577	.8180	1.5204	.1820	40	0.9890
0.5847	30	.5519	.7419	.8339	.9211	.6619	.8208	1.5108	.1792	30	0.9861
0.5876	40	.5544	.7438	.8323	.9203	.6661	.8235	1.5013	.1765	20	0.9832
0.5905	50	.5568	.7457	.8307	.9194	.6703	.8263	1.4919	.1737	10	0.9803
0.5934	34° 00′	.5592	9.7476	.8290	9.9186	.6745	9.8290	1.4826	0.1710	56° 00′	0.9774
0.5963	10	.5616	.7494	.8274	.9177	.6787	.8317	1.4733	.1683	50	0.9745
0.5992	20	.5640	.7513	.8258	.9169	.6830	.8344	1.4641	.1656	40	0.9716
0.6021	30	.5664	.7531	.8241	.9160	.6873	.8371	1.4550	.1629	30	0.9687
0.6050	40	.5688	.7550	.8225	.9151	.6916	.8398	1.4460	.1602	20	0.9657
0.6080	50	.5712	.7568	.8208	.9142	.6959	.8425	1.4370	.1575	10	0.9628
0.6109	35° 00′	.5736	9.7586	.8192	9.9134	.7002	9.8452	1.4281	0.1548	55° 00′	0.9599
0.6138	10	.5760	.7604	.8175	.9125	.7046	.8479	1.4193	.1521	50	0.9570
0.6167	20	.5783	.7622	.8158	.9116	.7089	.8506	1.4106	.1494	40	0.9541
0.6196	30	.5807	.7640	.8141	.9107	.7133	.8533	1.4019	.1467	30	0.9512
0.6225	40	.5831	.7657	.8124	.9098	.7177	.8559	1.3934	.1441	20	0.9483
0.6254	50	.5854	.7675	.8107	.9089	.7221	.8586	1.3848	.1414	10	0.9454
0.6283	36° 00′	.5878	9.7692	.8090	9.9080	.7265	9.8613	1.3764	0.1387	54° 00′	0.9425
		Nat.	Log.	Nat.	Log.	Nat.	Log.	Nat.	Log.		
		COSINES.		SINES.		COTANGENTS.		TANGENTS.		DEGREES.	RADIANS.

Trigonometric Functions.

RADIANS.	DEGREES.	SINES. Nat.	Log.	COSINES. Nat.	Log.	TANGENTS. Nat.	Log.	COTANGENTS. Nat.	Log.		
0.6283	36° 00′	.5878	9.7692	.8090	9.9080	.7265	9.8613	1.3764	0.1387	54° 00′	0.9425
0.6312	10	.5901	.7710	.8073	.9070	.7310	.8639	1.3680	.1361	50	0.9396
0.6341	20	.5925	.7727	.8056	.9061	.7355	.8666	1.3597	.1334	40	0.9367
0.6370	30	.5948	.7744	.8039	.9052	.7400	.8692	1.3514	.1308	30	0.9338
0.6400	40	.5972	.7761	.8021	.9042	.7445	.8718	1.3432	.1282	20	0.9308
0.6429	50	.5995	.7778	.8004	.9033	.7490	.8745	1.3351	.1255	10	0.9279
0.6458	37° 00′	.6018	9.7795	.7986	9.9023	.7536	9.8771	1.3270	0.1229	53° 00′	0.9250
0.6487	10	.6041	.7811	.7969	.9014	.7581	.8797	1.3190	.1203	50	0.9221
0.6516	20	.6065	.7828	.7951	.9004	.7627	.8824	1.3111	.1176	40	0.9192
0.6545	30	.6088	.7844	.7934	.8995	.7673	.8850	1.3032	.1150	30	0.9163
0.6574	40	.6111	.7861	.7916	.8985	.7720	.8876	1.2954	.1124	20	0.9134
0.6603	50	.6134	.7877	.7898	.8975	.7766	.8902	1.2876	.1098	10	0.9105
0.6632	38° 00′	.6157	9.7893	.7880	9.8965	.7813	9.8928	1.2799	0.1072	52° 00′	0.9076
0.6661	10	.6180	.7910	.7862	.8955	.7860	.8954	1.2723	.1046	50	0.9047
0.6690	20	.6202	.7926	.7844	.8945	.7907	.8980	1.2647	.1020	40	0.9018
0.6720	30	.6225	.7941	.7826	.8935	.7954	.9006	1.2572	.0994	30	0.8988
0.6749	40	.6248	.7957	.7808	.8925	.8002	.9032	1.2497	.0968	20	0.8959
0.6778	50	.6271	.7973	.7790	.8915	.8050	.9058	1.2423	.0942	10	0.8930
0.6807	39° 00′	.6293	9.7989	.7771	9.8905	.8098	9.9084	1.2349	0.0916	51° 00′	0.8901
0.6836	10	.6316	.8004	.7753	.8895	.8146	.9110	1.2276	.0890	50	0.8872
0.6865	20	.6338	.8020	.7735	.8884	.8195	.9135	1.2203	.0865	40	0.8843
0.6894	30	.6361	.8035	.7716	.8874	.8243	.9161	1.2131	.0839	30	0.8814
0.6923	40	.6383	.8050	.7698	.8864	.8292	.9187	1.2059	.0813	20	0.8785
0.6952	50	.6406	.8066	.7679	.8853	.8342	.9212	1.1988	.0788	10	0.8756
0.6981	40° 00′	.6428	9.8081	.7660	9.8843	.8391	9.9238	1.1918	0.0762	50° 00′	0.8727
0.7010	10	.6450	.8096	.7642	.8832	.8441	.9264	1.1847	.0736	50	0.8698
0.7039	20	.6472	.8111	.7623	.8821	.8491	.9289	1.1778	.0711	40	0.8668
0.7069	30	.6494	.8125	.7604	.8810	.8541	.9315	1.1708	.0685	30	0.8639
0.7098	40	.6517	.8140	.7585	.8800	.8591	.9341	1.1640	.0659	20	0.8610
0.7127	50	.6539	.8155	.7566	.8789	.8642	.9366	1.1571	.0634	10	0.8581
0.7156	41° 00′	.6561	9.8169	.7547	9.8778	.8693	9.9392	1.1504	0.0608	49° 00′	0.8552
0.7185	10	.6583	.8184	.7528	.8767	.8744	.9417	1.1436	.0583	50	0.8523
0.7214	20	.6604	.8198	.7509	.8756	.8796	.9443	1.1369	.0557	40	0.8494
0.7243	30	.6626	.8213	.7490	.8745	.8847	.9468	1.1303	.0532	30	0.8465
0.7272	40	.6648	.8227	.7470	.8733	.8899	.9494	1.1237	.0506	20	0.8436
0.7301	50	.6670	.8241	.7451	.8722	.8952	.9519	1.1171	.0481	10	0.8407
0.7330	42° 00′	.6691	9.8255	.7431	9.8711	.9004	9.9544	1.1106	0.0456	48° 00′	0.8378
0.7359	10	.6713	.8269	.7412	.8699	.9057	.9570	1.1041	.0430	50	0.8348
0.7389	20	.6734	.8283	.7392	.8688	.9110	.9595	1.0977	.0405	40	0.8319
0.7418	30	.6756	.8297	.7373	.8676	.9163	.9621	1.0913	.0379	30	0.8290
0.7447	40	.6777	.8311	.7353	.8665	.9217	.9646	1.0850	.0354	20	0.8261
0.7476	50	.6799	.8324	.7333	.8653	.9271	.9671	1.0786	.0329	10	0.8232
0.7505	43° 00′	.6820	9.8338	.7314	9.8641	.9325	9.9697	1.0724	0.0303	47° 00′	0.8203
0.7534	10	.6841	.8351	.7294	.8629	.9380	.9722	1.0661	.0278	50	0.8174
0.7563	20	.6862	.8365	.7274	.8618	.9435	.9747	1.0599	.0253	40	0.8145
0.7592	30	.6884	.8378	.7254	.8606	.9490	.9772	1.0538	.0228	30	0.8116
0.7621	40	.6905	.8391	.7234	.8594	.9545	.9798	1.0477	.0202	20	0.8087
0.7650	50	.6926	.8405	.7214	.8582	.9601	.9823	1.0416	.0177	10	0.8058
0.7679	44° 00′	.6947	9.8418	.7193	9.8569	.9657	9.9848	1.0355	0.0152	46° 00′	0.8029
0.7709	10	.6967	.8431	.7173	.8557	.9713	.9874	1.0295	.0126	50	0.7999
0.7738	20	.6988	.8444	.7153	.8545	.9770	.9899	1.0235	.0101	40	0.7970
0.7767	30	.7009	.8457	.7133	.8532	.9827	.9924	1.0176	.0076	30	0.7941
0.7796	40	.7030	.8469	.7112	.8520	.9884	.9949	1.0117	.0051	20	0.7912
0.7825	50	.7050	.8482	.7092	.8507	.9942	.9975	1.0058	.0025	10	0.7883
0.7854	45° 00′	.7071	9.8495	.7071	9.8495	1.0000	0.0000	1.0000	0.0000	45° 00′	0.7854
		Nat.	Log.	Nat.	Log.	Nat.	Log.	Nat.	Log.		
		COSINES.		SINES.		COTANGENTS.		TANGENTS.		DEGREES.	RADIANS.

Equivalents of Radians in Degrees, Minutes, and Seconds of Arc.

RADIANS.	EQUIVALENTS.	RADIANS.	EQUIVALENTS.
0.0001	0° 0′ 20″.6 or 0°.005730	0.0600	3° 26′ 15″.9 or 3°.437747
0.0002	0° 0′ 41″.3 or 0°.011459	0.0700	4° 0′ 38″.5 or 4°.010705
0.0003	0° 1′ 01″.9 or 0°.017189	0.0800	4° 35′ 01″.2 or 4°.583662
0.0004	0° 1′ 22″.5 or 0°.022918	0.0900	5° 9′ 23″.8 or 5°.156620
0.0005	0° 1′ 43″.1 or 0°.028648	0.1000	5° 43′ 46″.5 or 5°.729578
0.0006	0° 2′ 03″.8 or 0°.034377	0.2000	11° 27′ 33″.0 or 11°.459156
0.0007	0° 2′ 24″.4 or 0°.040107	0.3000	17° 11′ 19″.4 or 17°.188734
0.0008	0° 2′ 45″.0 or 0°.045837	0.4000	22° 55′ 05″.9 or 22°.918312
0.0009	0° 3′ 05″.6 or 0°.051566	0.5000	28° 38′ 52″.4 or 28°.647890
0.0010	0° 3′ 26″.3 or 0°.057296	0.6000	34° 22′ 38″.9 or 34°.377468
0.0020	0° 6′ 52″.5 or 0°.114592	0.7000	40° 6′ 25″.4 or 40°.107046
0.0030	0° 10′ 18″.8 or 0°.171887	0.8000	45° 50′ 11″.8 or 45°.836624
0.0040	0° 13′ 45″.1 or 0°.229183	0.9000	51° 33′ 58″.3 or 51°.566202
0.0050	0° 17′ 11″.3 or 0°.286479	1.0000	57° 17′ 44″.8 or 57°.295780
0.0060	0° 20′ 37″.6 or 0°.343775	2.0000	114° 35′ 29″.6 or 114°.591559
0.0070	0° 24′ 03″.9 or 0°.401070	3.0000	171° 53′ 14″.4 or 171°.887339
0.0080	0° 27′ 30″.1 or 0°.458366	4.0000	229° 10′ 59″.2 or 229°.183118
0.0090	0° 30′ 56″.4 or 0°.515662	5.0000	286° 28′ 44″.0 or 286°.478898
0.0100	0° 34′ 22″.6 or 0°.572958	6.0000	343° 46′ 28″.8 or 343°.774677
0.0200	1° 8′ 45″.3 or 1°.145916	7.0000	401° 4′ 13″.6 or 401°.070457
0.0300	1° 43′ 07″.9 or 1°.718873	8.0000	458° 21′ 58″.4 or 458°.366236
0.0400	2° 17′ 30″.6 or 2°.291831	9.0000	515° 39′ 43″.3 or 515°.662016
0.0500	2° 51′ 53″.2 or 2°.864789	10.0000	572° 57′ 28″.1 or 572°.957795

The Values in Circular Measure of Angles which are given in Degrees and Minutes.

1′	0.0003	9′	0.0026	3°	0.0524	20°	0.3491	100°	1.7453
2′	0.0006	10′	0.0029	4°	0.0698	30°	0.5236	110°	1.9199
3′	0.0009	20′	0.0058	5°	0.0873	40°	0.6981	120°	2.0944
4′	0.0012	30′	0.0087	6°	0.1047	50°	0.8727	130°	2.2689
5′	0.0015	40′	0.0116	7°	0.1222	60°	1.0472	140°	2.4435
6′	0.0017	50′	0.0145	8°	0.1396	70°	1.2217	150°	2.6180
7′	0.0020	1°	0.0175	9°	0.1571	80°	1.3963	160°	2.7925
8′	0.0023	2°	0.0349	10°	0.1745	90°	1.5708	170°	2.9671

Square Roots of Numbers.

N	0	1	2	3	4	5	6	7	8	9	Avg. diff.
1.0	1.000	1.005	1.010	1.015	1.020	1.025	1.030	1.034	1.039	1.044	5
1	1.049	1.054	1.058	1.063	1.068	1.072	1.077	1.082	1.086	1.091	
2	1.095	1.100	1.105	1.109	1.114	1.118	1.122	1.127	1.131	1.136	4
3	1.140	1.145	1.149	1.153	1.158	1.162	1.166	1.170	1.175	1.179	
4	1.183	1.187	1.192	1.196	1.200	1.204	1.208	1.212	1.217	1.221	
1.5	1.225	1.229	1.233	1.237	1.241	1.245	1.249	1.253	1.257	1.261	
6	1.265	1.269	1.273	1.277	1.281	1.285	1.288	1.292	1.296	1.300	
7	1.304	1.308	1.311	1.315	1.319	1.323	1.327	1.330	1.334	1.338	
8	1.342	1.345	1.349	1.353	1.356	1.360	1.364	1.367	1.371	1.375	
9	1.378	1.382	1.386	1.389	1.393	1.396	1.400	1.404	1.407	1.411	
2.0	1.414	1.418	1.421	1.425	1.428	1.432	1.435	1.439	1.442	1.446	
1	1.449	1.453	1.456	1.459	1.463	1.466	1.470	1.473	1.476	1.480	3
2	1.483	1.487	1.490	1.493	1.497	1.500	1.503	1.507	1.510	1.513	
3	1.517	1.520	1.523	1.526	1.530	1.533	1.536	1.539	1.543	1.546	
4	1.549	1.552	1.556	1.559	1.562	1.565	1.568	1.572	1.575	1.578	
2.5	1.581	1.584	1.587	1.591	1.594	1.597	1.600	1.603	1.606	1.609	
6	1.612	1.616	1.619	1.622	1.625	1.628	1.631	1.634	1.637	1.640	
7	1.643	1.646	1.649	1.652	1.655	1.658	1.661	1.664	1.667	1.670	
8	1.673	1.676	1.679	1.682	1.685	1.688	1.691	1.694	1.697	1.700	
9	1.703	1.706	1.709	1.712	1.715	1.718	1.720	1.723	1.726	1.729	
3.0	1.732	1.735	1.738	1.741	1.744	1.746	1.749	1.752	1.755	1.758	
1	1.761	1.764	1.766	1.769	1.772	1.775	1.778	1.780	1.783	1.786	
2	1.789	1.792	1.794	1.797	1.800	1.803	1.806	1.808	1.811	1.814	
3	1.817	1.819	1.822	1.825	1.828	1.830	1.833	1.836	1.838	1.841	
4	1.844	1.847	1.849	1.852	1.855	1.857	1.860	1.863	1.865	1.868	
3.5	1.871	1.873	1.876	1.879	1.881	1.884	1.887	1.889	1.892	1.895	
6	1.897	1.900	1.903	1.905	1.908	1.910	1.913	1.916	1.918	1.921	
7	1.924	1.926	1.929	1.931	1.934	1.936	1.939	1.942	1.944	1.947	
8	1.949	1.952	1.954	1.957	1.960	1.962	1.965	1.967	1.970	1.972	
9	1.975	1.977	1.980	1.982	1.985	1.987	1.990	1.992	1.995	1.997	
4.0	2.000	2.002	2.005	2.007	2.010	2.012	2.015	2.017	2.020	2.022	
1	2.025	2.027	2.030	2.032	2.035	2.037	2.040	2.042	2.045	2.047	2
2	2.049	2.052	2.054	2.057	2.059	2.062	2.064	2.066	2.069	2.071	
3	2.074	2.076	2.078	2.081	2.083	2.086	2.088	2.090	2.093	2.095	
4	2.098	2.100	2.102	2.105	2.107	2.110	2.112	2.114	2.117	2.119	
4.5	2.121	2.124	2.126	2.128	2.131	2.133	2.135	2.138	2.140	2.142	
6	2.145	2.147	2.149	2.152	2.154	2.156	2.159	2.161	2.163	2.166	
7	2.168	2.170	2.173	2.175	2.177	2.179	2.182	2.184	2.186	2.189	
8	2.191	2.193	2.195	2.198	2.200	2.202	2.205	2.207	2.209	2.211	
9	2.214	2.216	2.218	2.220	2.223	2.225	2.227	2.229	2.232	2.234	

$$\sqrt{\pi} = 1.77245+ \qquad 1/\sqrt{\pi} = 0.56419 \qquad \sqrt{\pi/2} = 1.25331 \qquad \sqrt{e} = 1.64872$$

Explanation of Table of Square Roots.

This table gives the values of $\sqrt{N}$ for values of N from 1 to 100, correct to four figures. (Interpolated values may be in error by 1 in the fourth figure.)

To find the square root of a number N outside the range from 1 to 100, divide the digits of the number into blocks of two (beginning with the decimal point), and note that moving the decimal point two places in N is equivalent to moving it one place in the square root of N. For example:

$$\sqrt{2.718} = 1.648; \quad \sqrt{271.8} = 16.48; \quad \sqrt{0.0002718} = 0.01648;$$

$$\sqrt{27.18} = 5.213; \quad \sqrt{2718} = 52.13; \quad \sqrt{0.002718} = 0.05213.$$

Square Roots.

N	0	1	2	3	4	5	6	7	8	9	Avg. diff.
5.0	2.236	2.238	2.241	2.243	2.245	2.247	2.249	2.252	2.254	2.256	2
1	2.258	2.261	2.263	2.265	2.267	2.269	2.272	2.274	2.276	2.278	
2	2.280	2.283	2.285	2.287	2.289	2.291	2.293	2.296	2.298	2.300	
3	2.302	2.304	2.307	2.309	2.311	2.313	2.315	2.317	2.319	2.322	
4	2.324	2.326	2.328	2.330	2.332	2.335	2.337	2.339	2.341	2.343	
5.5	2.345	2.347	2.349	2.352	2.354	2.356	2.358	2.360	2.362	2.364	
6	2.366	2.369	2.371	2.373	2.375	2.377	2.379	2.381	2.383	2.385	
7	2.387	2.390	2.392	2.394	2.396	2.398	2.400	2.402	2.404	2.406	
8	2.408	2.410	2.412	2.415	2.417	2.419	2.421	2.423	2.425	2.427	
9	2.429	2.431	2.433	2.435	2.437	2.439	2.441	2.443	2.445	2.447	
6.0	2.449	2.452	2.454	2.456	2.458	2.460	2.462	2.464	2.466	2.468	
1	2.470	2.472	2.474	2.476	2.478	2.480	2.482	2.484	2.486	2.488	
2	2.490	2.492	2.494	2.496	2.498	2.500	2.502	2.504	2.506	2.508	
3	2.510	2.512	2.514	2.516	2.518	2.520	2.522	2.524	2.526	2.528	
4	2.530	2.532	2.534	2.536	2.538	2.540	2.542	2.544	2.546	2.548	
6.5	2.550	2.551	2.553	2.555	2.557	2.559	2.561	2.563	2.565	2.567	
6	2.569	2.571	2.573	2.575	2.577	2.579	2.581	2.583	2.585	2.587	
7	2.588	2.590	2.592	2.594	2.596	2.598	2.600	2.602	2.604	2.606	
8	2.608	2.610	2.612	2.613	2.615	2.617	2.619	2.621	2.623	2.625	
9	2.627	2.629	2.631	2.632	2.634	2.636	2.638	2.640	2.642	2.644	
7.0	2.646	2.648	2.650	2.651	2.653	2.655	2.657	2.659	2.661	2.663	
1	2.665	2.666	2.668	2.670	2.672	2.674	2.676	2.678	2.680	2.681	
2	2.683	2.685	2.687	2.689	2.691	2.693	2.694	2.696	2.698	2.700	
3	2.702	2.704	2.706	2.707	2.709	2.711	2.713	2.715	2.717	2.718	
4	2.720	2.722	2.724	2.726	2.728	2.729	2.731	2.733	2.735	2.737	
7.5	2.739	2.740	2.742	2.744	2.746	2.748	2.750	2.751	2.753	2.755	
6	2.757	2.759	2.760	2.762	2.764	2.766	2.768	2.769	2.771	2.773	
7	2.775	2.777	2.778	2.780	2.782	2.784	2.786	2.787	2.789	2.791	
8	2.793	2.795	2.796	2.798	2.800	2.802	2.804	2.805	2.807	2.809	
9	2.811	2.812	2.814	2.816	2.818	2.820	2.821	2.823	2.825	2.827	
8.0	2.828	2.830	2.832	2.834	2.835	2.837	2.839	2.841	2.843	2.844	
1	2.846	2.848	2.850	2.851	2.853	2.855	2.857	2.858	2.860	2.862	
2	2.864	2.865	2.867	2.869	2.871	2.872	2.874	2.876	2.877	2.879	
3	2.881	2.883	2.884	2.886	2.888	2.890	2.891	2.893	2.895	2.897	
4	2.898	2.900	2.902	2.903	2.905	2.907	2.909	2.910	2.912	2.914	
8.5	2.915	2.917	2.919	2.921	2.922	2.924	2.926	2.927	2.929	2.931	
6	2.933	2.934	2.936	2.938	2.939	2.941	2.943	2.944	2.946	2.948	
7	2.950	2.951	2.953	2.955	2.956	2.958	2.960	2.961	2.963	2.965	
8	2.966	2.968	2.970	2.972	2.973	2.975	2.977	2.978	2.980	2.982	
9	2.983	2.985	2.987	2.988	2.990	2.992	2.993	2.995	2.997	2.998	
9.0	3.000	3.002	3.003	3.005	3.007	3.008	3.010	3.012	3.013	3.015	
1	3.017	3.018	3.020	3.022	3.023	3.025	3.027	3.028	3.030	3.032	
2	3.033	3.035	3.036	3.038	3.040	3.041	3.043	3.045	3.046	3.048	
3	3.050	3.051	3.053	3.055	3.056	3.058	3.059	3.061	3.063	3.064	
4	3.066	3.068	3.069	3.071	3.072	3.074	3.076	3.077	3.079	3.081	
9.5	3.082	3.084	3.085	3.087	3.089	3.090	3.092	3.094	3.095	3.097	
6	3.098	3.100	3.102	3.103	3.105	3.106	3.108	3.110	3.111	3.113	
7	3.114	3.116	3.118	3.119	3.121	3.122	3.124	3.126	3.127	3.129	
8	3.130	3.132	3.134	3.135	3.137	3.138	3.140	3.142	3.143	3.145	
9	3.146	3.148	3.150	3.151	3.153	3.154	3.156	3.158	3.159	3.161	

Moving the decimal point TWO places in N requires moving it ONE place in body of table.

Square Roots.

N	0	1	2	3	4	5	6	7	8	9	Avg. diff.
10.	3.162	3.178	3.194	3.209	3.225	3.240	3.256	3.271	3.286	3.302	16
1.	3.317	3.332	3.347	3.362	3.376	3.391	3.406	3.421	3.435	3.450	15
2.	3.464	3.479	3.493	3.507	3.521	3.536	3.550	3.564	3.578	3.592	14
3.	3.606	3.619	3.633	3.647	3.661	3.674	3.688	3.701	3.715	3.728	
4.	3.742	3.755	3.768	3.782	3.795	3.808	3.821	3.834	3.847	3.860	13
15.	3.873	3.886	3.899	3.912	3.924	3.937	3.950	3.962	3.975	3.987	
6.	4.000	4.012	4.025	4.037	4.050	4.062	4.074	4.087	4.099	4.111	12
7.	4.123	4.135	4.147	4.159	4.171	4.183	4.195	4.207	4.219	4.231	
8.	4.243	4.254	4.266	4.278	4.290	4.301	4.313	4.324	4.336	4.347	
9.	4.359	4.370	4.382	4.393	4.405	4.416	4.427	4.438	4.450	4.461	11
20.	4.472	4.483	4.494	4.506	4.517	4.528	4.539	4.550	4.561	4.572	
1.	4.583	4.593	4.604	4.615	4.626	4.637	4.648	4.658	4.669	4.680	
2.	4.690	4.701	4.712	4.722	4.733	4.743	4.754	4.764	4.775	4.785	
3.	4.796	4.806	4.817	4.827	4.837	4.848	4.858	4.868	4.879	4.889	10
4.	4.899	4.909	4.919	4.930	4.940	4.950	4.960	4.970	4.980	4.990	
25.	5.000	5.010	5.020	5.030	5.040	5.050	5.060	5.070	5.079	5.089	
6	5.099	5.109	5.119	5.128	5.138	5.148	5.158	5.167	5.177	5.187	
7.	5.196	5.206	5.215	5.225	5.235	5.244	5.254	5.263	5.273	5.282	
8.	5.292	5.301	5.310	5.320	5.329	5.339	5.348	5.357	5.367	5.376	
9.	5.385	5.394	5.404	5.413	5.422	5.431	5.441	5.450	5.459	5.468	9
30.	5.477	5.486	5.495	5.505	5.514	5.523	5.532	5.541	5.550	5.559	
1.	5.568	5.577	5.586	5.595	5.604	5.612	5.621	5.630	5.639	5.648	
2.	5.657	5.666	5.675	5.683	5.692	5.701	5.710	5.718	5.727	5.736	
3.	5.745	5.753	5.762	5.771	5.779	5.788	5.797	5.805	5.814	5.822	
4.	5.831	5.840	5.848	5.857	5.865	5.874	5.882	5.891	5.899	5.908	8
35.	5.916	5.925	5.933	5.941	5.950	5.958	5.967	5.975	5.983	5.992	
6.	6.000	6.008	6.017	6.025	6.033	6.042	6.050	6.058	6.066	6.075	
7.	6.083	6.091	6.099	6.107	6.116	6.124	6.132	6.140	6.148	6.156	
8.	6.164	6.173	6.181	6.189	6.197	6.205	6.213	6.221	6.229	6.237	
9.	6.245	6.253	6.261	6.269	6.277	6.285	6.293	6.301	6.309	6.317	
40.	6.325	6.332	6.340	6.348	6.356	6.364	6.372	6.380	6.387	6.395	
1.	6.403	6.411	6.419	6.427	6.434	6.442	6.450	6.458	6.465	6.473	
2.	6.481	6.488	6.496	6.504	6.512	6.519	6.527	6.535	6.542	6.550	
3.	6.557	6.565	6.573	6.580	6.588	6.595	6.603	6.611	6.618	6.626	
4.	6.633	6.641	6.648	6.656	6.663	6.671	6.678	6.686	6.693	6.701	
45.	6.708	6.716	6.723	6.731	6.738	6.745	6.753	6.760	6.768	6.775	
6.	6.782	6.790	6.797	6.804	6.812	6.819	6.826	6.834	6.841	6.848	
7.	6.856	6.863	6.870	6.877	6.885	6.892	6.899	6.907	6.914	6.921	
8.	6.928	6.935	6.943	6.950	6.957	6.964	6.971	6.979	6.986	6.993	
9.	7.000	7.007	7.014	7.021	7.029	7.036	7.043	7.050	7.057	7.064	

Square Roots of Certain Fractions.

N	$\sqrt{N}$	N	$\sqrt{N}$	N	$\sqrt{N}$	N	$\sqrt{N}$	N	$\sqrt{N}$	N	$\sqrt{N}$
$\frac{1}{2}$	0.7071	$\frac{3}{5}$	0.7746	$\frac{4}{7}$	0.7559	$\frac{1}{9}$	0.3333	$\frac{5}{12}$	0.6455	$\frac{9}{16}$	0.7500
$\frac{1}{3}$	0.5774	$\frac{4}{5}$	0.8944	$\frac{5}{7}$	0.8452	$\frac{2}{9}$	0.4714	$\frac{7}{12}$	0.7638	$\frac{11}{16}$	0.8292
$\frac{2}{3}$	0.8165	$\frac{1}{6}$	0.4082	$\frac{6}{7}$	0.9258	$\frac{4}{9}$	0.6667	$\frac{11}{12}$	0.9574	$\frac{13}{16}$	0.9014
$\frac{1}{4}$	0.5000	$\frac{5}{6}$	0.9129	$\frac{1}{8}$	0.3536	$\frac{5}{9}$	0.7454	$\frac{1}{16}$	0.2500	$\frac{15}{16}$	0.9682
$\frac{3}{4}$	0.8660	$\frac{1}{7}$	0.3780	$\frac{3}{8}$	0.6124	$\frac{7}{9}$	0.8819	$\frac{3}{16}$	0.4330	$\frac{1}{32}$	0.1768
$\frac{1}{5}$	0.4472	$\frac{2}{7}$	0.5345	$\frac{5}{8}$	0.7906	$\frac{8}{9}$	0.9428	$\frac{5}{16}$	0.5590	$\frac{1}{64}$	0.1250
$\frac{2}{5}$	0.6325	$\frac{3}{7}$	0.6547	$\frac{7}{8}$	0.9354	$\frac{1}{12}$	0.2887	$\frac{7}{16}$	0.6614	$\frac{1}{50}$	0.1414

Square Roots.

N	0	1	2	3	4	5	6	7	8	9	Avg. diff.
50.	7.071	7.078	7.085	7.092	7.099	7.106	7.113	7.120	7.127	7.134	7
1.	7.141	7.148	7.155	7.162	7.169	7.176	7.183	7.190	7.197	7.204	
2.	7.211	7.218	7.225	7.232	7.239	7.246	7.253	7.259	7.266	7.273	
3.	7.280	7.287	7.294	7.301	7.308	7.314	7.321	7.328	7.335	7.342	
4.	7.348	7.355	7.362	7.369	7.376	7.382	7.389	7.396	7.403	7.409	
55.	7.416	7.423	7.430	7.436	7.443	7.450	7.457	7.463	7.470	7.477	
6.	7.483	7.490	7.497	7.503	7.510	7.517	7.523	7.530	7.537	7.543	
7.	7.550	7.556	7.563	7.570	7.576	7.583	7.589	7.596	7.603	7.609	
8.	7.616	7.622	7.629	7.635	7.642	7.649	7.655	7.662	7.668	7.675	
9.	7.681	7.688	7.694	7.701	7.707	7.714	7.720	7.727	7.733	7.740	6
60.	7.746	7.752	7.759	7.765	7.772	7.778	7.785	7.791	7.797	7.804	
1.	7.810	7.817	7.823	7.829	7.836	7.842	7.849	7.855	7.861	7.868	
2.	7.874	7.880	7.887	7.893	7.899	7.906	7.912	7.918	7.925	7.931	
3.	7.937	7.944	7.950	7.956	7.962	7.969	7.975	7.981	7.987	7.994	
4.	8.000	8.006	8.012	8.019	8.025	8.031	8.037	8.044	8.050	8.056	
65.	8.062	8.068	8.075	8.081	8.087	8.093	8.099	8.106	8.112	8.118	
6.	8.124	8.130	8.136	8.142	8.149	8.155	8.161	8.167	8.173	8.179	
7.	8.185	8.191	8.198	8.204	8.210	8.216	8.222	8.228	8.234	8.240	
8.	8.246	8.252	8.258	8.264	8.270	8.276	8.283	8.289	8.295	8.301	
9.	8.307	8.313	8.319	8.325	8.331	8.337	8.343	8.349	8.355	8.361	
70.	8.367	8.373	8.379	8.385	8.390	8.396	8.402	8.408	8.414	8.420	
1.	8.426	8.432	8.438	8.444	8.450	8.456	8.462	8.468	8.473	8.479	
2.	8.485	8.491	8.497	8.503	8.509	8.515	8.521	8.526	8.532	8.538	
3.	8.544	8.550	8.556	8.562	8.567	8.573	8.579	8.585	8.591	8.597	
4.	8.602	8.608	8.614	8.620	8.626	8.631	8.637	8.643	8.649	8.654	
75.	8.660	8.666	8.672	8.678	8.683	8.689	8.695	8.701	8.706	8.712	
6.	8.718	8.724	8.729	8.735	8.741	8.746	8.752	8.758	8.764	8.769	
7.	8.775	8.781	8.786	8.792	8.798	8.803	8.809	8.815	8.820	8.826	
8.	8.832	8.837	8.843	8.849	8.854	8.860	8.866	8.871	8.877	8.883	
9.	8.888	8.894	8.899	8.905	8.911	8.916	8.922	8.927	8.933	8.939	
80.	8.944	8.950	8.955	8.961	8.967	8.972	8.978	8.983	8.989	8.994	
1.	9.000	9.006	9.011	9.017	9.022	9.028	9.033	9.039	9.044	9.050	
2.	9.055	9.061	9.066	9.072	9.077	9.083	9.088	9.094	9.099	9.105	
3.	9.110	9.116	9.121	9.127	9.132	9.138	9.143	9.149	9.154	9.160	
4.	9.165	9.171	9.176	9.182	9.187	9.192	9.198	9.203	9.209	9.214	5
85.	9.220	9.225	9.230	9.236	9.241	9.247	9.252	9.257	9.263	9.268	
6.	9.274	9.279	9.284	9.290	9.295	9.301	9.306	9.311	9.317	9.322	
7.	9.327	9.333	9.338	9.343	9.349	9.354	9.359	9.365	9.370	9.375	
8.	9.381	9.386	9.391	9.397	9.402	9.407	9.413	9.418	9.423	9.429	
9.	9.434	9.439	9.445	9.450	9.455	9.460	9.466	9.471	9.476	9.482	
90.	9.487	9.492	9.497	9.503	9.508	9.513	9.518	9.524	9.529	9.534	
1.	9.539	9.545	9.550	9.555	9.560	9.566	9.571	9.576	9.581	9.586	
2.	9.592	9.597	9.602	9.607	9.612	9.618	9.623	9.628	9.633	9.638	
3.	9.644	9.649	9.654	9.659	9.664	9.670	9.675	9.680	9.685	9.690	
4.	9.695	9.701	9.706	9.711	9.716	9.721	9.726	9.731	9.737	9.742	
95.	9.747	9.752	9.757	9.762	9.767	9.772	9.778	9.783	9.788	9.793	
6.	9.798	9.803	9.808	9.813	9.818	9.823	9.829	9.834	9.839	9.844	
7.	9.849	9.854	9.859	9.864	9.869	9.874	9.879	9.884	9.889	9.894	
8.	9.899	9.905	9.910	9.915	9.920	9.925	9.930	9.935	9.940	9.945	
9.	9.950	9.955	9.960	9.965	9.970	9.975	9.980	9.985	9.990	9.995	

$$\sqrt{\pi} = 1.77245+ \qquad 1/\sqrt{\pi} = 0.56419 \qquad \sqrt{\pi/2} = 1.25331 \qquad \sqrt{e} = 1.64872$$

NOTE. This page and the three that precede it are taken from Professor L. S. Marks's *Mechanical Engineers' Handbook*, published by McGraw-Hill Book Company, Inc.

PAGE INDEX.

INTEGRALS.